Electricity and Magnetism: Teacher's Edition

Contents in Brief

Teacher's Edition

See Program Component List on page ii

Student Edition

Prentice Hall Science Explorer

Series Tables of Contents

The Nature of Science and Technology

1. What Is Science?
2. The Work of Scientists
3. Technology and Engineering

Life Science

From Bacteria to Plants

1. Living Things
2. Viruses and Bacteria
3. Protists and Fungi
4. Introduction to Plants
5. Seed Plants

Animals

1. Sponges, Cnidarians, and Worms
2. Mollusks, Arthropods, and Echinoderms
3. Fishes, Amphibians, and Reptiles
4. Birds and Mammals
5. Animal Behavior

Cells and Heredity

1. Cell Structure and Function
2. Cell Processes and Energy
3. Genetics: The Science of Heredity
4. Modern Genetics
5. Changes Over Time

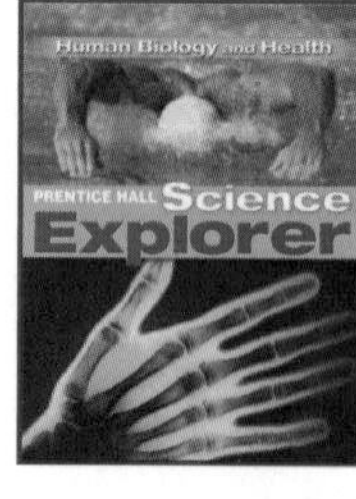

Human Biology and Health

1. Bones, Muscles, and Skin
2. Food and Digestion
3. Circulation
4. Respiration and Excretion
5. Fighting Disease
6. The Nervous System
7. The Endocrine System and Reproduction

Environmental Science

1. Populations and Communities
2. Ecosystems and Biomes
3. Living Resources
4. Land, Water, and Air Resources
5. Energy Resources

Earth Science

Inside Earth

1. Plate Tectonics
2. Earthquakes
3. Volcanoes
4. Minerals
5. Rocks

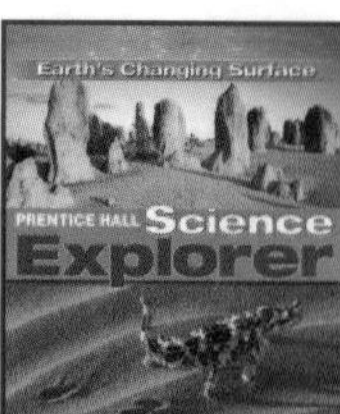

Earth's Changing Surface

1. Mapping Earth's Surface
2. Weathering and Soil Formation
3. Erosion and Deposition
4. A Trip Through Geologic Time

Earth's Waters

1. Earth: The Water Planet
2. Freshwater Resources
3. Ocean Motions
4. Ocean Zones

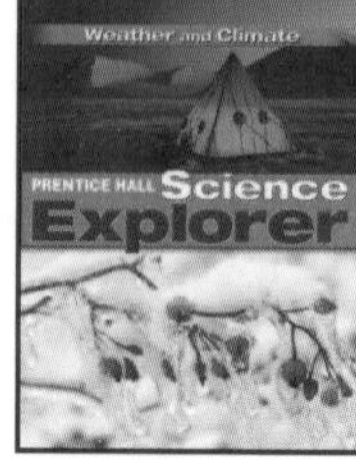

Weather and Climate

1. The Atmosphere
2. Weather Factors
3. Weather Patterns
4. Climate and Climate Change

Astronomy

1. Earth, Moon, and Sun
2. Exploring Space
3. The Solar System
4. Stars, Galaxies, and the Universe

Physical Science

Chemical Building Blocks

1. Introduction to Matter
2. Solids, Liquids, and Gases
3. Elements and the Periodic Table
4. Exploring Materials

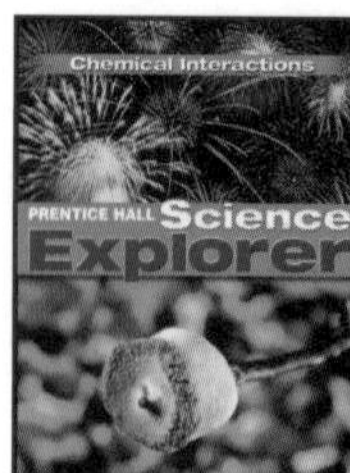

Chemical Interactions

1. Atoms and Bonding
2. Chemical Reactions
3. Acids, Bases, and Solutions
4. Carbon Chemistry

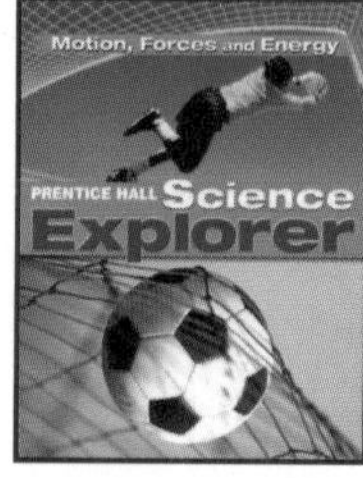

Motion, Forces, and Energy

1. Motion
2. Forces
3. Forces in Fluids
4. Work and Machines
5. Energy
6. Thermal Energy and Heat

Electricity and Magnetism

1. Magnetism
2. Electricity
3. Using Electricity and Magnetism
4. Electronics

Sound and Light

1. Characteristics of Waves
2. Sound
3. The Electromagnetic Spectrum
4. Light

Teacher's Edition

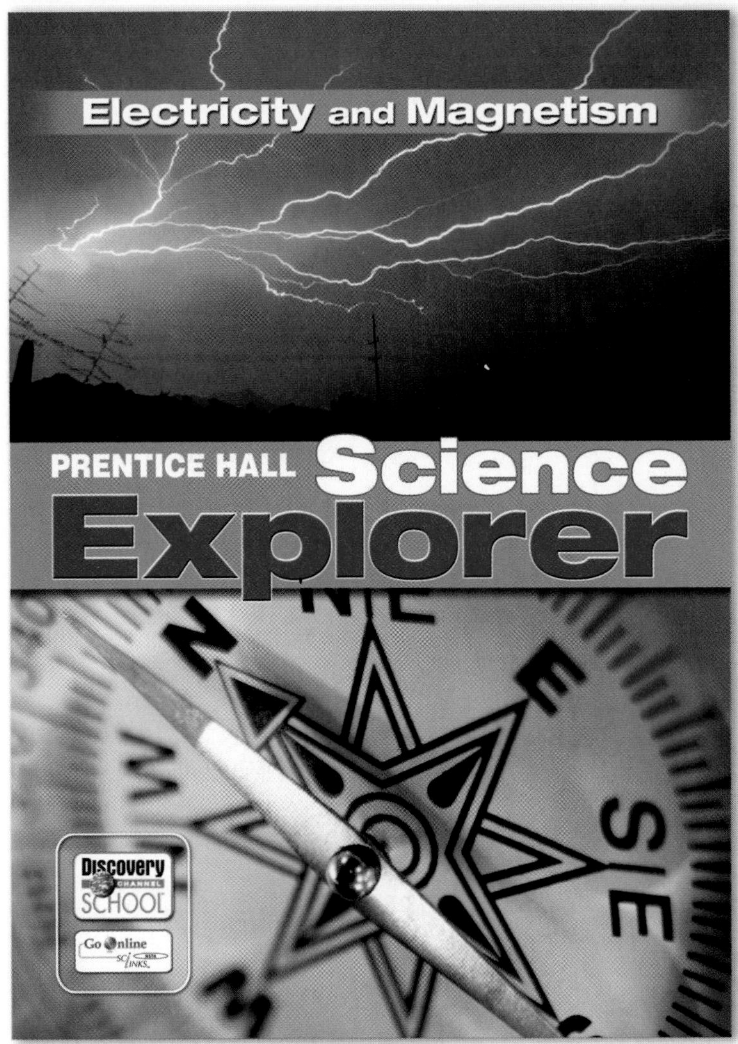

Boston, Massachusetts
Upper Saddle River, New Jersey

ISBN 0-13-201175-1

1 2 3 4 5 6 7 8 9 10 10 09 08 07 06

Pacing Options

PRENTICE HALL
TeacherEXPRESS™
Plan • Teach • Assess

SCIENCE EXPLORER offers many aids to help you plan your instruction time, whether regular class periods or block scheduling. Section-by-section lesson plans for each chapter include suggested times for Student Edition activities. TeacherExpress™ and the Lab zone™ Easy Planner CD-ROM will help you manage your time electronically.

Pacing Chart

	PERIODS	BLOCKS
Careers: When Illusion Is Better Than Reality	1–2	½–1
Chapter 1 Mapping Earth's Surface		
Chapter 1 Project *Magnetic Art*	Ongoing	Ongoing
1 What Is Magnetism?	3–4	1½–2
2 Inside a Magnet	3–4	1½–2
3 Magnetic Earth	2–3	1–1½
Chapter 1 Review and Assessment	1–2	½–1
Chapter 2 Electricity		
Chapter 2 Project *Cause for Alarm*	Ongoing	Ongoing
1 Electric Charge and Static Electricity	3–4	1–1½
2 Electric Current	3–4	1½–2
3 Batteries	2–3	1–1½
4 Electric Circuits	2–3	1–1½
5 Electric Power	1–2	½–1
6 Integrating Health: Electric Safety	1–2	½–1
Chapter 2 Review and Assessment	1–2	½–1
Chapter 3 Using Electricity and Magnetism		
Chapter 3 Project *Electrical Energy Audit*	Ongoing	Ongoing
1 What Is Electromagnetism?	2–3	1–1½
2 Electricity, Magnetism, and Motion	3–4	1½–2
3 Tech and Design: Electricity From Magnetism	3–4	1½–2
Chapter 3 Review and Assessment	1–2	½–1

	PERIODS	BLOCKS
Chapter 4 Using Electronics		
Chapter 4 Project *Bits and Bytes*	Ongoing	Ongoing
1 Electronic Signals and Semiconductors	3–4	1½–2
2 Electronic Communication	3–4	1½–2
3 Computers	3–4	1½–2
4 Tech and Design: The Information Superhighway	1–2	½–1
Chapter 4 Review and Assessment	1–2	½–1
Interdisciplinary Exploration: Edison—Genius of Invention	2–3	1–1½

Research-Based and Proven to Work

As the originator of the small book concept in middle school science, and as the nation's number one science publisher, Prentice Hall takes pride in the fact that we've always listened closely to teachers. In doing so, we've developed programs that effectively meet the needs of your classroom.

As we continue to listen, we realize that raising the achievement level of all students is the number one challenge facing teachers today. To assist you in meeting this latest challenge, Prentice Hall has combined the very best author team with solid research to create a program that meets your high standards and will ensure that no child is left behind.

With Prentice Hall, you can be confident that your students will not only be motivated, inspired, and excited to learn science, but that they will also achieve the success needed in today's environment of the No Child Left Behind (NCLB) legislation and testing reform.

On the following pages, you will read about the key elements found throughout *Science Explorer* that truly set this program apart and ensure success for you and your students.

As we continue to listen, we realize that raising the achievement level of all students is the number one challenge facing teachers today.

A Science Program Backed by Research

In developing Prentice Hall *Science Explorer*, we used research studies as a central, guiding element. Research on *Science Explorer* indicated key elements of a textbook program that ensure students' success: support for reading and mathematics in science, consistent opportunities for inquiry, and an ongoing assessment strand. This research was conducted in phases and continues today.

1. Exploratory: Needs Assessment

Along with periodic surveys concerning state and national standards as well as curriculum issues and challenges, we conducted specific product development research, which included discussions with teachers and advisory panels, focus groups, and quantitative surveys. We explored the specific needs of teachers, students, and other educators regarding each book we developed in Prentice Hall *Science Explorer*.

2. Formative: Prototype Development and Field-Testing

During this phase of research, we worked to develop prototype materials. Then we tested the materials by field-testing with students and teachers and by performing qualitative and quantitative surveys. In our early prototype testing, we received feedback about our lesson structure. Results were channeled back into the program development for improvement.

3. Summative: Validation Research

Finally, we conducted and continue to conduct long-term research based on scientific, experimental designs under actual classroom conditions. This research identifies what works and what can be improved in the next revision of Prentice Hall *Science Explorer*. We also continue to monitor the program in the market. We talk to our users about what works, and then we begin the cycle over again. The next section contains highlights of this research.

A Science Program With Proven Results

In a year-long study in 2000–2001, students in six states using Prentice Hall *Science Explorer* outscored students using other science programs on a nationally normed standardized test.

The study investigated the effects of science textbook programs at the eighth-grade level. Twelve eighth-grade science classes with a total of 223 students participated in the study. The selected classes were of similar student ability levels.

Each class was tested at the beginning of the school year using the TerraNova CTBS Basic Battery Plus, and then retested at the end of the school year. The final results, shown in the graph, show a significant improvement in test scores from the pre-test to the post-test evaluation.

- All tests were scored by CTB/McGraw-Hill, the publisher of the TerraNova exam. Statistical analyses and conclusions were performed by an independent firm, Pulse Analytics, Inc.

In Japan, Lesson Study Research has been employed for a number of years as a tool for teachers to improve their curriculum. In April 2003, Prentice Hall adapted this methodology to focus on a lesson from this edition. Our goal was to test the effectiveness of lesson pedagogy and improve it while in the program development stage. In all three classrooms tested, student learning increased an average of 10 points from the pre- to the post-assessment.

- Detailed results of these studies can be obtained at **www.PHSchool.com/research.**

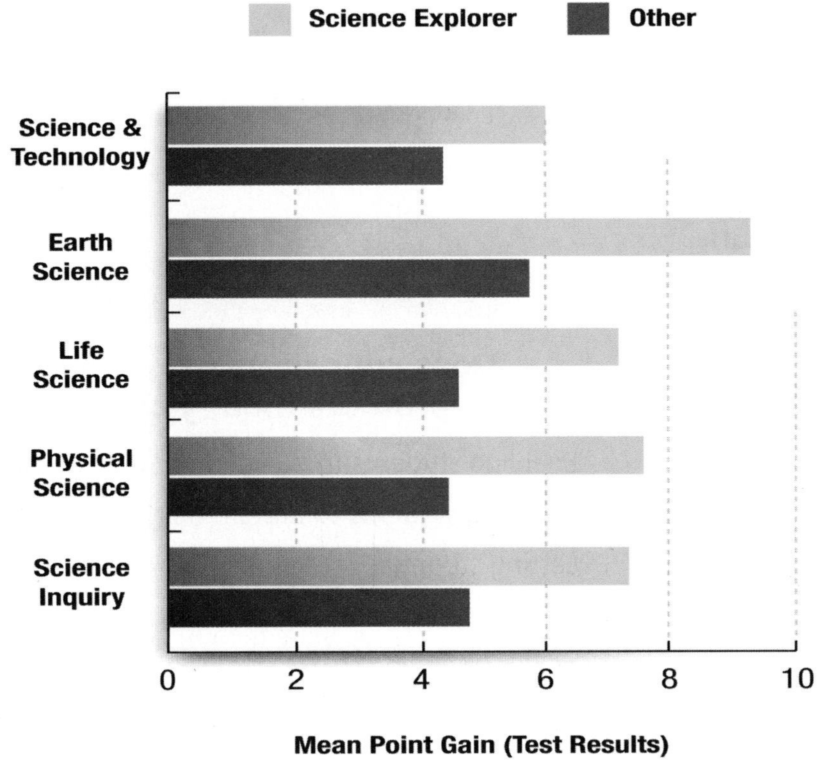

Foundational Research: Inquiry in the Science Classroom

"How do I know if my students are inquiring?" "If students are busy doing lots of hands-on activities, are they using inquiry?" "What is inquiry, anyway?" If you're confused, you are not alone. Inquiry is the heart and soul of science education, with most of us in continuous pursuit of achieving it with our students!

Defining Science Inquiry

What is it? Simply put, inquiry is the intellectual side of science. It is thinking like a scientist—being inquisitive, asking why, and searching for answers. The National Science Education Content Standards define inquiry as the process in which students begin with a question, design an investigation, gather evidence, formulate an answer to the original question, and communicate the investigative process and results. Since it is often difficult to accomplish all this in one class period, the standards also acknowledge that at times students need to practice only one or two inquiry components.

Understanding Inquiry

The National Research Council in Inquiry and the National Science Education Standards (2000) identified several "essential features" of classroom inquiry. We have modified these essential features into questions to guide you in your quest for enhanced and more thoughtful student inquiry.

1. ***Who asks the question?*** In most curricula, these focusing questions are an element given in the materials. As a teacher you can look for labs that, at least on a periodic basis, allow students to pursue their own questions.
2. ***Who designs the procedures?*** To gain experience with the logic underlying experimentation, students need continuous practice with designing procedures. Some labs in which the primary target is content acquisition designate procedures. But others should ask students to do so.
3. ***Who decides what data to collect?*** Students need practice in determining the data to collect.
4. ***Who formulates explanations based upon the data?*** Students should be challenged to think—to analyze and draw conclusions based on their data, not just copy answers from the text materials.
5. ***Who communicates and justifies the results?*** Activities should push students not only to communicate but also to justify their answers. Activities also should be thoughtfully designed and interesting so that students want to share their results and argue about conclusions.

Making Time for Inquiry

One last question—Must each and every activity have students do all of this? The answer is an obvious and emphatic "No." You will find a great variety of activities in *Science Explorer*. Some activities focus on content acquisition, and thus they specify the question and most of the procedures. But many others stress in-depth inquiry from start to finish. Because inquiry is an intellectual pursuit, it cannot merely be characterized by keeping students busy and active. Too many students have a knack for being physically but not intellectually engaged in science. It is our job to help them engage intellectually.

Michael J. Padilla, Ph.D.
Program Author of *Science Explorer*
Professor of Science Education
University of Georgia
Athens, Georgia

"Because inquiry is an intellectual pursuit, it cannot merely be characterized by keeping students busy and active."

Evaluator's Checklist

Does your science program promote inquiry by—

- ✔ Enabling students to pursue their own questions
- ✔ Allowing students to design their own procedures
- ✔ Letting students determine what data are best to collect
- ✔ Challenging students to think critically
- ✔ Pushing students to justify their answers

Inquiry in *Science Explorer*

Science Explorer offers the most opportunities to get students to think like a scientist. By providing inquiry opportunities throughout the program, *Science Explorer* enables students to enhance their understanding by participating in the discovery.

Student Edition Inquiry

Six lab and activity options are included in every chapter, structured from directed to open-ended—providing you the flexibility to address all types of learners and accommodate your class time and equipment requirements. As Michael Padilla notes, some activities focus on content acquisition, and thus the question and most of the procedures are specified. But many others stress in-depth inquiry from start to finish. The graph below shows how, in general, inquiry levels are addressed in the Student Edition.

Science Explorer encourages students to develop inquiry skills across the spectrum from teacher-guided to open-ended. Even more opportunities for real-life applications of inquiry are included in Science & Society, Technology & Society, Careers in Science, and Interdisciplinary Exploration features.

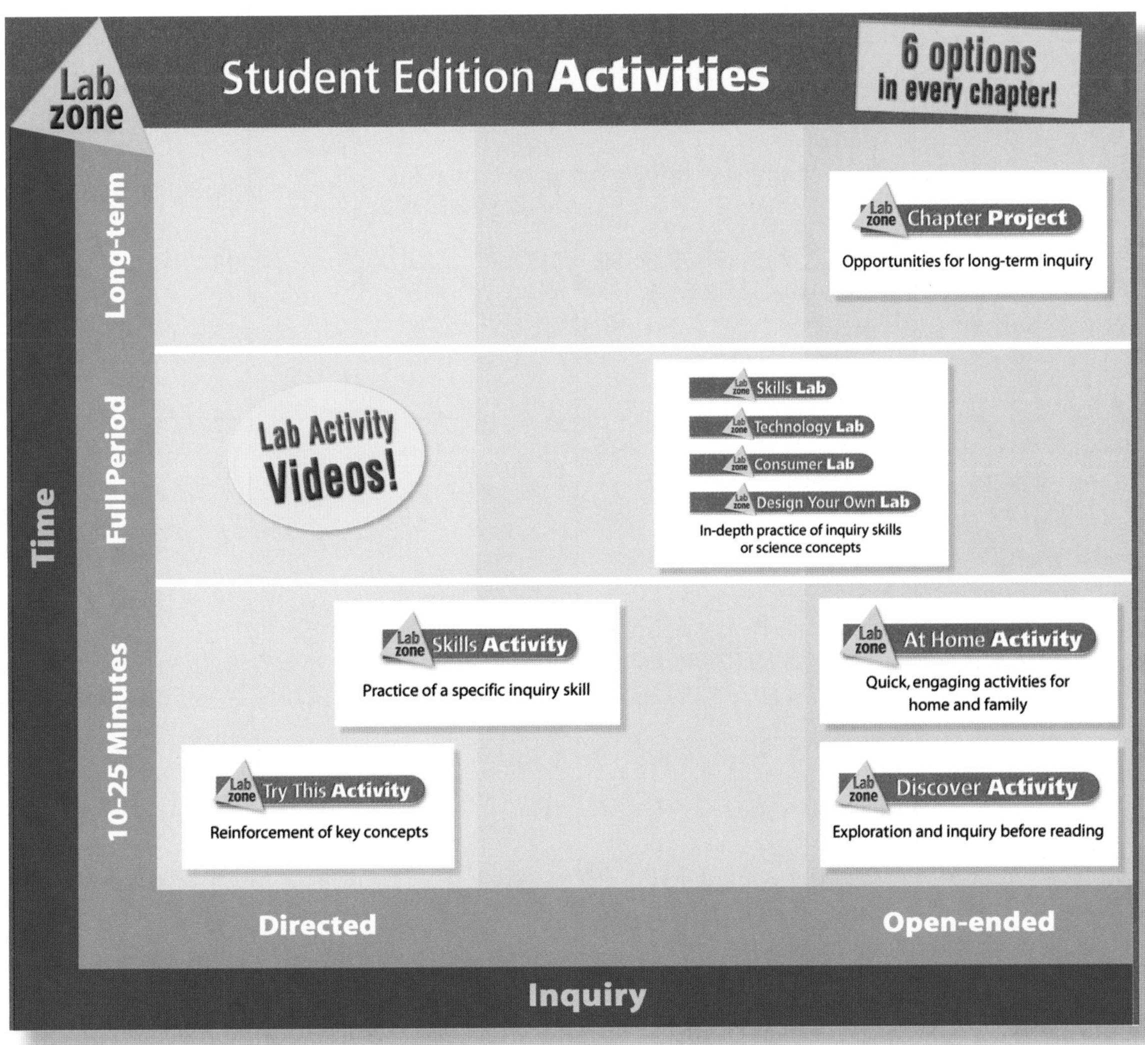

Inquiry Skills Chart

SCIENCE EXPLORER provides comprehensive teaching, practice, and assessment of science skills, with an emphasis on the process skills necessary for inquiry. This chart lists the skills covered in the program and cites the page numbers where each skill is covered.

Basic Process SKILLS				
	Student Text: Projects and Labs	**Student Text: Activities**	**Student Text: Caption and Review Questions**	**Teacher's Edition: Extensions**
Observing	5, 12–13, 42–43, 52–53, 79, 92–93, 107, 130–131	6, 8, 22, 54, 60, 68	23, 81, 88	63, 88
Inferring	20–21, 42–43, 58–59, 92–93	34, 38, 44, 80, 83, 85, 108, 123, 132	7, 30, 50, 104	
Predicting	12–13, 42–43, 52–53	65	8, 11, 30, 51, 57, 64, 65, 66, 73, 76, 89, 104, 109, 135, 140	
Classifying	42–43, 92–93, 130–131	114	47, 76, 104, 112, 140	
Making Models	130–131	49	76	16, 36, 49, 50, 82, 110
Communicating	5, 12–13, 21, 33, 42–43, 52–53, 58–59, 79, 92–93, 107, 113, 130–131	11, 19, 27, 41, 51, 57, 73, 84, 89, 97, 101, 110, 112, 122, 129, 133, 135	91	23
Measuring		25	61	87
Calculating	58–59, 79	24, 61, 62, 69, 72, 118, 124	66, 70, 140	69
Creating Data Tables	20, 42, 58			
Graphing	79	118		
Advanced Process SKILLS				
Posing Questions		67		10, 51
Developing Hypothesis	12–13, 113	94	71	
Designing Experiments	43, 59, 93, 131			

Advanced Process SKILLS (continued)				
	Student Text: Projects and Labs	Student Text: Activities	Student Text: Caption and Review Questions	Teacher's Edition: Extensions
Controlling Variables	12–13, 42–43, 52–53, 113		76	
Forming Operational Definitions	58–59			
Interpreting Data	20–21, 52–53		121	
Drawing Conclusions	12–13, 42–43, 52–53, 92–93, 113	14, 26, 35, 86	30	
Critical Thinking SKILLS				
Comparing and Contrasting			10, 16, 19, 41, 51, 66, 76, 82, 101, 104, 111, 112, 122, 129, 140	87
Applying Concepts	5, 33, 107	11, 27, 41, 57, 73, 101, 122, 135	19, 30, 41, 48, 51, 66, 76, 84, 89, 99, 104, 115, 129, 140	
Interpreting Diagrams, Graphs, Photographs, and Maps			11, 27, 30, 35, 41, 45, 55, 63, 66, 68, 73, 76, 95, 101, 116, 119, 120, 124, 134, 140	10, 11, 17, 18, 39, 46, 117
Relating Cause and Effect			11, 18, 19, 26, 27, 37, 40, 51, 57, 66, 84, 86, 89, 100, 101, 104, 112, 122, 140	
Making Generalizations			70	
Making Judgments	20–21		81, 135, 137, 140	
Problem Solving	5, 20–21, 33, 52–53, 107		30, 76	
Informational Organizational SKILLS				
Concept Maps			29, 75, 103	28, 74, 102, 127, 138
Compare/Contrast Tables				39, 97
Venn Diagrams				
Flowcharts			139	99, 115
Cycle Diagrams				

The ***Science Explorer*** program provides additional teaching, reinforcement, and assessment of skills in the *Inquiry Skills Activities Book* and the *Integrated Science Laboratory Manual*.

A National Look at Science Education

Project 2061 was established by the American Association for the Advancement of Science (AAAS) as a long-term project to improve science education nationwide. A primary goal of Project 2061 is to define a "common core of learning"—the knowledge and skills we want all students to achieve. Project 2061 published *Science for All Americans* in 1989 and followed this with *Benchmarks for Science Literacy* in 1993. *Benchmarks* recommends what students should know and be able to do by the end of grades 2, 5, 8, and 12. Project 2061 clearly states that *Benchmarks* is not a curriculum but a tool for designing successful curricula.

The National Research Council (NRC) used *Science for All Americans* and *Benchmarks* to develop the National Science Education Standards (NSES), which were published in 1996. The NSES are organized into six categories (Content, Teaching, Assessment, Professional Development, Program, and System) to help schools establish the conditions necessary to achieve scientific literacy for all students.

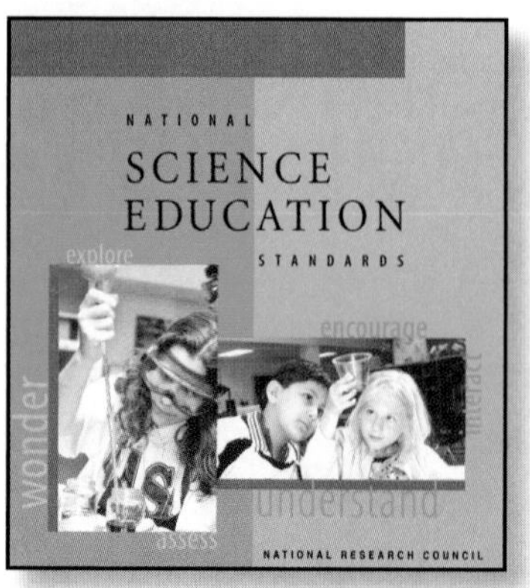

Michael Padilla, the program author of *Science Explorer,* guided one of six teams of teachers whose work led to the publication of *Benchmarks.* He also was a contributing writer of the National Science Education Standards. Under his guidance, *Science Explorer* has implemented these standards through its inquiry approach, a focus on student learning of important concepts and skills, and teacher support aligned with the NSES teaching standards.

Neither *Benchmarks* nor the NSES requires a single, uniform national curriculum, and in fact there is a great diversity nationwide in science curricula. The correlations that follow are designed to help you use the *Science Explorer* program to meet your particular curriculum needs.

Meeting the National Science Education Standards

MAGNETISM

Science as Inquiry (Content Standard A)

- **Design and conduct a scientific investigation** Students conduct an investigation of how magnets can be used to detect fake coins. *(Skills Lab)*

Physical Science (Content Standard B)

- **Properties and changes of properties in matter** The attraction or repulsion of magnetic materials is called magnetism. A material that shows strong magnetic properties is said to be a ferromagnetic material. *(What Is Magnetism?; Inside a Magnet)*

Earth and Space Science (Content Standard D)

- **Structure of the Earth system** The circulation of molten material in Earth's core is related to Earth's magnetism. *(Magnetic Earth)*
- **Earth's history** When molten material hardens into rock on the ocean floor, the direction of Earth's magnetic field at that time is permanently recorded. *(Magnetic Earth)*
- **Earth in the solar system** Earth's magnetic field affects the movement of electrically charged particles in space. *(Magnetic Earth)*

Science and Technology (Content Standard E)

- **Design a solution or product** Students use magnetism to create art. Students design and construct a magnetic paper clip holder. *(Chapter Project; Design Your Own Lab)*

ELECTRICITY

Science as Inquiry (Content Standard A)

- **Design and conduct a scientific investigation** Students determine why a versorium turns. *(Skills Lab)*

Physical Science (Content Standard B)

- **Transfer of energy** The interaction between electric charges is called electricity. Electric current is the continuous flow of electric charges through a material. An electromagnetic cell is a device that transforms chemical energy into electrical energy. Electrical circuits have devices that are run by electrical energy, have a source of electrical energy, and are connected by conducting wires. The rate at which energy is transformed from one form to another is known as power. *(Electric Charge and Static Electricity; Electric Current; Batteries; Electric Circuits; Electric Power)*

A National Look at Science Education *(continued)*

Science and Technology (Content Standard E)

- **Design a solution or product** Students design and construct an alarm circuit. Students design and construct a dimmer switch. *(Chapter Project; Skills Lab)*

Science in Personal and Social Perspectives (Content Standard F)

- **Personal health** Potential dangers of electric current include short circuits, electric shocks, and ungrounded wires. *(Electrical Safety)*

USING ELECTRICITY AND MAGNETISM

Science as Inquiry (Content Standard A)

- **Design and conduct a scientific investigation** Students investigate how an electric motor operates. *(Skills Lab)*
- **Use appropriate tools and techniques to gather, analyze, and interpret data** Students conduct electrical energy audits of their homes. *(Chapter Project)*

Physical Science (Content Standard B)

- **Transfer of energy** The relationship between electricity and magnetism is called electromagnetism. When a wire with a current is placed in a magnetic field, electrical energy is transformed into mechanical energy. An electric current is induced in a conductor when the conductor moves through a magnetic field. *(What Is Electricity?; Electricity, Magnetism, and Motion; Electricity From Magnetism)*

Science and Technology (Content Standard E)

- **Understandings about science and technology** Electromagnets have many uses. Generators are used to produce electrical energy, and transformers are used in the transmission of electrical energy. *(What Is Electromagnetism?; Electricity From Magnetism)*

Science in Personal and Social Perspectives (Content Standard F)

- **Science and technology in society** Students weigh the impact of magnetic resonance imaging. *(Technology and Society)*

History and Nature of Science (Content Standard G)

- **History of science** Several scientists over the years were responsible for bringing electrical energy into everyday use. *(Technology and History)*

ELECTRONICS

Science as Inquiry (Content Standard A)

- **Design and conduct a scientific investigation** Students investigate how to tell if a battery is installed correctly. *(Technology Lab)*
- **Develop descriptions, explanations, predictions, and models using evidence** Students make a model of a computer program. *(Skills Lab)*

Physical Science (Content Standard B)

- **Transfer of energy** Electronic signals can be carried over long distances by electromagnetic waves. *(Electronic Communication)*

Science and Technology (Content Standard E)

- **Evaluate completed technological designs or products** Students study an existing computer application and then propose a new one. *(Chapter Project)*
- **Understandings about science and technology** Electronics is the use of electric current to control, communicate, and process information. *(Electronic Signals and Devices; Electronic Communication; Computers; The Information Superhighway)*

Science in Personal and Social Perspectives (Content Standard F)

- **Science and technology in society** Computer networks provide great benefits but also pose potential problems. Digital manipulation provides advantages and disadvantages in modern society. *(The Information Superhighway; Science and Society)*

History and Nature of Science (Content Standard G)

- **History of science** Computers have come a long way in a relatively short period of time. *(Science and History)*

Note: To see how the benchmarks are supported by *SCIENCE EXPLORER,* go to **PHSchool.com.**

Reading Comprehension in the Science Classroom

Q&A

Q: Why are science texts often difficult for students to read and comprehend?

A: In general, science texts make complex literacy and knowledge demands on learners. They have a more technical vocabulary and a more demanding syntax, and place a greater emphasis on inferential reasoning.

Q: What does research say about facilitating comprehension?

A: Studies comparing novices and experts show that the conceptual organization of experts' knowledge is very different from that of novices. For example, experts emphasize core concepts when organizing knowledge, while novices focus on superficial details. To facilitate comprehension, effective teaching strategies should support and scaffold students as they build an understanding of the key concepts and concept relationships within a text unit.

Q: What strategies can teachers use to facilitate comprehension?

A: Three complementary strategies are very important in facilitating student comprehension of science texts. First, guide student interaction with the text using the built-in strategies. Second, organize the curriculum in terms of core concepts (e.g., the **Key Concepts** in each section). Third, develop visual representations of the relationships among the key concepts and vocabulary that can be referred to during instruction.

Nancy Romance, Ph.D.
Professor of Science Education
Florida Atlantic University
Fort Lauderdale, Florida

"Effective teaching strategies should support and scaffold students as they build an understanding of the key concepts and concept relationships within a text unit."

Reading Support in *Science Explorer*

The latest research emphasizes the importance of activating learners' prior knowledge and teaching them to distinguish core concepts from less important information. These skills are now more important than ever, because success in science requires students to read, understand, and connect complex terms and concepts.

Before students read—

Reading Preview introduces students to the key concepts and key terms they'll find in each section. The **Target Reading Skill** is identified and applied with a graphic organizer.

During the section—

Boldface Sentences identify each key concept and encourage students to focus on the big ideas of science.

Reading Checkpoints reinforce students' understanding by slowing them down to review after every concept is discussed.

Caption Questions draw students into the art and photos, helping them connect the content to the images.

After students read—

Section Assessment revisits the **Target Reading Skill** and encourages students to use the graphic organizer.

Each review question is scaffolded and models the way students think, by first easing them into a review and then challenging them with increasingly more difficult questions.

Evaluator's Checklist

Does your science program promote reading comprehension with—

- ✔ Text structured in an outline format and key concepts highlighted in boldface type
- ✔ Real-world applications to activate prior knowledge
- ✔ Key concepts, critical vocabulary, and a reading skill for every section
- ✔ Sample graphic organizers for each section
- ✔ Relevant photos and carefully constructed graphics with questions
- ✔ Reading checkpoints that appear in each section
- ✔ Scaffolded questions in section assessments

Math in the Science Classroom

Why should students concern themselves with mathematics in your science class?

Good science requires good data from which to draw conclusions. Technology enhances the ability to measure in a variety of ways. Often the scientist must measure large amounts of data, and thus an aim of analysis is to reduce the data to a summary that makes sense and is consistent with established norms of communication—i.e., mathematics.

Calculating measures of central tendency (e.g., mean, median, or mode), variability (e.g., range), and shape (graphic representations) can effectively reduce 500 data points to 3 without losing the essential characteristics of the data. Scientists understand that a trade-off exists between precision and richness as data are folded into categories, and so margins of error can be quantified in mathematical terms and factored into all scientific findings.

Mathematics is the language used by scientists to model change in the world. Understanding change is a vital part of the inquiry process. Mathematics serves as a common language to communicate across the sciences. Fields of scientific research that originated as separate disciplines are now integrated, such as happened with bioengineering. What do the sciences have in common? Each uses the language of mathematics to communicate about data and the process of data analysis. Recognizing this need, *Science Explorer* integrates mathematics practice throughout the program and gives students ample opportunity to hone their math skills.

Clearly, mathematics plays an important role in your science classroom!

William Tate, Ph.D.
Professor of Education and Applied Statistics and Computation
Washington University
St. Louis, Missouri

"Mathematics is the language used by scientists to model change in the world."

Integrated Math Support

In the Student Edition

The math instruction is based on principles derived from Prentice Hall's research-based mathematics program.

Sample Problems, Math Practice, Analyzing Data, and a Math Skills Handbook all help to provide practice at point of use, encouraging students to Read and Understand, Plan and Solve, and then Look Back and Check.

Color-coded variables aid student navigation and help reinforce their comprehension.

In the Teacher's Edition

Math teaching notes enable the science teacher to support math instruction and math objectives on high-stakes tests.

In the Guided Reading and Study Workbook

These unique worksheets help students master reading and enhance their study and math skills. Students can create a record of their work for study and review.

Evaluator's Checklist

Does your science program promote math skills by—

- ✔ Giving students opportunities to collect data
- ✔ Providing students opportunities to analyze data
- ✔ Enabling students to practice math skills
- ✔ Helping students solve equations by using color-coded variables
- ✔ Using sample problems to apply science concepts

Technology and Design in the Science Classroom

Much of the world we live in is designed and made by humans. The buildings in which we live, the cars we drive, the medicines we take, and often the food we eat are products of technology. The knowledge and skills needed to understand the processes used to create these products should be a component of every student's basic literacy.

Some schools offer hands-on instruction on how technology development works through industrial arts curricula. Even then, there is a disconnect among science (understanding how nature works), mathematics (understanding data-driven models), and technology (understanding the human-made world). The link among these fields of study is the engineering design process—that process by which one identifies a human need and uses science knowledge and human ingenuity to create a technology to satisfy the need. Engineering gives students the problem-solving and design skills they will need to succeed in our sophisticated, three-dimensional, technological world.

As a complement to "science as inquiry," the National Science Education Standards (NRC, 1996) call for students at all age levels to develop the abilities related to "technology as design," including the ability to identify and frame a problem and then to design, implement, and evaluate a solution. At the 5–8 grade level, the standards call for students to be engaged in complex problem-solving and to learn more about how science and technology complement each other. It's also important for students to understand that there are often constraints involved in design as well as trade-offs and unintended consequences of technological solutions to problems.

As the *Standards for Technological Literacy* (ITEA, 2000) state, "Science and technology are like conjoined twins. While they have separate identities they must remain inextricably connected." Both sets of standards emphasize how progress in science leads to new developments in technology, while technological innovation in turn drives advances in science.

Ioannis Miaoulis, Ph.D.
President
Museum of Science
Boston, Massachusetts

"Engineering gives students the problem-solving and design skills they will need to succeed in our sophisticated, three-dimensional, technological world."

Evaluator's Checklist

Does your science program promote technology and design by—

- ✔ Incorporating technology and design concepts and skills into the science curriculum
- ✔ Giving students opportunities to identify and solve technological design problems
- ✔ Providing students opportunities to analyze the impact of technology on society
- ✔ Enabling students to practice technology and design skills

Technology and Design in *Science Explorer*

How often do you hear your students ask: "Why do I need to learn this?" Connecting them to the world of technology and design in their everyday life is one way to help answer this question. It is also why so many state science curricula are now emphasizing technology and design concepts and skills.

Science Explorer makes a special effort to include a technology and design strand that encourages students to not only identify a need but to take what they learned in science and apply it to design a possible solution, build a prototype, test and evaluate the design, and/or troubleshoot the design. This strand also provides definitions of technology and engineering and discusses the similarities and differences between these endeavors and science. Students will learn to analyze the risks and benefits of a new technology and to consider the tradeoffs, such as safety, costs, efficiency, and appearance.

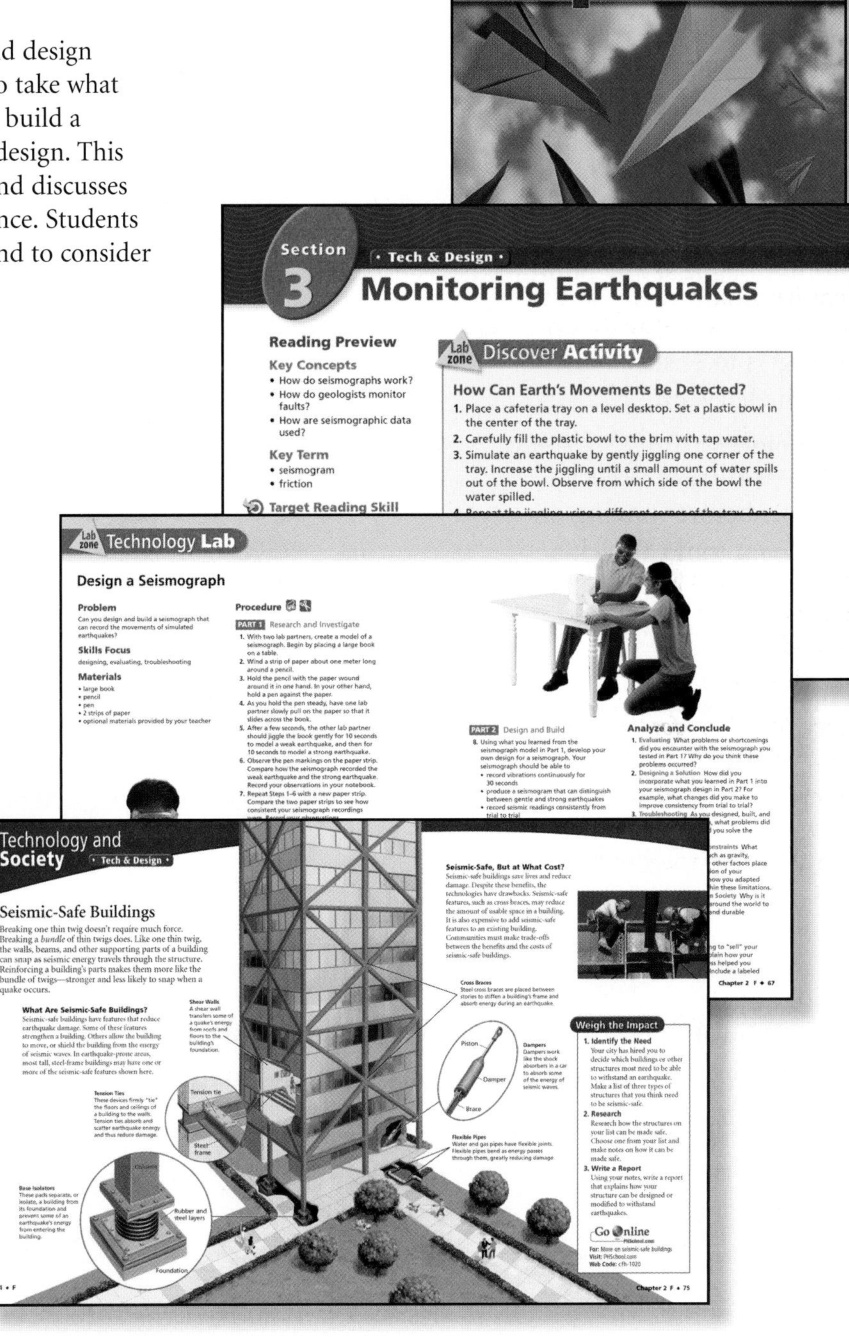

In the Student Edition

Integrated Technology & Design Sections

Sections throughout *Science Explorer* specifically integrate technology and design with the content of the text. For example, students not only learn how seismographs work but also learn what role seismographs play in society and how people use the data that are gathered.

Technology Labs

These labs help students gain experience in designing and building a device or product that meets a particular need or solves a problem. Students follow a design process of Research and Investigate, Design and Build, and Evaluate and Redesign.

Chapter Projects

Chapter Projects work hand-in-hand with the chapter content. Students design, build, and test based on real-world situations. They have the opportunity to apply the knowledge and skills learned to building a product.

Special Features

This technology and design strand is also reflected in Technology & Society and Science & Society features as well as Science & History timelines and Tech & Design in History timelines. These highly visual features introduce a technology and its impact on society. For example, students learn how a hybrid car differs from a traditional car.

Assessment

Assessment in the Science Curriculum

No Child Left Behind clearly challenges school districts across the nation to raise expectations for all students with testing of student achievement in science beginning in 2007–2008.

A primary goal of NCLB is to provide classroom teachers with better data from scientifically valid assessments in order to inform instructional planning and to identify students who are at risk and require intervention. It has been a common practice to teach a science lesson, administer a test, grade it, and move on. This practice is a thing of the past. With the spotlight now on improving student performance, it is essential to use assessment results as a way to identify student strengths and challenges. Providing student feedback and obtaining student input is a valuable, essential part of the assessment process.

Assessment is a never-ending cycle, as is shown in the following diagram. Although you may begin at any point in the assessment cycle, the basic process is the same.

An important assessment strategy is to ensure that students have ample opportunities to check their understanding of skills and concepts before moving on to the next topic. Checking for understanding also includes asking appropriate, probing questions with each example presented. This enables students and teachers to know whether the skills or concepts being introduced are actually understood.

ASSESS: Use a variety of assessment tools to gain information and strengthen student understanding.

ANALYZE: Analyze assessment results to create a picture of student strengths and challenges.

TARGET: Choose a target to create a focused path on which to proceed.

STRATEGIZE: Identify strategies to achieve the target, create a plan for implementation, and choose assessments tools.

IMPLEMENT: Implement the plan with a focus on gathering and using assessment information throughout.

Eileen Depka
Supervisor of Standards and Assessment
Waukesha, Wisconsin

"Meeting the NCLB challenge will necessitate an integrated approach to assessment with a variety of assessment tools."

Evaluator's Checklist

Does your science program include assessments that—

- ✔ Are embedded before, during, and after lesson instruction
- ✔ Align to standards and to the instructional program
- ✔ Assess both skill acquisition and understanding
- ✔ Include meaningful rubrics to guide students
- ✔ Mirror the various formats of standardized tests

Prentice Hall *Science Explorer* now includes Success Tracker, an online tool to help teachers monitor and assess student progress with built-in remediation. Ask your sales rep about Success Tracker today!

Success  Tracker™
Online at PHSchool.com

Assessment in *Science Explorer*

Science Explorer's **remarkable range of strategies for checking progress will help teachers find the right opportunity for reaching all their students.**

The assessment strategies in *Science Explorer* will help both students and teachers alike ensure student success in content mastery as well as high-stakes test performance. A wealth of opportunities built into the Student Edition helps students monitor their own progress. Teachers are supported with ongoing assessment opportunities in the Teacher's Edition and an easy-to-use, editable test generator linked to content objectives. These integrated, ongoing assessment tools assure success.

Especially to support state and national testing objectives, Prentice Hall has developed test preparation materials that model the NCLB approach.

- **Diagnostic Assessment** tools provide in-depth analysis of strengths and weaknesses, areas of difficulty, and probable underlying causes that can help teachers make instructional decisions and plan intervention strategies.
- **Progress Monitoring** tools aligned with content objectives and state tests provide ongoing, longitudinal records of student achievement detailing individual student progress toward meeting end-of-year and end-of-schooling grade level, district, or state standards.
- **Outcomes** tools that mimic state and national tests show whether individual students have met the expected standards and can help a school system judge whether it has made adequate progress in improving its performance year by year.

Caption Questions enhance critical thinking skills.

Reading Checkpoints reinforce students' understanding.

Scaffolded Section Assessment Questions model the way students think.

Comprehensive Chapter Reviews and Assessments provide opportunities for students to check their own understanding and practice valuable high-stakes test-taking skills.

***ExamView*® Computer Test Bank CD-ROM** provides teachers access to thousands of modifiable test questions in English and Spanish.

Test Preparation Blackline Masters and Student Workbook include diagnostic and prescription tools, progress-monitoring aids, and practice tests that help teachers focus on improving test scores.

Section 3 Assessment

Target Reading Skill Sequencing Refer to your flowchart about seismographs as you answer Question 1.

Reviewing Key Concepts

1. a. Defining What is a seismogram?
   b. Explaining How can geologists tell apart the different types of seismic waves on a seismogram?
   c. Comparing and Contrasting Two identical seismographs are located 1,000 km and 1,200 km from an earthquake's epicenter. How would the two seismograms for the earthquake compare?
2. a. Reviewing What changes are measured by the instruments used to monitor faults?
   b. Describing How are satellites used to measure movements along a fault?
   c. Inferring A satellite that monitors a fault detects an increasing tilt in the land surface along the fault. What could this change in the land surface indicate?
3. a. Listing What are three ways in which geologists use seismographic data?
   b. Explaining How do geologists use seismographic data to make maps of faults?
   c. Making Generalizations Why is it difficult to predict earthquakes?

Writing in Science

Dialogue Geologists in Alaska have just detected an earthquake and located the earthquake's epicenter. Write a dialogue in which the geologists notify a disaster response team that will help people in the earthquake area.

Chapter 2 F ◆ 65

Standardized Test Prep

Test-Taking Tip
When answering questions about diagrams, read all parts of the diagram carefully, including title, captions, and labels. Make sure that you understand the meaning of arrows and other symbols. Determine exactly what the question asks. Then eliminate those answer choices that are not supported by the diagram.

Practice answering this question.
The diagram shows how stress affects a mass of rock in a process called
A compression.
B tension.
C squeezing.
D shearing.
The correct answer is D because the arrows show rock being pulled in opposite directions.

Choose the letter that best answers the question or completes the statement.

1. In a strike-slip fault, rock masses along the fault move
   A in the same direction.
   B down only.
   C together.
   D sideways past each other.
2. Stress will build until an earthquake occurs if friction along a fault is
   F decreasing. G high.
   H low. J changed to heat.

Use the information below and your knowledge of science to answer Questions 3 and 4.

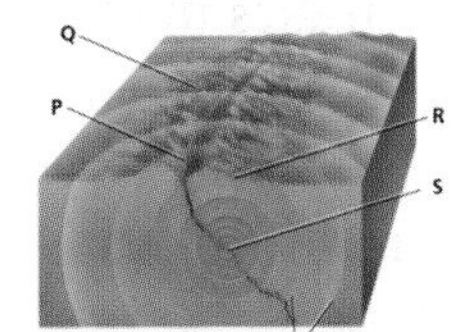

3. When an earthquake occurs, seismic waves travel
   A from P in all directions.
   B from R to S.
   C from S in all directions.
   D from Q to P.
4. At point R, seismic waves from an earthquake would be
   F weaker than at P.
   G likely to cause little damage.
   H weaker than at Q.
   J likely to cause the most damage.
5. To estimate the total energy released by an earthquake, a geologist should use the
   A Mercalli scale. B Richter scale.
   C epicenter scale. D moment magnitude scale.

Constructed Response

6. A geologist discovers a large fault beneath a major city. Why would this information be helpful in determining earthquake risk in the area? What three safety steps should the geologist recommend?

Chapter 2 F ◆ 79

Master Materials List

SCIENCE EXPLORER offers an abundance of activity options in the Student Edition so you can pick and choose those that suit your needs. Prentice Hall has worked with Neo/SCI Corporation to develop Consumable Kits and Nonconsumable Kits that precisely match the needs of the *SCIENCE EXPLORER* labs. Use this Master Materials List or the Materials Ordering CD-ROM to help order your supplies. For more information on materials kits for this program, contact your local Prentice Hall sales representative or Neo/SCI Corporation at 1-800-526-6689 or **www.neosci.com**.

Consumable Materials

Description	Textbook Section(s)	Quantity per class
Aluminum foil, roll	2-1(Lab), 2-3(DIS), 2-3(Lab)	1
Ball, cork, 1"	1-3(DIS)	5
Ball, styrofoam, 1"	1-3(DIS)	5
Balloon, 9", pkg/20	2-1(DIS)	1
Battery, 6 V	2-4(SA), 2-4(DIS), 3-2(TT)	10
Battery, D-cell	2-1(CP), 2-2(DIS), 2-2(Lab), 2-3(Lab), 2-4(DIS), 2-4(SA), 2-6(DIS), 3-1(DIS), 3-1(TT), 3-2(DIS), 3-2(Lab), 4-1(DIS), 4-1(Lab)	10
Bulb, light, mini, pkg/10	2-1(CP), 2-2(DIS), 2-2(Lab), 2-3(Lab), 2-4(DIS), 2-4(SA), 2-5(DIS), 2-6(DIS), 3-1(DIS), 4-1(Lab)	2
*Can, aluminum, empty	2-1(DIS)	5
Cardboard, 32 x 32 cm	1-1(Lab)	5
*Chalk	1-3(SA)	1
Cup, foam, 6 oz, pkg/50	1-1(SA), 1-2(Lab), 2-1(Lab)	1
Fabric, wool, 12 x 60"	2-1(Lab)	1
Iron filings, 8 oz	1-2(DIS)	2
Lead, pencil, 0.9 mm	2-2(Lab)	5
Marker, permanent	2-3(Lab)	5
Modeling clay, white, 1 lb	1-2(Lab), 2-2(DIS), 3-2(Lab), 3-3(DIS)	4
*Newspaper, local	3-4(Lab), 4-3(Lab), 4-4(DIS)	1
Pan, aluminum, 9"	2-1(TT)	5
*Paper towel, roll	2-3(DIS)	1
Paper, tissue	2-1(SA)	5
*Paper, white, ream	1-3(TT), 2-1(Lab), 3-4(Lab), 4-1(DIS)	1
Paper clips, pkg/100	1-1(DIS), 1-2(Lab), 2-3(Lab), 3-1(TT), 3-2(Lab)	9
Paper clips, jumbo, pkg/100	3-2(Lab)	1
*Pencil	1-1(SA), 1-1(Lab), 2-1(Lab), 3-4(Lab)	15
Plate, foam, 9", pkg/15	2-1(TT), 2-1(Lab)	1
Salt, 100 g	2-3(DIS)	1
Sandpaper, pkg/5	3-2(Lab)	1
Soap, dishwashing, 14.7 oz	1-3(DIS)	1
Spoon, plastic, pkg/25	2-3(DIS)	1
Steel wool, pkg/5	2-6(DIS)	1
Stick, craft, pkg/25	1-1(Lab)	1
String, ball	1-2(Lab)	1
Tape, duct, roll	2-3(Lab)	1
Tape, electrical, roll	2-2(DIS), 2-3(Lab), 3-1(TT), 4-1(Lab)	1
Tape, masking, roll	1-1(Lab), 1-2(Lab), 1-3(SA), 2-1(TT), 2-2(DIS), 2-2(Lab), 2-3(Lab)	1
Vinegar, 30 mL	2-3(DIS)	1
Water, tap, gallon	1-3(DIS), 2-2(TT)	1

KEY: CP: Chapter Project; **DIS:** Discover; **SA:** Skills Activity; **TT:** Try This; **Lab:** Skills, Consumer, Design Your Own, or Technology
* items school supplied

Quantities based on five groups of six students per class.

Master Materials List

Nonconsumable Materials

Description	Textbook Section(s)	Quantity per class
Alligator clips	2-2(Lab), 2-2(DIS), 2-3(Lab), 2-6(DIS), 4-1(Lab)	20
Battery holder, D-cell	2-1(CP), 2-2(DIS), 2-2(Lab), 2-4(DIS), 2-4(SA), 2-6(DIS), 3-1(DIS), 3-2(DIS), 3-2(Lab), 4-1(Lab)	10
Beaker, polypropylene, 250 mL	2-2(TT)	5
Bolt, 4"	3-2(DIS)	5
*Book	3-2(DIS)	15
Bricks, interlocking, set	4-3(Lab)	10
*Calculator	4-3(DIS)	5
Cap, for plastic vial	1-2(DIS)	5
*Clamp, ring stand	2-2(TT)	5
*Coins, variety	1-1(Lab)	25
Comb, plastic	2-1(SA)	5
Compass	1-3(SA), 1-3(TT), 2-2(DIS), 3-1(DIS)	15
*Dish or bowl	1-3(DIS)	5
Film canister	3-2(Lab)	5
Flashlight, D-cell	2-3(Lab), 4-1(DIS), 4-1(Lab)	10
Funnel	2-2(TT)	5
*Galvanometer	3-3(DIS)	5
*Generator, hand	2-5(DIS)	5
*Glass, drinking	2-3(DIS)	5
Hand lens, pkg/5	4-2(DIS)	1
*Hole punch	2-1(SA)	5
LED	4-1(Lab)	5
Magnet, bar	1-1(CP), 1-1(DIS), 1-1(Lab), 1-1(SA), 1-2(Lab), 1-2(DIS), 1-3(DIS), 1-3(TT), 3-2(TT)	10
Magnet, circular	1-1(SA), 1-2(Lab), 3-2(Lab)	10
Magnet, horseshoe	1-1(DIS), 1-2(Lab), 3-2(DIS), 3-3(DIS)	5
*Map, local	1-3(DIS), 1-3(SA)	5
*Nail, iron	3-1(TT)	5
*Nail, steel	3-2(DIS)	5
Needle, large	1-3(DIS)	5
*Penny	2-3(DIS)	5
*Pliers	3-2(Lab)	5
Protractor	1-1(Lab), 1-3(SA)	5
*Ring stand	2-2(TT)	5
Ruler, 15 cm, pkg/10	1-1(Lab), 2-2(DIS), 3-2(DIS)	5
*Scissors	2-1(TT), 2-1(Lab), 2-3(DIS), 2-3(Lab)	5
Socket, mini	2-1(CP), 2-2(DIS), 2-2(Lab), 2-4(DIS), 2-4(SA), 2-5(DIS), 2-6(DIS), 3-1(DIS), 4-1(Lab)	20
Stirring Rod	2-3(DIS)	5
*Stopwatch	2-2(TT), 2-3(Lab)	5
Switch	2-1(CP), 2-2(DIS), 2-4(DIS), 2-4(SA), 3-2(DIS)	5
*Television, color	4-2(DIS)	1
Tube, cardboard, 1 x 4"	2-3(Lab)	5
Tube, plastic, rigid, 6 x 1.5"	1-2(DIS)	5
Tubing, clear plastic, 3/8 x 1/16", 1 ft	1-2(DIS), 2-2(TT)	5
Tubing, rubber, 1/8 x 1/16", 1 ft	2-2(Lab)	2
*Voltmeter	2-3(DIS)	5
Washer, steel, 3/4 x 5/16", pkg/140	1-1(Lab)	1
Wire, enamel-coated, 4 oz	3-2(Lab)	2
Wire, insulated, copper, 4 oz	2-1(CP), 2-2(Lab), 2-2(DIS), 2-3(Lab), 2-4(DIS), 2-4(SA), 3-1(DIS), 3-1(TT), 3-2(DIS), 3-2(TT), 3-2(Lab), 3-3(DIS), 4-1(Lab)	1
Wire, noninsulated, copper, 4 oz	2-2(Lab)	1
Wire cutter and strippers	2-2(DIS)	1

KEY: CP: Chapter Project; **DIS:** Discover; **SA:** Skills Activity; **TT:** Try This; **Lab:** Skills, Consumer, Design Your Own, or Technology
* items school supplied

Quantities based on five groups of six students per class.

Electricity and Magnetism

Book-Specific Resources
Student Edition
StudentExpress™ with Interactive Textbook
Teacher's Edition
All-in-One Teaching Resources
Color Transparencies
Guided Reading and Study Workbook
Student Edition on Audio CD
Discovery Channel School® Video
Lab Activity Video
Consumable and Nonconsumable Materials Kits

Program Print Resources
Integrated Science Laboratory Manual
Computer Microscope Lab Manual
Inquiry Skills Activity Books
Progress Monitoring Assessments
Test Preparation Workbook
Test-Taking Tips With Transparencies
Teacher's ELL Handbook
Reading Strategies for Science Content

Differentiated Instruction Resources
Adapted Reading and Study Workbook
Adapted Tests
Differentiated Instruction Guide for Labs and Activities

Program Technology Resources
TeacherExpress™ CD-ROM
Interactive Textbooks Online
PresentationExpress™ CD-ROM
ExamView®, Computer Test Bank CD-ROM
Lab zone™ Easy Planner CD-ROM
Probeware Lab Manual With CD-ROM
Computer Microscope and Lab Manual
Materials Ordering CD-ROM
Discovery Channel School® DVD Library
Lab Activity DVD Library
Web Site at PHSchool.com

Spanish Print Resources
Spanish Student Edition
Spanish Guided Reading and Study Workbook
Spanish Teaching Guide With Tests

Acknowledgments appear on page 182, which constitutes an extension of this copyright page.

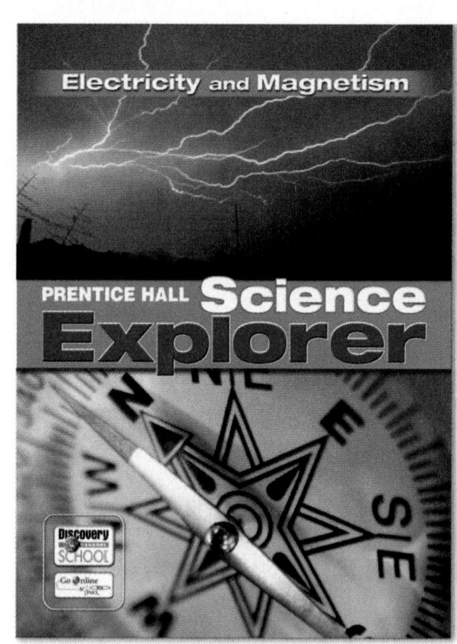

Cover
A spectacular discharge of static electricity flashes across the night sky (top). The north magnetic pole to which a compass needle points slowly moves over time (bottom).

ISBN 0-13-201158-1
1 2 3 4 5 6 7 8 9 10 10 09 08 07 06

Program Authors

Michael J. Padilla, Ph.D.
Professor of Science Education
University of Georgia
Athens, Georgia

Michael Padilla is a leader in middle school science education. He has served as an author and elected officer for the National Science Teachers Association and as a writer of the National Science Education Standards. As lead author of Science Explorer, Mike has inspired the team in developing a program that meets the needs of middle grades students, promotes science inquiry, and is aligned with the National Science Education Standards.

Ioannis Miaoulis, Ph.D.
President
Museum of Science
Boston, Massachusetts

Originally trained as a mechanical engineer, Ioannis Miaoulis is in the forefront of the national movement to increase technological literacy. As dean of the Tufts University School of Engineering, Dr. Miaoulis spearheaded the introduction of engineering into the Massachusetts curriculum. Currently he is working with school systems across the country to engage students in engineering activities and to foster discussions on the impact of science and technology on society.

Martha Cyr, Ph.D.
Director of K–12 Outreach
Worcester Polytechnic Institute
Worcester, Massachusetts

Martha Cyr is a noted expert in engineering outreach. She has over nine years of experience with programs and activities that emphasize the use of engineering principles, through hands-on projects, to excite and motivate students and teachers of mathematics and science in grades K–12. Her goal is to stimulate a continued interest in science and mathematics through engineering.

Book Author

Camille L. Wainwright, Ph.D.
Professor of Science Education
Pacific University
Forest Grove, Oregon

Contributing Writers

Edward Evans
Former Science Teacher
Hilton Central School
Hilton, New York

Mark Illingworth
Teacher
Hollis Public Schools
Hollis, New Hampshire

Thomas L. Messer
Science Teacher
Cape Cod Academy
Osterville, Massachusetts

Thomas R. Wellnitz
Science Teacher
The Paideia School
Atlanta, Georgia

Consultants

Reading Consultant

Nancy Romance, Ph.D.
Professor of Science Education
Florida Atlantic University
Fort Lauderdale, Florida

Mathematics Consultant

William Tate, Ph.D.
Professor of Education and Applied Statistics and Computation
Washington University
St. Louis, Missouri

N • iii

Reviewers

Tufts University Content Reviewers

Faculty from Tufts University in Medford, Massachusetts, developed *Science Explorer* chapter projects and reviewed the student books.

Astier M. Almedom, Ph.D.
Department of Biology

Wayne Chudyk, Ph.D.
Department of Civil and Environmental Engineering

John L. Durant, Ph.D.
Department of Civil and Environmental Engineering

George S. Ellmore, Ph.D.
Department of Biology

David Kaplan, Ph.D.
Department of Biomedical Engineering

Samuel Kounaves, Ph.D.
Department of Chemistry

David H. Lee, Ph.D.
Department of Chemistry

Douglas Matson, Ph.D.
Department of Mechanical Engineering

Karen Panetta, Ph.D.
Department of Electrical Engineering and Computer Science

Jan A. Pechenik, Ph.D.
Department of Biology

John C. Ridge, Ph.D.
Department of Geology

William Waller, Ph.D.
Department of Astronomy

Content Reviewers

Paul Beale, Ph.D.
Department of Physics
University of Colorado
Boulder, Colorado

Jeff Bodart, Ph.D.
Chipola Junior College
Marianna, Florida

Michael Castellani, Ph.D.
Department of Chemistry
Marshall University
Huntington, West Virginia

Eugene Chiang, Ph.D.
Department of Astronomy
University of California – Berkeley
Berkeley, California

Charles C. Curtis, Ph.D.
Department of Physics
University of Arizona
Tucson, Arizona

Daniel Kirk-Davidoff, Ph.D.
Department of Meteorology
University of Maryland
College Park, Maryland

Diane T. Doser, Ph.D.
Department of Geological Sciences
University of Texas at El Paso
El Paso, Texas

R. E. Duhrkopf, Ph.D.
Department of Biology
Baylor University
Waco, Texas

Michael Hacker
Co-director, Center for Technological Literacy
Hofstra University
Hempstead, New York

Michael W. Hamburger, Ph.D.
Department of Geological Sciences
Indiana University
Bloomington, Indiana

Alice K. Hankla, Ph.D.
The Galloway School
Atlanta, Georgia

Donald C. Jackson, Ph.D.
Department of Molecular Pharmacology, Physiology, & Biotechnology
Brown University
Providence, Rhode Island

Jeremiah N. Jarrett, Ph.D.
Department of Biological Sciences
Central Connecticut State University
New Britain, Connecticut

David Lederman, Ph.D.
Department of Physics
West Virginia University
Morgantown, West Virginia

Becky Mansfield, Ph.D.
Department of Geography
Ohio State University
Columbus, Ohio

Elizabeth M. Martin, M.S.
Department of Chemistry and Biochemistry
College of Charleston
Charleston, South Carolina

Joe McCullough, Ph.D.
Department of Natural and Applied Sciences
Cabrillo College
Aptos, California

Robert J. Mellors, Ph.D.
Department of Geological Sciences
San Diego State University
San Diego, California

Joseph M. Moran, Ph.D.
American Meteorological Society
Washington, D.C.

David J. Morrissey, Ph.D.
Department of Chemistry
Michigan State University
East Lansing, Michigan

Philip A. Reed, Ph.D.
Department of Occupational & Technical Studies
Old Dominion University
Norfolk, Virginia

Scott M. Rochette, Ph.D.
Department of the Earth Sciences
State University of New York, College at Brockport
Brockport, New York

Laurence D. Rosenhein, Ph.D.
Department of Chemistry
Indiana State University
Terre Haute, Indiana

Ronald Sass, Ph.D.
Department of Biology and Chemistry
Rice University
Houston, Texas

George Schatz, Ph.D.
Department of Chemistry
Northwestern University
Evanston, Illinois

Sara Seager, Ph.D.
Carnegie Institution of Washington
Washington, D.C.

Robert M. Thornton, Ph.D.
Section of Plant Biology
University of California
Davis, California

John R. Villarreal, Ph.D.
College of Science and Engineering
The University of Texas – Pan American
Edinburg, Texas

Kenneth Welty, Ph.D.
School of Education
University of Wisconsin–Stout
Menomonie, Wisconsin

Edward J. Zalisko, Ph.D.
Department of Biology
Blackburn College
Carlinville, Illinois

Teacher Reviewers

David R. Blakely
Arlington High School
Arlington, Massachusetts

Jane E. Callery
Two Rivers Magnet Middle School
East Hartford, Connecticut

Melissa Lynn Cook
Oakland Mills High School
Columbia, Maryland

James Fattic
Southside Middle School
Anderson, Indiana

Dan Gabel
Hoover Middle School
Rockville, Maryland

Wayne Goates
Eisenhower Middle School
Goddard, Kansas

Katherine Bobay Graser
Mint Hill Middle School
Charlotte, North Carolina

Darcy Hampton
Deal Junior High School
Washington, D.C.

Karen Kelly
Pierce Middle School
Waterford, Michigan

David Kelso
Manchester High School Central
Manchester, New Hampshire

Benigno Lopez, Jr.
Sleepy Hill Middle School
Lakeland, Florida

Angie L. Matamoros, Ph.D.
ALM Consulting, Inc.
Weston, Florida

Tim McCollum
Charleston Middle School
Charleston, Illinois

Bruce A. Mellin
Brooks School
North Andover, Massachusetts

Ella Jay Parfitt
Southeast Middle School
Baltimore, Maryland

Evelyn A. Pizzarello
Louis M. Klein Middle School
Harrison, New York

Kathleen M. Poe
Fletcher Middle School
Jacksonville, Florida

Shirley Rose
Lewis and Clark Middle School
Tulsa, Oklahoma

Linda Sandersen
Greenfield Middle School
Greenfield, Wisconsin

Mary E. Solan
Southwest Middle School
Charlotte, North Carolina

Mary Stewart
University of Tulsa
Tulsa, Oklahoma

Paul Swenson
Billings West High School
Billings, Montana

Thomas Vaughn
Arlington High School
Arlington, Massachusetts

Susan C. Zibell
Central Elementary
Simsbury, Connecticut

Safety Reviewers

W. H. Breazeale, Ph.D.
Department of Chemistry
College of Charleston
Charleston, South Carolina

Ruth Hathaway, Ph.D.
Hathaway Consulting
Cape Girardeau, Missouri

Douglas Mandt, M.S.
Science Education Consultant
Edgewood, Washington

Activity Field Testers

Nicki Bibbo
Witchcraft Heights School
Salem, Massachusetts

Rose-Marie Botting
Broward County Schools
Fort Lauderdale, Florida

Colleen Campos
Laredo Middle School
Aurora, Colorado

Elizabeth Chait
W. L. Chenery Middle School
Belmont, Massachusetts

Holly Estes
Hale Middle School
Stow, Massachusetts

Laura Hapgood
Plymouth Community Intermediate School
Plymouth, Massachusetts

Mary F. Lavin
Plymouth Community Intermediate School
Plymouth, Massachusetts

James MacNeil, Ph.D.
Cambridge, Massachusetts

Lauren Magruder
St. Michael's Country Day School
Newport, Rhode Island

Jeanne Maurand
Austin Preparatory School
Reading, Massachusetts

Joanne Jackson-Pelletier
Winman Junior High School
Warwick, Rhode Island

Warren Phillips
Plymouth Public Schools
Plymouth, Massachusetts

Carol Pirtle
Hale Middle School
Stow, Massachusetts

Kathleen M. Poe
Fletcher Middle School
Jacksonville, Florida

Cynthia B. Pope
Norfolk Public Schools
Norfolk, Virginia

Anne Scammell
Geneva Middle School
Geneva, New York

Karen Riley Sievers
Callanan Middle School
Des Moines, Iowa

David M. Smith
Eyer Middle School
Allentown, Pennsylvania

Gene Vitale
Parkland School
McHenry, Illinois

N • v

Contents

Electricity and Magnetism

Reference Section

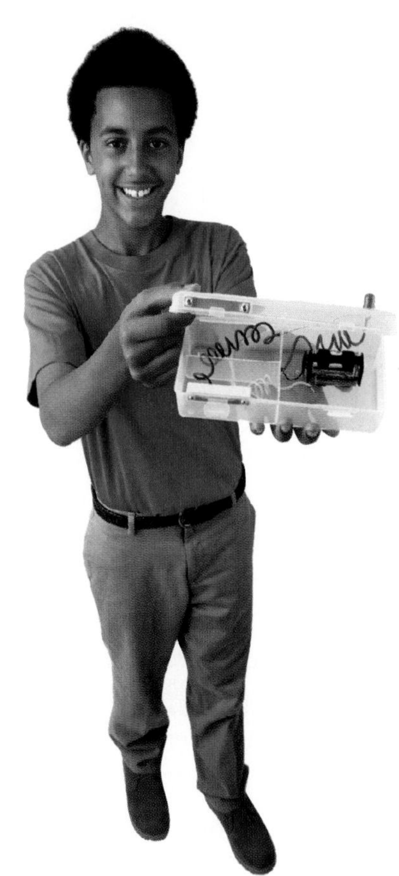

VIDEO

Enhance understanding through dynamic video.

Preview Get motivated with this introduction to the chapter content.

Field Trip Explore a real-world story related to the chapter content.

Assessment Review content and take an assessment.

Web Links

Get connected to exciting Web resources in every lesson.

SCI LINKS NSTA Find Web links on topics relating to every section.

Active Art Interact with selected visuals from every chapter online.

Planet Diary® Explore news and natural phenomena through weekly reports.

Science News® Keep up to date with the latest science discoveries.

Experience the complete textbook online and on CD-ROM.

Activities Practice skills and learn content.

Videos Explore content and learn important lab skills.

Audio Support Hear key terms spoken and defined.

Self-Assessment Use instant feedback to help you track your progress.

Activities

Lab zone™ Chapter Project — Opportunities for long-term inquiry

Lab zone Discover Activity — Exploration and inquiry before reading

Lab zone Try This Activity — Reinforcement of key concepts

Lab zone Skills Activity — Practice of specific science inquiry skills

viii ◆ N

Lab zone Labs — In-depth practice of inquiry skills and science concepts

Lab zone At-Home Activity — Quick, engaging activities for home and family

• Tech & Design • — Design, build, test, and communicate

Math — Point-of-use math practice

active art — Illustrations come alive online

N • ix

Careers in Science

When Illusion Is Better Than Reality

Inquiry and Aeronautical Engineering

Working scientist, engineer Estela Hernandez develops computer programs that simulate flying the space shuttle. This article shows how she uses observing, designing solutions, and making models as key elements of scientific inquiry. While electronics and computers are studied elsewhere in this book, students need not have any previous knowledge of those concepts to understand this real-world application of scientific inquiry.

Build Background Knowledge

Playing Computer Games

Invite students to share information about their favorite computer games. Ask: **What features do you like best about that game?** *(Sample answer: Cool graphics, seems real)* Then have students consider how that game was made. Help them realize that engineers and computer scientists write the computer programs that make the games work.

Introduce the Career

Before students read the article, let them read the title, examine the pictures, and read the captions on their own. Then ask: **What questions came into your mind as you looked at these pictures?** *(Sample questions: How can you fly without leaving the ground? What is a simulator? What are simulations used for?)* Point out to students that just as they had questions about what they were seeing, scientists too have questions about what they observe.

Careers in **Science**

When Illusion Is Better Than Reality

One of the best parts of her job, says engineer Estela Hernandez, is that she gets to fly the space shuttle. "And I'm pretty good at it," she adds.

It is not the real space shuttle, but it is as close as anyone ever gets without going through astronaut training. Estela logs her shuttle hours on a flight simulator—a flight training program. The flight simulator is at the Ames Research Center at NASA (National Aeronautics and Space Administration). As a flight simulation engineer, Estela helps develop computer programs that simulate the real world of flying. So it's her job to help create the nearest thing to flying an aircraft that anyone can experience without leaving the ground.

The flight simulations may at first seem like very high-tech computer games. But they have a very serious purpose: They save lives. Estela and other engineers create flight simulations that allow pilots and astronauts to train. The pilots and astronauts make their mistakes on the ground, where no one gets hurt.

Estela flies the space shuttle—without leaving the ground.

Talking With Estela Hernandez

The Role of Computers

Estela and her fellow engineers use computers to create the illusion of flying. Because a computer can make lightning-fast calculations, it can monitor what a pilot is doing. Computers can direct the various instruments and controls to respond just as they would in a real aircraft under the same conditions. "When the pilot moves the stick," Estela says, "those inputs go back to the computer. The computer calculates how the aircraft would move, what the instruments will display, and even what the pilot sees out the window." None of the simulation would be possible without a computer.

Background

Facts and Figures Engineering is the study of mathematical and natural sciences and their real-world application. In practice, however, engineering is not a single field. Engineers specialize in various kinds of engineering such as automotive, mechanical, aeronautical, chemical, civil, electrical, industrial, and many more.

Regardless of which field of engineering a person specializes in, he or she usually has a basic knowledge of many other fields. Real-world engineering involves problems that are complex and related to more than one field of engineering, so a general knowledge is essential.

Career Path

Estela Hernandez was born in Mexico and grew up in Valencia, California. She earned a bachelor's degree in aeronautical engineering from California Polytechnic State University in San Luis Obispo. She worked as a summer intern at NASA. After graduation, she worked at Lockheed Martin Corporation on the company's missile program. Today, Estela works as a flight simulation engineer at NASA's Ames Research Center in California. Recently, she earned a master's degree in engineering management from Santa Clara University in California.

An Unexpected Career

Estela did not set out to be a flight simulation engineer. "When I got out of high school, I wasn't sure just what I wanted to do," she says, "but I had always liked taking things apart and figuring out how they worked." Estela studied science and math for two years. Then, she took the advice of a math professor and went on to study engineering at California Polytechnic. Still, she wasn't sure what type of engineering she should choose. In the end she says, "I chose aeronautical engineering instead of mechanical engineering."

"I wasn't really sure I liked engineering until I spent a summer working for NASA," she says. She was part of a team using simulations to figure out how to refuel blimps while they are in the air. "This was really cool," she says. "Quickly, I was hooked." For the first time, she knew what career she wanted. As soon as an engineering job in flight simulation came up at NASA, Estela jumped at the chance.

Explore the Career

Choose from among the teaching strategies on these pages as you help your students explore the practical application of inquiry skills in the real world.

Help Students Read Point out that the word *similar* is close to *simulate.* Challenge students to define the word *simulate* based on their knowledge of the meaning of *similar. (Sample answer:* Simulate *means "to work or act like something else.")* You may wish to say that *simulate* means to imitate.

Build Inquiry Skills Many people who are engineers have always liked taking things apart and figuring out how they worked. Encourage students to engage in this activity by making available several different simple devices such as mechanical clocks, radios, electric hand mixers, and toasters. Make sure the devices are unplugged and that their batteries are removed. Allow students to unscrew the protective panels of these devices and take them all apart. Encourage them to identify the functions of various parts and how each part contributes to the function of the device. Then, challenge students to reassemble the device, without leaving any extra parts.

Show Examples Make available a flight simulator program for students to use or some other simulator program. Allow time for every student to have at least one chance to fly the airplane. Consider tallying the number of students who flew successfully. Then ask: **Why are flight simulators so important for training?** *(Sample answer: Flight simulators enable pilots to make their mistakes on the ground without hurting people or destroying equipment.)*

Background

Facts and Figures Aeronautical engineers design, build, test, and operate systems that either operate in Earth's atmosphere, such as airplanes or helicopters, or operate in space, such as satellites and rockets. Some aeronautical engineers specialize in aerodynamics, or the way in which air moves around a body traveling through the atmosphere. Others are more interested in the structural components of an aircraft or spacecraft. They study the properties of different materials. Some aeronautical engineers specialize in moving the aircraft. They study propulsion, which applies the properties of gases to motion.

Discuss Ask: **How is the Vertical Motion Simulator similar to a flight simulator video game?** *(In both, you use controls to steer the aircraft and to adjust its speed. You also can see an image of what you are flying through and see instrument readings.)* **How is the VMS different from a video game?** *(The controls and instruments on the VMS are on an instrument panel just like the one in a real aircraft. You are looking at different screens that show changing scenes out the windows. You are also sitting in a cab that moves like a real aircraft.)* Some students may have been on a simulator ride at an amusement park or shopping mall. Explain that these rides give the sensation of movement like the VMS.

Research Encourage interested students to find out about the requirements for becoming a pilot or an astronaut. Suggest they find requirements for training, education, and licensing and whether or not flight simulation is required.

The VMS can simulate the flight of a Harrier jet (above). The cab (left) contains a cockpit with the sounds and images of flight. The cab rests on a motion base that simulates the motion of flight. The out-of-the-window graphic (below) shows the Harrier pilot's view as the aircraft approaches the runway.

The Vertical Motion Simulator

Estela works on a machine called the Vertical Motion Simulator, or VMS. You can compare the VMS to a flight simulator video game that you may have played. You use the usual video game controls to steer the aircraft up, down, right, and left. You can also speed up the aircraft or slow it down. On the video game screen, you see an image of what you're flying through—the ground below and various objects visible in the sky around you. The video screen will also show such instrument readings as your speed, direction, and altitude.

However, unlike video game controls, the controls and instruments of the Vertical Motion Simulator are on an instrument panel like one in a real aircraft.

Instead of a single computer screen, you have several screens. These screens provide a view of what you would see looking out the windows of the real aircraft. The controls and instruments, the video screens, and your chair are all inside a large box, called a cab. The cab is laid out like the cockpit of the actual aircraft. Large motors move the cab around—forward and back, up and down, side to side. This movement reproduces the motion of the real aircraft as it bounces around in flight. When a tire blows, for instance, you feel your vehicle lurch.

It is this capacity for motion that makes the Vertical Motion Simulator valuable to astronauts and other pilots. "Most of the flight simulators don't have motion," she says. "They may look like the real thing, but they don't feel like the real thing."

Background

Facts and Figures The Vertical Motion Simulator, or VMS, is located at the NASA Ames Research Center in California. Unlike other flight simulators, VMS has flexible software and hardware that can be easily changed to simulate the flight of various aircraft and spacecraft. It can even be used to simulate the behavior of aircraft in the design stages so that engineers can assess the aircraft design and modify it as needed.

Engineers can control the simulation by changing variables in the experiment while it is occurring. They can also stop and start the simulation at any time.

Vehicles that have been simulated in the VMS include a blimp, helicopters, fighter jets, and the space shuttle.

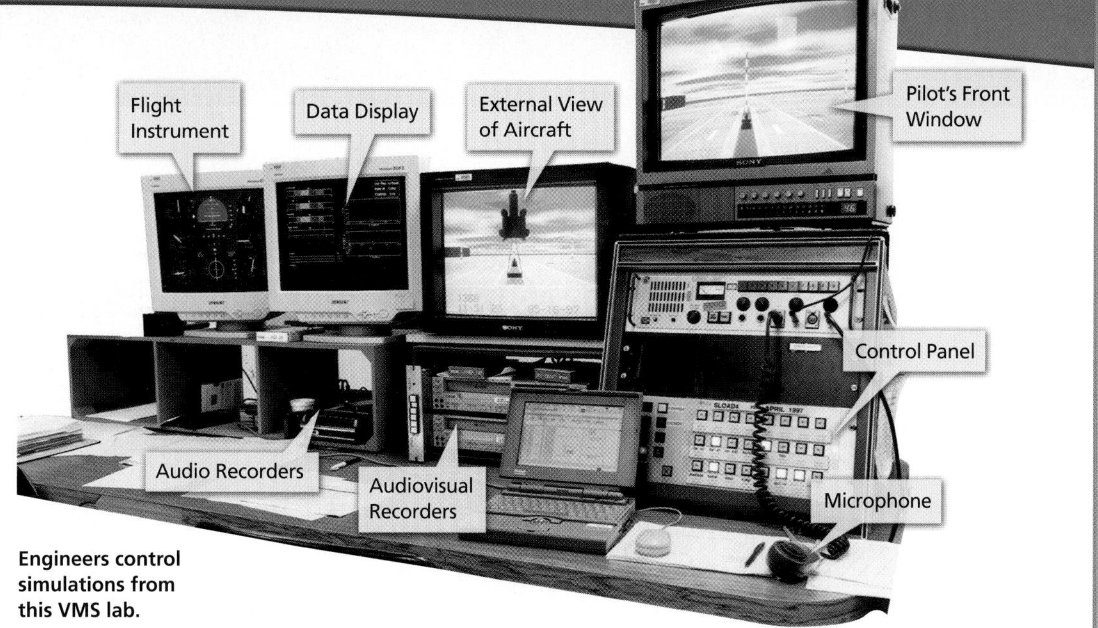

Engineers control simulations from this VMS lab.

Behind the illusion

Creating the illusion of flight can be as challenging and as fun as actual flying. "First, you have to know how an aircraft works," she says. "You have to understand what is being controlled." She and the other engineers who work on the VMS start with mathematical equations. These equations describe the motion of an aircraft as it flies through the air—or touches down on the ground. The engineers feed those equations into a computer. The computer can calculate just how the craft will move under different circumstances.

Estela and her co-workers must write the programming codes or instructions that tell the computer precisely what to do. Each simulation generally takes several months to develop. The engineers are responsible for the computer graphics that provide the visual images that make the simulation look so realistic. The engineers also must tell the computer how to shake the cockpit in just the right way to make it seem as though it is really moving. "We do a little bit of everything," Hernandez says, which is one of the reasons she loves what she does. "A lot of other places you are doing just one thing."

The Best Part of the Job

"Perhaps the best part of the job," she says, "is seeing how the simulation all comes together at the end to create the illusion of flying. It is very neat to write the code and then get to see how it works."

Writing in Science

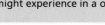

Career Link Estela's job as an engineer is to develop computer programs that simulate flight. Suppose you are a simulation engineer. Plan a simulation you'd like to develop to represent driving a car, a snowmobile, a tractor, or a helicopter. In a paragraph, describe the sounds, sights, and motions you might experience in a one-minute simulation.

For: More on this career
Visit: PHSchool.com
Web Code: cgb-4000

Use Visuals Invite students to examine the photograph of the control panel on this page. Emphasize that this is the panel used by the engineers who are monitoring and controlling the simulation. Point out that not only is the pilot practicing how to control the aircraft, but engineers are gathering data in order to assess the aircraft's design and response to controls. Challenge students to identify a function for each part of the control panel that is labeled. Ask such questions as: **What would an engineer use the microphone for?** *(To communicate with the pilot in the simulator)* **Why does the engineer need an external view of the aircraft?** *(Sample answer: To observe how the aircraft moves in response to simulated weather conditions or cues given by the pilot)*

Writing in Science

Writing in Science Description

Scoring Rubric

4 Exceeds criteria; includes a concise, grammatically correct paragraph with detailed and highly imagined descriptions of the sounds, sights, and motions experienced in a specific simulation
3 Meets criteria
2 Includes sketchy details and/or minor errors
1 Paragraph is incomplete and/or has serious errors

For: More on this career
Visit: PHSchool.com
Web Code: cgb-4000

Students can research this career and others that are related to the study of physics.

Chapter at a Glance

PRENTICE HALL TeacherEXPRESS™ Plan • Teach • Assess

Magnetic Art

Technology

Local Standards

All in One Teaching Resources

- Chapter Project Teacher Notes, pp. 38–39
- Chapter Project Student Overview, pp. 40–41
- Chapter Project Student Worksheets, pp. 42–43
- Chapter Project Scoring Rubric, p. 44

Video Preview

What Is Magnetism?

3–4 periods
1 1/2–2 blocks

N.1.1.1 Explain what the properties of a magnet are.
N.1.1.2 Explain how magnetic poles interact.
N.1.1.3 Describe the shape of a magnetic field.

Inside a Magnet

3–4 periods
1 1/2–2 blocks

N.1.2.1 Explain how an atom can behave like a magnet.
N.1.2.2 Describe how magnetic domains are arranged in a magnetic material.
N.1.2.3 Explain how magnets can be changed.

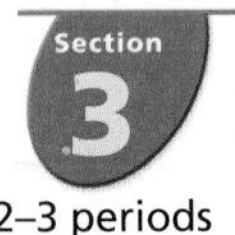

Magnetic Earth

2–3 periods
1–1 1/2 blocks

N.1.3.1 Explain how Earth is like a bar magnet.
N.1.3.2 Describe the effects of Earth's magnetic field.

Video Field Trip

All in One Teaching Resources

- Key Terms Review, p. 76
- Transparency N11
- Performance Assessment Teacher Notes, p. 83
- Performance Assessment Scoring Rubric, p. 84
- Performance Assessment Student Worksheet, p. 85
- Chapter Test, pp. 86–89

Video Assessment

Test Preparation

Test Preparation Blackline Masters

Chapter Activities Planner

For more activities
LAB ZONE Easy Planner CD-ROM

Student Edition	Inquiry	Time	Materials	Skills	Resources
Chapter Project, p. 5	Open-ended	1–2 weeks	All in One **Teaching Resources** p. 38		**Lab zone Easy Planner** All in One **Teaching Resources** pp. 38–39
Section 1					
Discover Activity, p. 6	Guided	15 minutes	Bar magnet, horseshoe magnet, paper clips	Observing	**Lab zone Easy Planner**
Skills Activity, p. 8	Directed	10 minutes	Pencil, foam cup, 2 circular magnets	Observing	**Lab zone Easy Planner**
At-Home Activity, p. 11	Guided			Classifying	**Lab zone Easy Planner**
Skills Lab, pp. 12–13	Guided	Prep: 15 minutes; Class: 40 minutes	Various coins, craft stick, tape, metric ruler, pencil, protractor, coin-size steel washers, small bar magnet (about 2 cm wide), thin stiff cardboard (about 25 cm × 30 cm)	Predicting, observing, developing hypotheses	**Lab zone Easy Planner** **Lab Activity Video** All in One **Teaching Resources** Skills Lab: *Detecting Fake Coins,* pp. 52–55
Section 2					
Discover Activity, p. 14	Guided	15 minutes	Clear plastic tube, iron filings, strong bar magnet	Drawing conclusions	**Lab zone Easy Planner**
Technology Lab, pp. 20–21	Guided	Prep: 10 minutes; Class: 40 minutes	2 bar magnets, masking tape, container of 150 regular-size paper clips, an assortment of magnets (different types, shapes, and sizes), modeling clay, string, various other materials	Designing the solution, evaluating the design, troubleshooting	**Lab zone Easy Planner** **Lab Activity Video** All in One **Teaching Resources** Technology Lab: *Design and Build a Magnetic Paper Clip Holder,* pp. 64–67
Section 3					
Discover Activity, p. 22	Guided	15 minutes	Large needle, strong bar magnet, dish, water, dishwashing soap, cork or foam ball	Observing	**Lab zone Easy Planner**
Skills Activity, p. 25	Directed	10 minutes	Local map, tape or chalk, compass, protractor	Measuring	**Lab zone Easy Planner**
Try This Activity, p. 26	Directed	10 minutes	Bar magnet, sheet of paper, compass	Drawing conclusions	**Lab zone Easy Planner**
At-Home Activity, p. 27	Open-ended		Compass	Communicating	**Lab zone Easy Planner**

Section 1 What Is Magnetism?

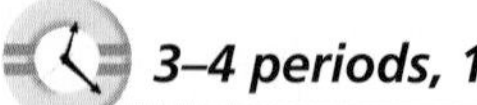
3–4 periods, 1/2–2 blocks

ABILITY LEVELS

L1 Basic to Average
L2 For All Students
L3 Average to Advanced

Objectives

N.1.1.1 Explain what the properties of a magnet are.
N.1.1.2 Explain how magnetic poles interact.
N.1.1.3 Describe the shape of a magnetic field.

Key Terms

• magnet • magnetic pole • magnetic force • magnetic field • magnetic field lines

Local Standards

Preteach

Build Background Knowledge

Students think about how magnets are used in home kitchens.

What Do All Magnets Have in Common? 

Targeted Print and Technology Resources

L2 Reading Strategy Transparency N1: Using Prior Knowledge

Instruct

Properties of Magnets Have students identify the properties of the magnetic rock shown in Figure 1.

Magnetic Poles Have students explain what will happen when like poles are near and unlike poles are near.

Magnetic Fields Use Figure 4 to reinforce students' understanding of where a magnetic field is strongest.

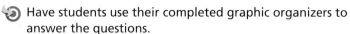

Detecting Fake Coins 

Targeted Print and Technology Resources

All in One Teaching Resources

L2 Guided Reading, pp. 47–49
L2 Transparencies N2, N3
L2 Skills Lab: *Detecting Fake Coins* pp. 52–55

Lab Activity Video/DVD
Skills Lab: *Detecting Fake Coins*

PHSchool.com Web Code: cgp-4011

Student Edition on Audio CD

Assess

Section Assessment Questions

Have students use their completed graphic organizers to answer the questions.

Reteach

Students explain concepts related to magnets by using Figure 5 as a reference.

Targeted Print and Technology Resources

All in One Teaching Resources

• Section Summary, p. 46
L1 Review and Reinforce, p. 50
L3 Enrich, p. 51

Section 2 Inside a Magnet

 *3–4 periods, 1 1/2–2 blocks*

ABILITY LEVELS
L1 Basic to Average
L2 For All Students
L3 Average to Advanced

Objectives

N.1.2.1 Explain how an atom can behave like a magnet.
N.1.2.2 Describe how magnetic domains are arranged in a magnetic material.
N.1.2.3 Explain how magnets can be changed.

Local Standards

Key Terms

• atom • element • nucleus • proton • neutron • electron • magnetic domain
• ferromagnetic material • temporary magnet • permanent magnet

Preteach

Build Background Knowledge

Students recall concepts about atoms learned in previous science classes.

 *How Can Materials Become Magnetic?* 

Targeted Print and Technology Resources

All in One Teaching Resources

L2 Reading Strategy Transparency N4: Asking Questions

 **PresentationExpress™ CD-ROM**

Instruct

The Atom Ask students to describe the electrons in a strong magnet.

Magnetic Domains Use the diagrams in Figure 8 to differentiate between magnetized and unmagnetized material.

Making and Changing Magnets Demonstrate how to make a temporary magnet by rubbing a paper clip with one pole of a bar magnet.

 *Design and Build a Magnetic Paper Clip Holder* L3

Targeted Print and Technology Resources

All in One Teaching Resources

L2 Guided Reading, pp. 58–61
L2 Transparencies N5, N6, N7
L3 Technology Lab: *Design and Build a Magnetic Paper Clip Holder,* pp. 64–67

Lab Activity Video/DVD
Technology Lab: *Design and Build a Magnetic Paper Clip Holder*

www.SciLinks.org Web Code: scn-1412
PHSchool.com Web Code: cgd-4034

 **Student Edition on Audio CD**

Assess

Section Assessment Questions

Have students use their completed graphic organizers to answer the questions.

Reteach

Call on volunteers to explain what magnetic domains are and how they are arranged in different materials.

Targeted Print and Technology Resources

All in One Teaching Resources

• Section Summary, p. 57
L1 Review and Reinforce, p. 62
L3 Enrich, p. 63

Section 3 Magnetic Earth

2–3 periods, 1–1 1/2 blocks

ABILITY LEVELS
L1 Basic to Average
L2 For All Students
L3 Average to Advanced

Local Standards

Objectives

N.1.3.1 Explain how Earth is like a bar magnet.
N.1.3.2 Describe the effects of Earth's magnetic field.

Key Terms

• compass • magnetic declination • Van Allen belts • solar wind • magnetosphere • aurora

Preteach

Build Background Knowledge

Students recall their experiences using a compass.

 *Can You Use a Needle to Make a Compass?* 

Targeted Print and Technology Resources

All in One Teaching Resources

L2 Reading Strategy: Building Vocabulary

PresentationExpress™ CD-ROM

Instruct

Earth as a Magnet Have students observe a compass and explain why the needle points north.

Earth's Magnetic Field Ask leading questions for a discussion about evidence of Earth's magnetic field in rocks hardened from molten material.

The Magnetosphere Use Figure 16 to have students explain the cause of an aurora.

Targeted Print and Technology Resources

All in One Teaching Resources

L2 Guided Reading, pp. 70–73
L2 Transparencies N8, N9, N10

Video Field Trip

PHSchool.com Web Code: cgd-4013

Student Edition on Audio CD

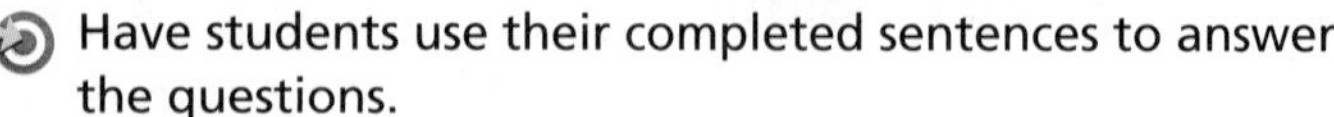

Section Assessment Questions

Have students use their completed sentences to answer the questions.

Reteach

Call on volunteers to define the key terms *magnetic declination*, *magnetosphere*, and *aurora* and explain the cause of each.

Targeted Print and Technology Resources

All in One Teaching Resources

• Section Summary, p. 69
L1 Review and Reinforce, p. 74
L3 Enrich, p. 75

Chapter 1 Content Refresher

Go Online
NSTA-PD LINKS
For: Professional development support
Visit: www.SciLinks.org/PDLinks
Web Code: scf-1410
Professional Development

Section 1 What Is Magnetism?

Magnetite Several minerals have magnetic properties. The most notable of these is magnetite (Fe_3O_4), a black or brownish-red, lustrous mineral. It is found throughout the world and is an important source of iron ore. The variety of magnetite that is magnetic is commonly called lodestone (or loadstone).

Magnetite crystals are also found in organisms. The neck muscles of pigeons and sparrows, for instance, contain magnetite crystals, which may help in navigation. Some bacteria, called magnetotactic bacteria, contain magnetite crystals. Each magnetite crystal inside a cell is a magnet, with a north and a south pole. These tiny internal compasses orient the bacteria to Earth's magnetic field lines, which are aligned north and south. Magnetotactic bacteria can determine which direction is down. These bacteria do not thrive where oxygen is abundant. They seek deep aquatic environments, because there is less oxygen in deeper water than in shallow water.

Address Misconceptions

Students may be confused by the concept of a field force, a force that can act without physically touching. For a strategy for overcoming this misconception, see **Address Misconceptions** in the section *What Is Magnetism?*

Section 2 Inside a Magnet

Attraction and Magnetic Domains Ferromagnetic materials are composed of tiny regions in which millions of atoms are aligned almost parallel to one another. These regions are called magnetic domains, and they can be seen with a microscope. A magnetic domain can be as large as 1 mm in width or length. When a ferromagnetic material is brought within a strong magnetic field, domains in the material actually rotate into alignment with the magnetic field. When such a ferromagnetic material is brought within a weak magnetic field, something different occurs. The domains that are already aligned with the magnetic field grow, and the domains that are not aligned shrink. The result is a temporary magnet, and if the magnetic field is taken away, the material quickly demagnetizes. This is what occurs, for example, when a bar magnet picks up steel paper clips or when a magnet is placed on a metal refrigerator door.

Section 3 Magnetic Earth

Earth's Magnetic Field Scientists hypothesize that Earth's magnetic field is produced through the so-called dynamo effect. Earth's core is composed mainly of nickel and iron, both of which are good electrical conductors. The heat of Earth's interior produces convection currents in the molten core. At the same time, Earth is rotating on its axis. The rotation of these currents of core material produces electric currents, which are thought to be responsible for the planet's magnetic field.

Earth's magnetic field affects iron-rich minerals—including magnetite—that are abundant in lava flows that form igneous rock on the sea floor. The lava is too hot to be magnetic. As the molten material cools, the iron-rich rocks align with Earth's magnetic field. As a result, these rocks possess paleomagnetism. By studying the paleomagnetism of the rock layers on the ocean floor and elsewhere, geologists can determine when Earth's magnetic field has reversed itself as well as how continents have moved over time. The study of paleomagnetism has contributed greatly to the understanding of plate tectonics.

Help Students Read

Relating Text and Figures

Using Graphic Elements to Clarify and Extend

Strategy Help students relate figures to text in order to clarify difficult concepts in the text or to understand information beyond that stated in the text. Students can learn to make use of figures to support comprehension. Before students begin, choose a subsection in this chapter, such as the *Alignment of Domains* subsection.

Example

1. Have students keep their books closed as you read a few paragraphs aloud, including text that refers to a figure. You may want to think aloud as you read, saying, for example, "I wonder what that would look like?"
2. Then have students open their books to the passage that you have read. Tell them to reread it and study the figure and its caption carefully. Ask what parts of the passage make more sense when students look at the figure.
3. Point out that visuals also sometimes communicate information that is not in the text. Have students identify any new information that can be learned from the figure.
4. Have students work in pairs, with one reading aloud the next reference to a figure, and then both working together to discuss how the figure helps them understand the passage or provides additional information.

Interactive Textbook

- Complete student edition
- Video and audio
- Simulations and activities
- Section and chapter activities

Chapter 1 Magnetism

Chapter Preview

Interactive Textbook

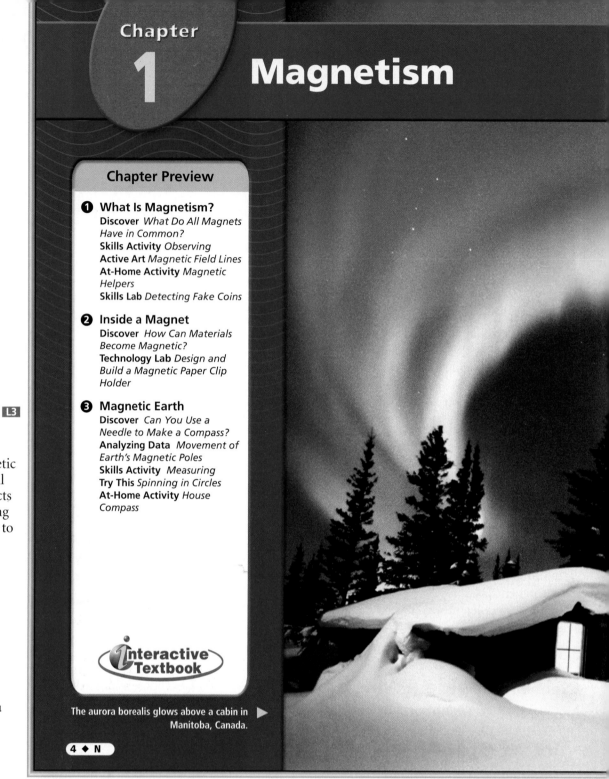

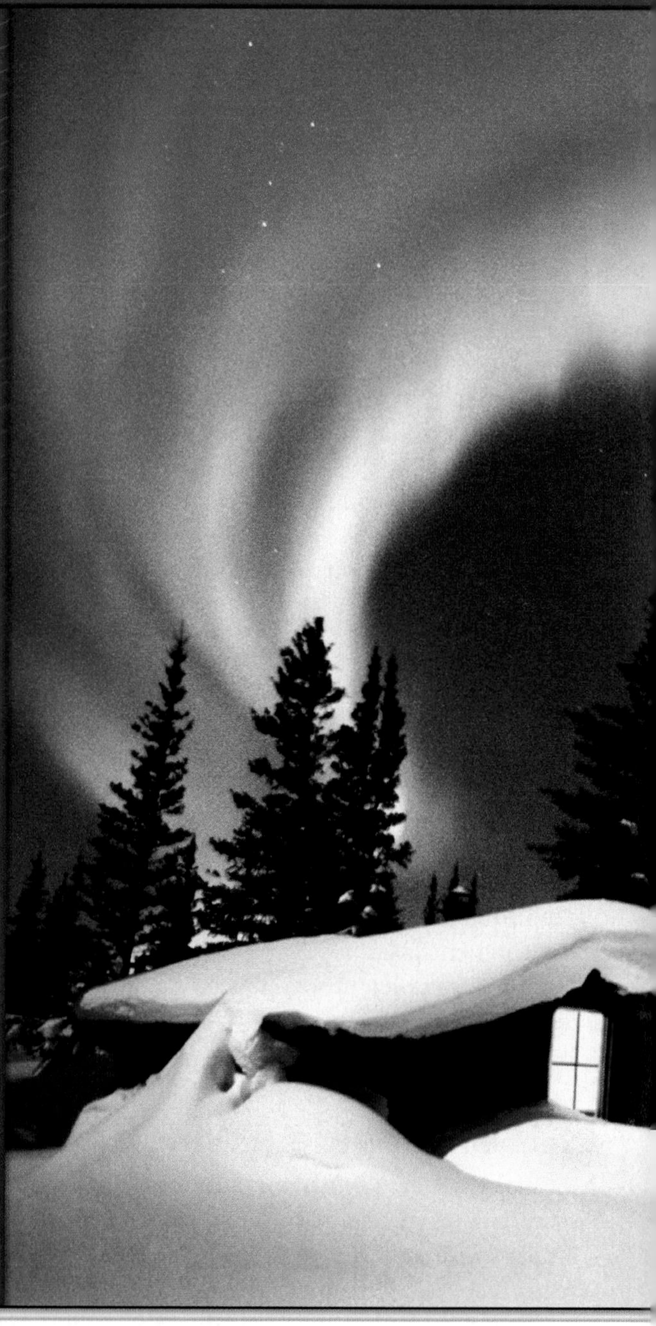

The aurora borealis glows above a cabin in Manitoba, Canada.

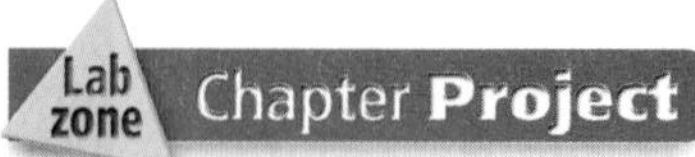

Lab zone Chapter Project L3

Objectives

Students will design and create a magnetic sculpture that is at least 20 centimeters tall and is held together by magnets and objects with magnetic properties. After completing this Chapter Project, students will be able to

- observe what materials are attracted to magnets and what materials are not
- apply concepts related to making temporary magnets
- design a solution to the problem of creating a sculpture held together by magnets
- communicate results to the class

Skills Focus

Observing, applying concepts, designing a solution, communicating

Project Time Line 1–2 weeks

All in One Teaching Resources

- Chapter Project Teacher Notes
- Chapter Project Overview
- Chapter Project Worksheet 1
- Chapter Project Worksheet 2
- Chapter Project Scoring Rubric

Developing a Plan

Divide the class into small groups for work on this Chapter Project. Students should first read and research how magnets can be used to make temporary magnets. Next, groups test objects for magnetic properties and plan how to use materials in creating their sculptures. Groups then build their sculptures using magnets, temporary magnets, and other materials. Finally, each group makes a diagram showing how the materials in the sculpture are connected and presents the magnetic sculpture to the class.

Possible Materials

Provide students with a variety of magnets of different sizes, strengths, and shapes including bar magnets, disk-shaped magnets, horseshoe magnets, ceramic magnets, flexible magnetic sheets, and neodymium magnets. Also provide a variety of metallic objects such as coins, pieces of lodestone or magnetite (natural magnets), washers, nuts and bolts, screws, paper clips without plastic coverings, nails, flexible wire, and scraps of aluminum foil. Note that while some coins and the foil are metallic, these items—among many others—will not be attracted to a magnet. Such materials are suggested to eliminate the common misconception that all metals are attracted to a magnet.

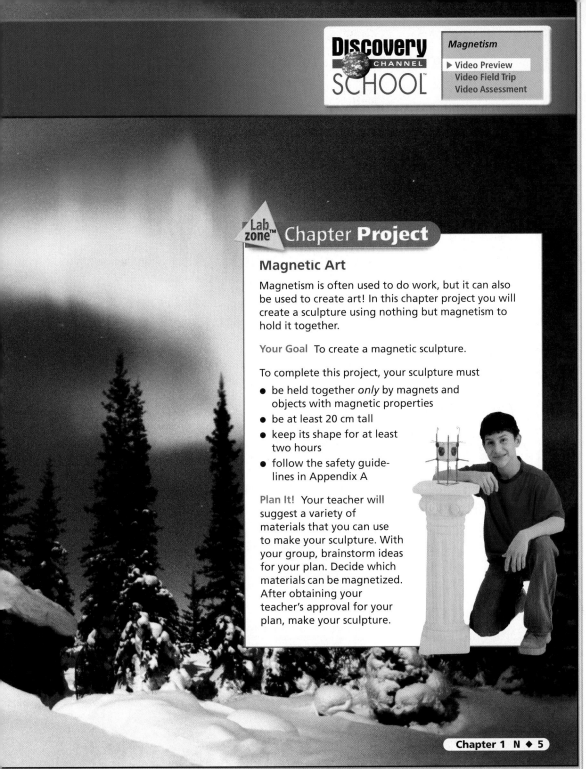

Chapter Project

Magnetic Art

Magnetism is often used to do work, but it can also be used to create art! In this chapter project you will create a sculpture using nothing but magnetism to hold it together.

Your Goal To create a magnetic sculpture.

To complete this project, your sculpture must

- be held together *only* by magnets and objects with magnetic properties
- be at least 20 cm tall
- keep its shape for at least two hours
- follow the safety guidelines in Appendix A

Plan It! Your teacher will suggest a variety of materials that you can use to make your sculpture. With your group, brainstorm ideas for your plan. Decide which materials can be magnetized. After obtaining your teacher's approval for your plan, make your sculpture.

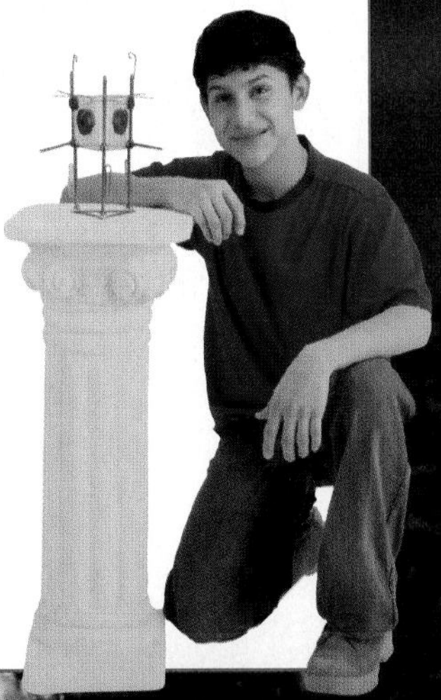

Magnetism

Show the Video Preview to introduce the Chapter Project and overview the chapter content. Discussion question: **Why do scientists think that lobsters are able to detect Earth's magnetic field?** *(The lobsters' ability to navigate suggests that there may be a strong relationship between their bodies and Earth's magnetism.)*

Possible Shortcuts

You can make this project shorter by providing small groups of students several magnets and an assortment of materials. Then challenge each group to create a magnetic sculpture in one period hour using only the given materials. After all groups have completed their sculptures, discuss how they used magnets and temporary magnets.

Launching the Project

To introduce the project, obtain a small amount of ferrofluid and put a few drops into a Petri dish. Allow students to observe the fluid as you place a magnet beneath the Petri dish. Ask: **What do you think has caused the fluid to take the pattern it has?** *(Sample answer: The magnet has affected the fluid.)* Explain that they will use the same force they have just observed in the Chapter Project to create a sculpture.

Performance Assessment

The Chapter Project Scoring Rubric will help you evaluate how well students complete the Chapter Project. You may want to share the scoring rubric with your students so they are clear about what will be expected of them. Students will be assessed on

- how well they build a sculpture that meets the criteria of being held together by magnets and objects with magnetic properties
- how well their diagram shows how their sculpture is held together
- how effectively they present the magnet sculptures to the class
- their group participation

Students can keep their diagrams in their portfolios.

Section 1

What Is Magnetism?

Objectives

After this lesson, students will be able to

N.1.1.1 Explain what the properties of a magnet are.

N.1.1.2 Explain how magnetic poles interact.

N.1.1.3 Describe the shape of a magnetic field.

Target Reading Skill

Using Prior Knowledge Explain that using prior knowledge helps students connect what they already know to what they are about to read.

Answers

Possible answers:

What You Know:

1. Magnets stick to refrigerators.
2. Magnets have north and south poles.
3. Magnets have magnetic fields around them.

What You Learned:

1. A magnet attracts iron and materials that contain iron.
2. Magnetic poles that are alike repel each other, and magnetic poles that are unlike attract each other.
3. Magnetic forces are exerted all around a magnet, and magnets can interact without touching.

All in One Teaching Resources

- Transparency N1

Preteach

Build Background Knowledge L2

Magnets in the Kitchen

Challenge students to think about how magnets are used in the kitchen. Ask: **What often keeps kitchen cabinet doors closed?** *(Sample answer: A small magnet on the edge of the cabinet attracts a small piece of metal on the inside of the door, keeping the door closed.)* **What holds the top of a can to an electric can opener after the top has been cut off?** *(A magnet)* **What holds notes on the front of a refrigerator?** *(Magnets)*

Section 1

What Is Magnetism?

Reading Preview

Key Concepts

- What are the properties of a magnet?
- How do magnetic poles interact?
- What is the shape of a magnetic field?

Key Terms

- magnet
- magnetic pole
- magnetic force
- magnetic field
- magnetic field lines

Target Reading Skill

Using Prior Knowledge Before you read, look at the headings and visuals to see what this section is about. Then write what you know about magnetism in a graphic organizer like the one below. As you read, write what you learn.

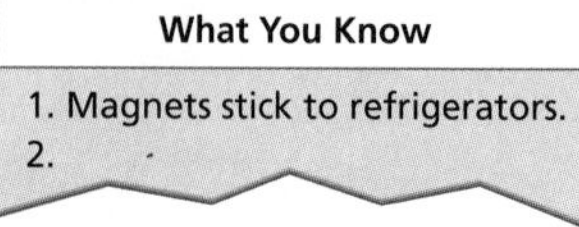

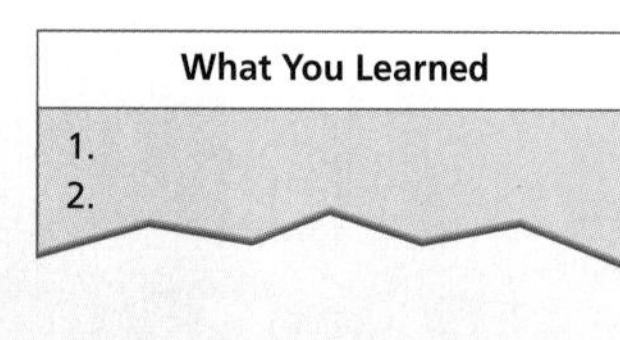

Lab zone Discover Activity

What Do All Magnets Have in Common?

1. Obtain a bar magnet and a horseshoe magnet.
2. See how many paper clips you can attract to different parts of each magnet.
3. Draw a diagram showing the number and location of paper clips on each magnet.

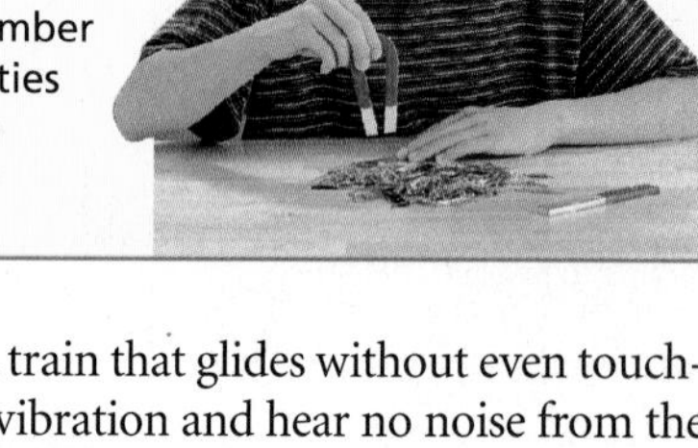

Think It Over

Observing Where does each magnet hold the greatest number of paper clips? What similarities do you observe between the two magnets?

Imagine zooming along in a train that glides without even touching the ground. You feel no vibration and hear no noise from the steel tracks below. You can just sit back and relax as you speed toward your destination at nearly 500 kilometers per hour.

Are you dreaming? No, you are not. You are floating a few centimeters in the air on a magnetically levitating train, or maglev train. Although you have probably not ridden on such a train, they do exist. What makes them float? Believe it or not, it is magnetism that makes them float.

◀ Strong magnets move this Japanese maglev train.

Lab zone Discover Activity

Skills Focus Observing L1

Materials bar magnet, horseshoe magnet, paper clips

Time 15 minutes

Tips Tell students they will observe how two different types of magnets attract materials.

Expected Outcome Most paper clips will be attracted to the magnets' poles. Few or none will be attracted to the middle of the bar magnet or to the curved part of the horseshoe magnet.

Think It Over Sample answer: Most paper clips are attracted to the ends of the magnets. Most of the magnetic pull seems to come from the poles, or ends, of the bar magnet and the horseshoe magnet.

Properties of Magnets

When you think of magnets, you might think about the objects that hold notes to your refrigerator. But magnets can also be found in many other everyday items such as wallets, kitchen cabinets, and security tags at a store. A **magnet** is any material that attracts iron and materials that contain iron.

Magnets have many modern uses, but they are not new. More than 2,000 years ago, people living in the ancient Greek city of Magnesia (in what is now Turkey) discovered an unusual kind of rock. This kind of rock contained a mineral called magnetite. Both the word *magnetite* and the word *magnet* come from the name Magnesia. Rocks containing magnetite attracted materials that contained iron. They also attracted or repelled other magnetic rocks. The attraction or repulsion of magnetic materials is called magnetism.

About a thousand years ago, people in other parts of the world discovered another property of magnetic rocks. If they allowed such a rock to swing freely from a string, one part of the rock would always point in the same direction. That direction was toward the North Star, Polaris. This star is also called the leading star, or lodestar. For this reason, magnetic rocks are known as lodestones.

Magnets have the same properties as magnetic rocks. **Magnets attract iron and materials that contain iron. Magnets attract or repel other magnets. In addition, one part of a magnet will always point north when allowed to swing freely.**

Reading Checkpoint **What mineral found in rocks can attract materials containing iron?**

FIGURE 1
A Natural Magnet
Some magnets are found in nature. This rock attracts iron nails because it contains the magnetic mineral called magnetite.

FIGURE 2
Modern Magnets
Magnets come in a variety of shapes and sizes, but they share certain characteristics.
Inferring *What substance might the scissors, paper clips, and spoon have in common?*

Instruct

Properties of Magnets

Teach Key Concepts L2

The Attraction of Magnets

Focus Tell students that a magnet is any material that attracts iron or materials that contain iron.

Teach Ask: **What is magnetism?** *(The attraction or repulsion of magnetic materials)* **What are three properties of magnets?** *(Magnets attract iron and materials that contain iron. Magnets attract or repel other magnets. One part of a magnet always points north when allowed to swing freely.)*

Apply Have students look at Figure 1 and read the caption. Ask: **This rock is identified as a natural magnet. What do you know about this rock?** *(It attracts iron and materials that contain iron. It attracts or repels other magnets. One part of the rock will point north when allowed to swing freely.)* **learning modality: visual**

Independent Practice L2

All in One Teaching Resources

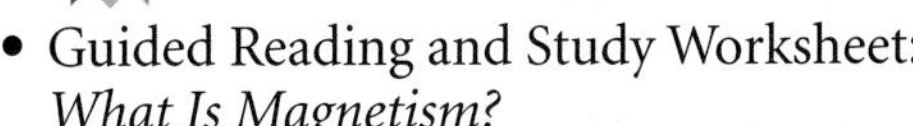

- Guided Reading and Study Worksheet: *What Is Magnetism?*

Student Edition on Audio CD

Monitor Progress L2

Writing Ask students to write a definition of magnetism in their own words.

Answers

Figure 2 The objects might contain iron.

Reading Checkpoint The mineral magnetite can attract materials containing iron.

Magnetic Poles

Teach Key Concepts

L2

A Magnet Has Two Poles

Focus Explain to students that any magnet always has two poles, called a north pole and a south pole.

Teach Show students a bar magnet on which the two poles are labeled. Ask: **What is each end of the magnet called?** *(A magnetic pole)* **Which part of this magnet will always point north if it hangs free on a string?** *(The north pole)* **What is the rule about what happens when the poles of two magnets are brought together?** *(Magnetic poles that are alike repel each other, and magnetic poles that are unlike attract each other.)*

Apply Show students a bar magnet. Ask: **If you bring this north pole near another magnet's north pole, what will happen?** *(The two like poles will push away from each other.)* **If you bring this south pole near another magnet's north pole, what will happen?** *(The two unlike poles will attract each other.)* **learning modality: verbal**

L1

Attraction and Repulsion

Materials 2 bar magnets

Time 5 minutes

Focus Tell students that unlike poles attract each other and like poles repel each other.

Teach Have students place the magnets on their desks. Have them slide unlike poles of the magnets closer together until they can first feel the attraction. Then have them slide like poles of the magnets closer together until they can first feel the repulsion.

Apply Encourage students to experiment with the magnets to find out how close they can put unlike poles before the magnets are "pulled" together and how close they can put like poles before the magnets are "pushed" apart. **learning modality: kinesthetic**

FIGURE 3
Attraction and Repulsion
Two bar magnets suspended by strings are brought near each other. Unlike poles attract each other; like poles repel each other.
Predicting *What would happen if two south poles were brought near one another?*

Magnetic Poles

The magnets in your everyday life have the same properties as magnetic rocks because they are made to have them. Recall that one end of a magnet always points north. Any magnet, no matter what its shape, has two ends, each one called a **magnetic pole.** The magnetic effect of a magnet is strongest at the poles. The pole of a magnet that points north is labeled the north pole. The other pole is labeled the south pole. A magnet always has a pair of poles, a north pole and a south pole.

Magnetic Interactions What happens if you bring two magnets together? The answer depends on how you hold the poles of the magnets. If you bring the north pole of one magnet near the south pole of another, the two unlike poles attract one another. However, if you bring two north poles together, the like poles move away from each other. The same is true if two south poles are brought together. **Magnetic poles that are unlike attract each other, and magnetic poles that are alike repel each other.** Figure 3 shows how two bar magnets interact.

Magnetic Force The attraction or repulsion between magnetic poles is **magnetic force.** A force is a push or a pull that can cause an object to move. A magnetic force is produced when magnetic poles interact. Any material that exerts a magnetic force is considered to be a magnet.

The maglev train you read about earlier depends on magnetic force to move. Magnets in the bottom of the train and in the guideway on the ground have like poles facing each other. Because like poles repel, the two magnets move away from each other. The result is that the train car is lifted up, or levitated. Other magnets make the train move forward.

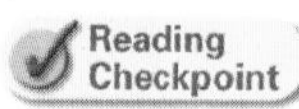

What does every magnet have in common?

Lab zone Skills Activity

Observing

1. Use a pencil to poke a hole in the bottom of a foam cup. Turn the cup upside down and stand the pencil in the hole.
2. Place two circular magnets on the pencil, so that their like sides are together, and observe them.
3. Remove the top magnet. Flip it over, replace it on the pencil, and observe it.

What happens to the magnets in each case? Explain your observations.

8 ◆ N

Lab zone Skills Activity

Skills Focus Observing L2

Materials pencil, foam cup, 2 circular magnets

Time 10 minutes

Tips Have students predict what will happen when they place the two magnets together on the pencil.

Expected Outcome In the first trial, the top magnet will levitate. The levitation is caused by the repulsion between like poles. In the second trial, the top magnet will be attracted to the bottom magnet. This is caused by the attraction of unlike poles.

Extend Have students use more magnets to increase the height of the levitating magnet. **learning modality: visual**

Magnetic Fields

A magnetic force is strongest at the poles of a magnet, but it is not limited to the poles. Magnetic forces are exerted all around a magnet. The area of magnetic force around a magnet is known as its **magnetic field.** Because of magnetic fields, magnets can interact without even touching.

Figure 4 shows the magnetic field of a bar magnet. Notice the red lines, called magnetic field lines, around the magnet. **Magnetic field lines** are invisible lines that map out the magnetic field around a magnet. **Magnetic field lines spread out from one pole, curve around the magnet, and return to the other pole.** The lines form complete loops from pole to pole and never cross. Arrows are used to indicate the direction of the magnetic field lines—always leaving the north pole and entering the south pole.

The distance between magnetic field lines indicates the strength of a magnetic field. The closer together the lines are, the stronger the field. A magnet's magnetic field lines are closest together at the poles.

Reading Checkpoint **Where is the magnetic field strongest?**

Go Online active art
For: Magnetic Field Lines activity
Visit: PHSchool.com
Web Code: cgp-4011

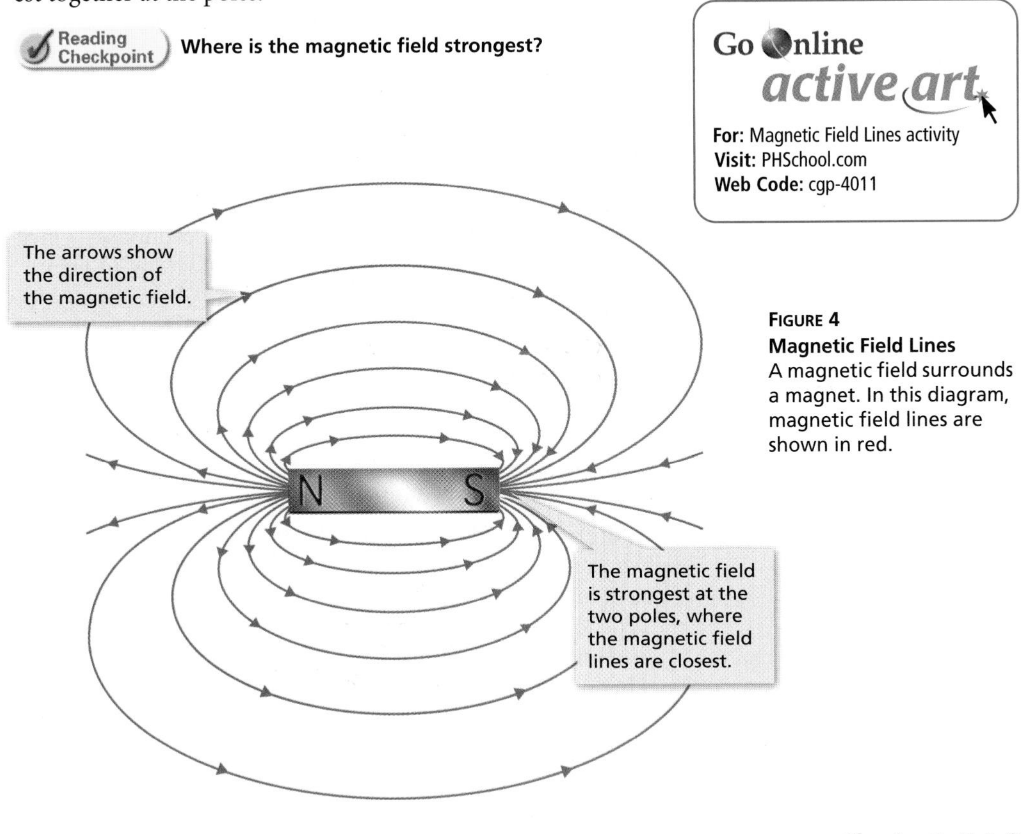

FIGURE 4
Magnetic Field Lines
A magnetic field surrounds a magnet. In this diagram, magnetic field lines are shown in red.

Magnetic Fields

Teach Key Concepts L2

An Area of Magnetic Force

Focus Tell students that magnetic forces are exerted all around a magnet.

Teach Ask: **What is a magnetic field?** *(The area of magnetic force around a magnet)* Explain that a force is a push or pull. Magnetic forces are exerted all around a magnet, but the forces are stronger in some areas. Ask: **Where are the magnetic forces of a magnet strongest?** *(Around the poles)* **In Figure 4, what are the lines around the magnet called?** *(Magnetic field lines)*

Apply Ask: **In Figure 4, how can you tell by the lines where this magnet's magnetic field is strongest?** *(The closer together the lines, the stronger the field. Therefore, the magnetic field is strongest near the poles.)*

Extend The ***active art*** shows how magnetic field lines spread out from one pole, curve around, and return to the other pole. **learning modality: visual**

For: Magnetic Fields Lines activity
Visit: PHSchool.com
Web Code: cgp-4011

Students can interact with the art of magnetic field lines online.

All in One Teaching Resources

- Transparency N2

Differentiated Instruction

Less Proficient Readers L1

Comprehension: Key Concept On the board, rewrite the boldface sentence about magnetic poles into two sentences: "Magnetic poles that are alike repel each other. Magnetic poles that are unlike attract each other." Then, review the meanings of *magnetic pole, attract,* and *repel.* Finally, use the illustrations in Figure 3 to clarify the meanings of the two sentences. **learning modality: verbal**

Monitor Progress L2

Answers

Figure 3 They would repel each other.

 Two magnetic poles

 At the poles

Using Visuals: Figure 5 L2

Magnetic Field Lines

Focus Tell students that iron filings can be used to map out a magnet's magnetic field.

Teach Have students observe the magnetic field lines in Figure 5. Ask: **Where does the field seem to be the strongest?** *(Around the poles)* **What evidence can you see for this conclusion?** *(The lines of iron filings are densest near the poles.)* **How can you tell that the magnet's magnetic field gets weaker farther from the magnet?** *(The iron filings are more spread out farther from the magnet.)*

Apply Challenge students to explain why the lines curve between the two poles. Ask: **Find an iron filing that is on the curve about halfway between the two poles. How are the forces acting at that point?** *(At that point, the filing is equally attracted to both poles.)* **learning modality: visual**

All in One Teaching Resources

- Transparency N3

Address Misconceptions L2

Contact Forces and Field Forces

Focus Some students may be confused by the concept of a magnetic field. Explain that scientists recognize two kinds of forces, contact forces and field forces.

Teach Tell students that contact forces act when two objects are in physical contact, but field forces can act without physically touching. Ask: **Is the force of gravity a contact force or a field force?** *(It is a field force, since it acts without objects being in physical contact.)*

Apply Have students look at the photo of iron filings around the bar magnet in Figure 5. Ask: **If the iron filings were not present around the magnet, would the field forces still be present around the poles of the magnet?** *(Yes, the field forces are always present. The iron filings simply make the effects of the field visible.)* **learning modality: verbal**

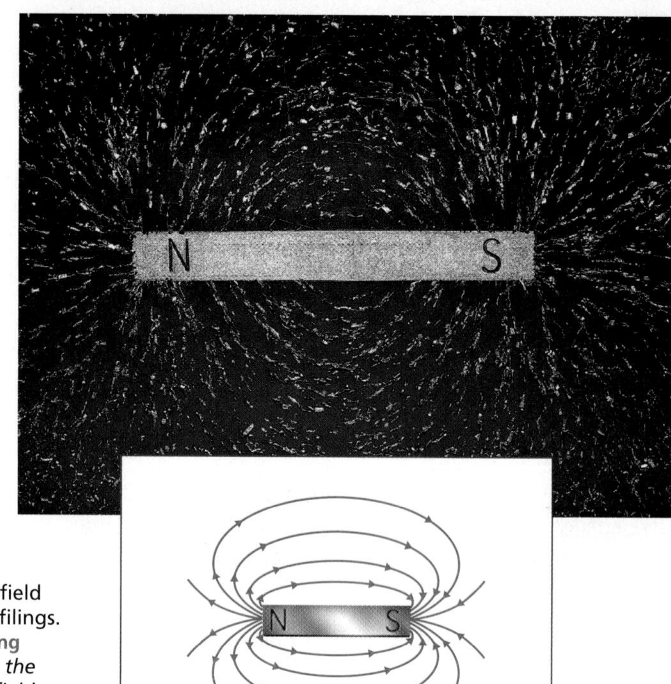

FIGURE 5
A Single Magnetic Field
A bar magnet's magnetic field is mapped out using iron filings.
Comparing and Contrasting
How do the iron filings in the photo and the magnetic field lines in the illustration compare?

A Single Magnetic Field Although you cannot see a magnetic field, you can see its effects. The photograph in Figure 5 shows iron filings sprinkled on a sheet of plastic that covers one magnet. The magnetic forces of the magnet act on the iron filings and align them along the invisible magnetic field lines. The result is that the iron filings form a pattern similar to the magnetic field lines shown in the diagram in Figure 5.

Combined Magnetic Fields When the magnetic fields of two or more magnets overlap, the result is a combined field. Figure 6 shows the magnetic field produced when the poles of two bar magnets are brought near each other. Compare the combined field of two like poles to that of two unlike poles. Depending on which poles are near each other, the magnetic field lines are different. The fields from the like poles repel each other. But the fields from unlike poles attract each other. They combine to form a strong field between the two poles.

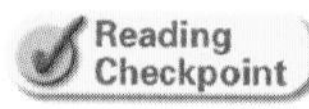

What happens when the magnetic fields of two or more magnets overlap?

Differentiated Instruction

English Learners/Beginning L1
Comprehension: Ask Questions To help students understand the importance of magnetic fields, distribute a rewritten, simplified version of the subsection Magnetic Fields. Then ask students simple questions that can be answered directly from the rewritten text. **learning modality: verbal**

English Learners/Intermediate L2
Comprehension: Ask Questions Have students read the simplified subsection you have prepared for the Beginning students, and then have them read the actual text again. Ask whether anything in the text subsection confused students, and help them clarify the meanings. **learning modality: verbal**

FIGURE 6
Combined Magnetic Fields
The magnetic field of a single bar magnet is altered when another bar magnet is brought near it.

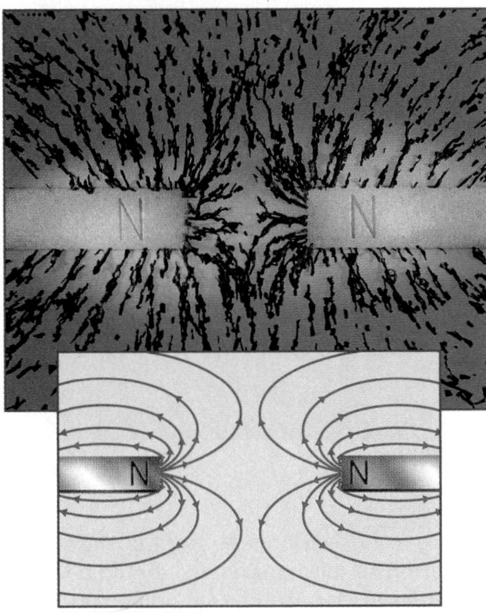

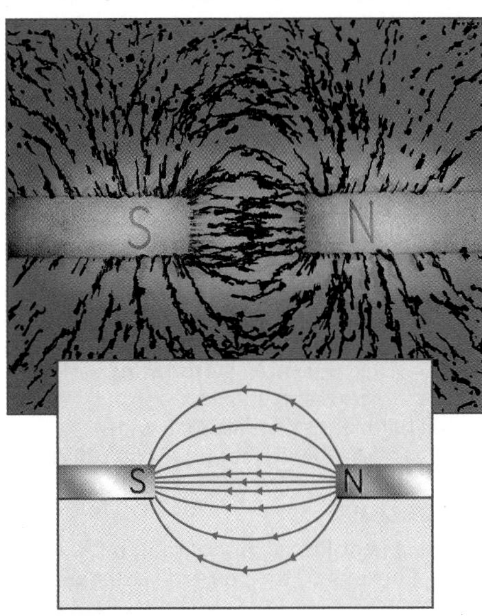

Section 1 Assessment

Target Reading Skill Using Prior Knowledge Review your graphic organizer and revise it based on what you just learned in the section.

Reviewing Key Concepts

1. a. Reviewing What is a magnet?
   b. Summarizing What are three properties of a magnet?
   c. Predicting What will happen to a bar magnet that is allowed to swing freely?
2. a. Describing What area of a magnet has the strongest magnetic effect?
   b. Explaining How does a magnet's north pole behave when brought near another north pole? Near a magnet's south pole?
   c. Relating Cause and Effect How can the behavior of two magnets show the presence of a magnetic force?
3. a. Defining What is a magnetic field?
   b. Interpreting Diagrams Look at Figure 4. What is the shape of the magnetic field?

Lab zone At-Home Activity

Magnetic Helpers Explain the properties of magnets to a member of your family. Then make a list of objects around your home that are most likely to contain or use one or more magnets. For example, magnets are used to hold some cabinet doors closed. Have your family member make a separate list. Compare the two lists and explain to your family member why each object is or is not likely to contain or use magnets.

Lab zone At-Home Activity

Magnetic Helpers L1 Students should compare their lists with the lists of their families. Recommend that students lead family discussions about whether or not objects contain or use magnets, basing their classifications on the objects' properties and uses. Ask students to compare their lists and share their findings with classmates.

Lab zone Chapter Project

Keep Students on Track By this point, groups should have tested a variety of objects and materials for magnetic properties. If students do not already know how to make a temporary magnet, demonstrate this technique. Encourage groups to begin to plan a design for a magnetic sculpture.

Monitor Progress L2

Answers

Figure 5 The iron filings align along the magnetic field lines.

Reading Checkpoint The magnetic fields combine to form a stronger field between the magnets when unlike poles are near each other and a weaker field when like poles are near each other.

Assess

Reviewing Key Concepts

1. a. A magnet is any material that attracts iron and materials that contain iron. **b.** A magnet attracts materials that contain iron, attracts or repels other magnets, and has one pole that points north when allowed to swing freely. **c.** The bar magnet will align itself in a north-south direction.
2. a. A magnet's poles have the strongest magnetic effect. **b.** Two magnetic north poles repel each other. A magnetic north and a magnetic south pole attract each other.
c. When unlike magnetic poles of two magnets are brought near one another, a force of attraction will tend to pull them together. When magnetic poles that are alike are brought near each other, a force of repulsion will tend to push them apart.
3. a. A magnetic field is the area of magnetic force around a magnet. **b.** Sample answer: The shape of a magnetic field resembles two side-by-side ovals, with the bar magnet lying along the long sides of the ovals where they contact each other.

Reteach L1

Have volunteers explain concepts related to magnets by using the photos in Figure 5 as reference. Ask students to describe properties of magnets, magnetic interactions, magnetic force, and magnetic fields.

Performance Assessment L2

Drawing Have students draw a bar magnet and label its poles. Then have students sketch the magnetic fields around the poles and indicate the alignment of the domains in the magnet.

All in One Teaching Resources

- Section Summary: *What Is Magnetism?*
- Review and Reinforce: *What Is Magnetism?*
- Enrich: *What Is Magnetism?*

L2

Detecting Fake Coins

Prepare for Inquiry

Key Concept

U.S. coins are made from metals that are not magnetic, and thus they can be separated from magnetic metal slugs using a magnet.

Skills Objectives

After this lab, students will be able to:

- predict how different metals will react to the presence of a magnetic field
- observe how coins will slide straight down the cardboard and washers will be deflected and will slide along the stick
- develop hypotheses about the roles of the magnet and the stick in this lab

Prep Time 15 minutes

Class Time 40 minutes

Advance Planning

Collect the appropriate number of cardboard sheets, craft sticks, washers of various sizes, and small bar magnets. You will need the type of cardboard used to make file folders. Test the washers to make sure they are attracted to the magnets. Supply coins or have students bring their own.

All in One Teaching Resources

- Lab Worksheet: *Detecting Fake Coins*

Guide Inquiry

Invitation

Tell students that vending machines have to have a way of telling the difference between a real coin and a fake coin, often called a slug. Ask: **What are some characteristics of coins and slugs by which a vending machine could detect one from the other?** *(Students may list properties of coins, such as size, shape, mass, density, and magnetic properties.)*

Introduce the Procedure

As students observe, place a pile of coins and washers mixed together on a desk. Move a magnet around the top of the pile and lift up the magnet. Students will observe that washers have stuck to the magnet, while the coins have been left behind.

Lab zone **Skills Lab**

Detecting Fake Coins

Problem

How can you use a magnet to tell the difference between real and fake coins?

Skills Focus

predicting, observing, developing hypotheses

Materials

- various coins
- craft stick
- tape
- metric ruler
- pencil
- protractor
- coin-size steel washers
- small bar magnet, about 2 cm wide
- thin, stiff cardboard, about 25 cm × 30 cm

Procedure

1. Use a pencil to label the front, back, top, and bottom of the piece of cardboard.
2. Draw a line lengthwise down the middle of both sides of the cardboard.
3. On the back of the cardboard, draw a line parallel to the first and about 2 cm to the right.
4. Place a magnet, aligned vertically, about a third of the way down the line you drew in Step 3. Tape the magnet in place.

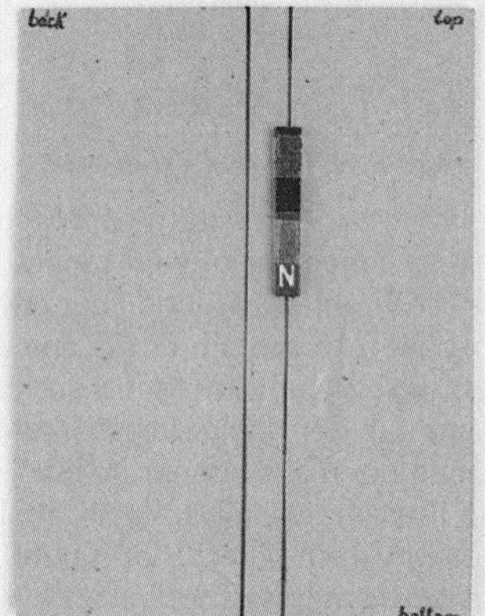

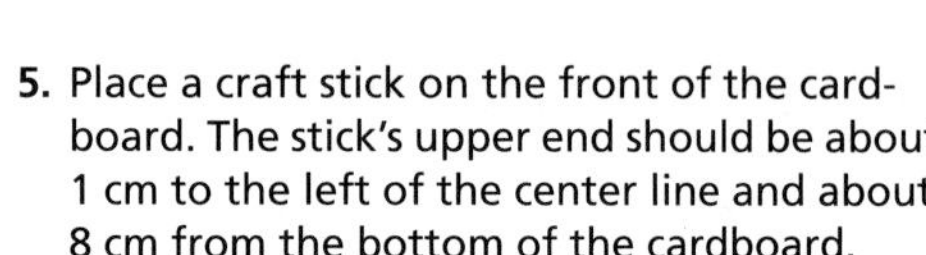

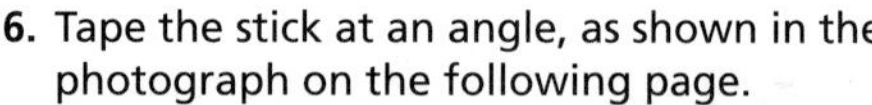

5. Place a craft stick on the front of the cardboard. The stick's upper end should be about 1 cm to the left of the center line and about 8 cm from the bottom of the cardboard.
6. Tape the stick at an angle, as shown in the photograph on the following page.
7. Prop the cardboard against something that will hold it at an angle of about 45°. Predict what will happen when you slide a coin down the front of the cardboard.
8. Place a coin on the center line and slide the coin down the front of the cardboard. (*Hint*: If the coin gets stuck, slowly increase the angle.)
9. Predict what will happen when you slide a steel washer.
10. Test your prediction by sliding a washer down the cardboard. Again, if the washer gets stuck, slowly increase the angle and try again.
11. Once you have reached an angle at which the objects slide easily, send down a randomly mixed group of coins and washers one at a time.

Troubleshooting the Experiment

- One factor that can affect the effectiveness of students' devices is the angle of the inclined cardboard. When the angle is increased to more than 45°, the coins and washers will move down more quickly, decreasing a washer's chance of being attracted to the magnet.
- Another factor to consider is the strength of the magnet. If a strong magnet is used, a steeper angle of incline may be indicated. An alternative is to place the magnet farther than 1 centimeter from the center line.

Analyze and Conclude

1. **Predicting** What was your prediction from Step 7? Explain your reasoning.
2. **Predicting** What was your prediction from Step 9? Explain your reasoning.
3. **Observing** Describe how observations made during the lab either supported or did not support your predictions.
4. **Developing Hypotheses** What is the role of the magnet in this lab?
5. **Developing Hypotheses** What is the role of the craft stick?
6. **Drawing Conclusions** What can you conclude about the metals from which the coins are made? About the metals in the washers?
7. **Controlling Variables** Why does the steepness of the cardboard affect how the coin-separating device works?
8. **Predicting** Some Canadian coins contain metals that are attracted to magnets. Would this device be useful in Canada to detect fake coins? Explain your answer.
9. **Communicating** Write a brochure that explains how the device could be used to separate real coins from fake coins and what advantages it might have for vending machine owners.

More to Explore

Go to a store that has vending machines. Find out who owns the vending machines. Ask the owners if they have a problem with counterfeit coins (sometimes called "slugs"). Ask how they or the makers of the vending machines solve the problem. How is their solution related to the device you built in this lab?

Analyze and Conclude

1. Students' predictions will vary. Sample answer: The coins will slide straight down because they are not attracted by a magnet.

2. Sample answer: The washers will slide straight and then slide along the stick, because the magnet attracts washers.

3. Answers will depend on predictions. Sample answer: As predicted, the coins slid straight down the cardboard and the washers veered off and slid along the stick.

4. Sample answer: The magnet attracts any magnetic materials as they slide down the cardboard.

5. Sample answer: The craft stick serves to separate the two groups into piles at the bottom of the cardboard.

6. The coins are composed of nonmagnetic metals, which a magnet does not attract. The washers are composed of magnetic metals, which a magnet does attract.

7. The steepness of the cardboard affects the speed of objects sliding down. When objects are moving slowly, there is more chance that the magnet will attract objects made of magnetic materials.

8. The device would not be useful in Canada because some Canadian coins are magnetic and would be attracted by the magnet, just as fake coins are.

9. In their brochures, students should explain the difference between materials that are ferromagnetic and materials that are not. Students also describe how the device uses that difference to separate coins from slugs.

Extend Inquiry

More to Explore The device built in this lab is similar to the device used in many vending machines long ago. Today, magnetic fields are set up using electromagnets, and the size and mass of the coins are analyzed closely to differentiate real coins from fake coins.

Expected Outcome Coins should slide straight down the center line on the cardboard and be deposited in a pile. Washers should be deflected to the side by the magnet and then slide down along the craft stick to be deposited in a separate pile.

Section 2 Inside a Magnet

Objectives

After this lesson, students will be able to

N.1.2.1 Explain how an atom can behave like a magnet.

N.1.2.2 Describe how magnetic domains are arranged in a magnetic material.

N.1.2.3 Explain how magnets can be changed.

Target Reading Skill

Asking Questions Explain that changing a heading into a question helps students anticipate the ideas, facts, and events they are about to read.

Answers

Sample questions and answers: **What are the three particles that make up an atom?** *(Protons, neutrons, and electrons.)* **What are magnetic domains?** *(A grouping of atoms that have their magnetic fields aligned is called a magnetic domain.)* **How can magnets be made and changed?** *(A magnet can be made by placing an unmagnetized ferromagnetic material in a strong magnetic field or by rubbing the material with one pole of a magnet. A permanent magnet can lose some or all of its magnetism if it is hit hard or heated. If a magnet is broken in two, you have two smaller magnets.)*

All in One Teaching Resources

- Transparency N4

Preteach

Build Background Knowledge L2

Remind students that they have learned about atoms in past science classes. Ask: **What is an atom?** *(Sample answer: An atom is the smallest part of an element that has the properties of that element.)* **What are the particles that make up an atom?** *(Some students may know that protons, neutrons, and electrons make up atoms.)* Tell students that it is the electrons that give some materials magnetic properties. **Do any of those particles have a charge?** *(Some students may know that protons are positively charged and electrons are negatively charged.)*

Section 2 Inside a Magnet

Reading Preview

Key Concepts

- How can an atom behave like a magnet?
- How are magnetic domains arranged in a magnetic material?
- How can magnets be changed?

Key Terms

- atom • element • nucleus
- proton • neutron • electron
- magnetic domain
- ferromagnetic material
- temporary magnet
- permanent magnet

Target Reading Skill

Asking Questions Before you read, preview the red headings. In a graphic organizer like the one below, ask a *what* or *how* question for each heading. As you read, write the answers to your questions.

Inside an Atom

Question	Answer
What are the three particles that make up an atom?	The three particles that make up an atom are . . .

Lab zone Discover Activity

How Can Materials Become Magnetic?

1. Fill a clear plastic tube about two-thirds full with iron filings.
2. Observe the arrangement of the filings.
3. Rub the tube lengthwise about 30 times in the same direction with one end of a strong magnet.
4. Again, observe the arrangement of the filings.

Think It Over

Drawing Conclusions What can you conclude from your observations?

You've probably noticed that if you bring a magnet near the door of your refrigerator, it clings. But what happens if you bring a piece of paper near the same refrigerator door? Nothing. You have to use a magnet to hold the paper against the door. Materials such as paper, plastic, rubber, and glass do not have magnetic properties. They will not cling to magnets and certain metals. Why are some materials magnetic while others are not?

Only certain materials will ▶ cling to the refrigerator using magnetism.

Lab zone Discover Activity

Skills Focus Drawing conclusions L1

Materials clear plastic tube, iron filings, strong bar magnet

Time 15 minutes

Tips Make sure students rub their plastic tubes in one direction. Suggest they start at the top of the tube, rub down to the bottom, and then begin again at the top.

Expected Outcome When a student rubs the tube, the iron filings become aligned and point in the same direction.

Think It Over Sample answer: The iron filings line up and point in the same direction because they have become magnetized by the rubbing of the bar magnet.

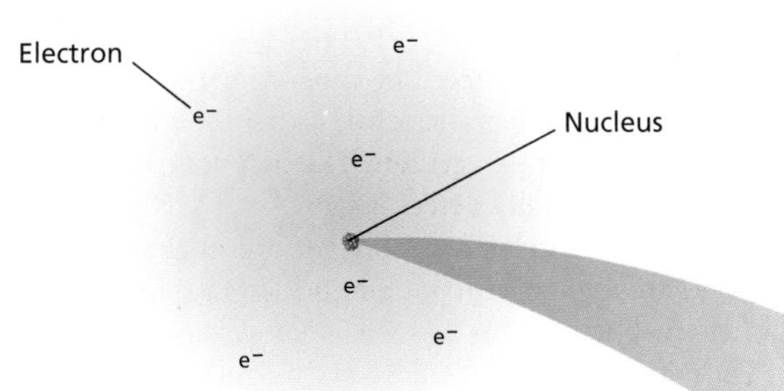

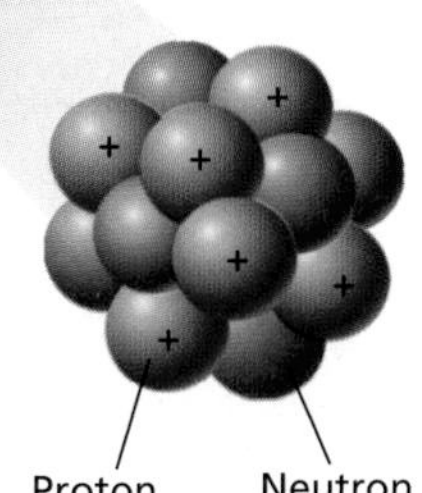

FIGURE 7
Structure of an Atom
An atom contains neutrons and positively charged protons in its nucleus. Negatively charged electrons move randomly throughout the atom.

The Atom

The magnetic properties of a material depend on the structure of its atoms. Because materials take up space and have mass, they are classified as matter. All matter is made up of atoms. An **atom** is the smallest particle of an element. An **element** is one of about 100 basic substances that make up all matter. The structure and composition of the atoms that make up a particular element make that element different from any other element.

Structure of an Atom Although atoms can differ, they have some characteristics in common. Every atom has a center region and an outer region. The center region of an atom is called a **nucleus.** Inside the nucleus two kinds of particles may be found: protons and neutrons. A **proton** is a particle that carries a positive charge. A **neutron** is a particle that does not carry a charge.

The outer region of an atom is mainly empty space. However, particles called electrons usually exist there. An **electron** is a particle that carries a negative charge. Electrons move randomly throughout the atom. They are much smaller than neutrons and protons. Look at Figure 7 to see the structure of an atom.

Electron Spin Each electron in an atom has a property called electron spin, so it behaves as if it were spinning. **A spinning electron produces a magnetic field that makes the electron behave like a tiny magnet in an atom.**

In most atoms, electrons form pairs that spin in opposite directions. Opposite spins produce opposite magnetic fields that cancel. Therefore, most atoms have weak magnetic properties. But some atoms contain electrons that are not paired. These atoms tend to have strong magnetic properties.

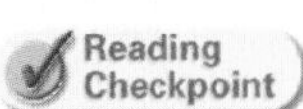 **Why are most materials not magnetic?**

Instruct

The Atom

Teach Key Concepts L2

Electrons in Atoms

Focus Tell students that the magnetic properties of a material depend on the electrons of its atoms.

Teach Have a volunteer read the definition of an atom out loud. Ask: **What are the charges of the particles in an atom?** *(A proton has a positive charge, a neutron has no charge, and an electron has a negative charge.)* **What makes an electron behave like a tiny magnet in an atom?** *(The spinning of the electron produces a magnetic field.)* **What characteristic does an atom with strong magnetic properties have?** *(The atom has electrons that are not paired.)*

Apply Show students a strong magnet, and demonstrate its magnetic field by showing that it is attracted to iron. Ask: **What do this object's magnetic properties tell you about the electrons in its atoms?** *(This object has atoms that contain electrons that are not paired.)* **learning modality: verbal**

All in One Teaching Resources
- Transparency N5

Independent Practice L2

All in One Teaching Resources
- Guided Reading and Study Worksheet: *Inside a Magnet*

Student Edition on Audio CD

Differentiated Instruction

Special Needs L1
Interpreting Diagrams and Communicating Refer students to Figure 8, and tell them to use the figure as a guide in making their own drawings of magnetic domains in magnetized material and in unmagnetized material. Students should label their drawings and write a brief annotation explaining why each drawing is classified as it is. **learning modality: visual**

Gifted L3
Communicating Ask students to prepare a presentation to the class about why a refrigerator magnet sticks to a refrigerator door. Suggest these students create visual aids to help in their presentation. Through research, students will discover that the magnetic field of the refrigerator magnet aligns the magnetic domains of the door. **learning modality: verbal**

Monitor Progress L2

Drawing Have students make their own labeled drawing of an atom.

Students can keep their drawings in their portfolios. Portfolio

Answer

 Reading Checkpoint In most atoms, electrons form pairs that spin in opposite directions. Opposite spins create opposite magnetic fields that cancel, leaving no net magnetic field.

Magnetic Domains

Teach Key Concepts

L2

Lining Up in the Same Direction

Focus Tell students that in magnetic materials, groups of atoms are lined up in the same direction.

Teach Ask: **What is a magnetic domain?** *(A grouping of atoms that have their magnetic fields lined up in the same direction)* Explain that individual atoms have magnetic fields, and billions of atoms together make up a magnetic domain. Ask: **How is a magnetic domain like a bar magnet?** *(A magnetic domain has a north pole and a south pole.)* **In a magnetic material, how are all or most of the magnetic domains arranged?** *(Most or all are arranged in the same direction.)*

Apply Use Figure 8 to differentiate between magnetized material and unmagnetized material. Ask: **How can you tell the top diagram in Figure 8 represents unmagnetized material?** *(The magnetic domains point in random directions.)* **How does this random arrangement prevent the material from being magnetic?** *(The magnetic fields of some domains cancel the magnetic fields of other domains.)* **learning modality: visual**

All in One **Teaching Resources**

- Transparency N6

L2

Modeling Magnetic Domains

Materials 10-cm by 4-cm strips of construction paper, enough for each student to have 12 strips

Time 10 minutes

Focus Tell students they will model the magnetic domains in magnetized material and in unmagnetized material

Teach Give each student at least 12 strips of paper, and tell them to label the ends of each strip N and S to represent magnetic poles of individual magnetic domains. First have students arrange the strips in a way that shows an unmagnetized material. Then, have students arrange the strips in a way that shows a magnetized material.

Apply Ask: **When you model a magnetized material, how are the north poles of the magnetic domains aligned?** *(They all point in the same direction.)* **learning modality: kinesthetic**

Magnetic Domains

The magnetic fields of the atoms in most materials point in random directions. The result is that the magnetic fields cancel one another almost entirely. The magnetic force is so weak that you cannot usually detect it.

In certain materials, however, the magnetic fields of many atoms are aligned with one another. A grouping of atoms that have their magnetic fields aligned is known as a **magnetic domain.** The entire domain acts like a bar magnet with a north pole and a south pole.

Alignment of Domains The direction in which the domains point determines if the material is magnetized or not magnetized. In a material that is not magnetized, the magnetic domains point in random directions, as shown in Figure 8. Therefore, the magnetic fields of some domains cancel the magnetic fields of other domains. The result is that the material is not a magnet.

Figure 8 has a diagram showing the arrangement of the domains in a magnetized material. You can see that most of the domains are pointing in the same direction. **In a magnetized material, all or most of the magnetic domains are arranged in the same direction.** In other words, the magnetic fields of the domains are aligned. If you did the Discover Activity at the beginning of this section you aligned the magnetic domains of the iron filings.

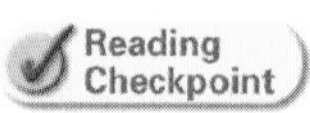
What is the arrangement of the magnetic domains in a material that is not magnetized?

FIGURE 8
Magnetic Domains
The arrows represent the magnetic domains of a material. The arrows point toward the north pole of each magnetic domain.
Comparing and Contrasting *How does the arrangement of domains differ between magnetized iron and unmagnetized iron?*

Unmagnetized Iron

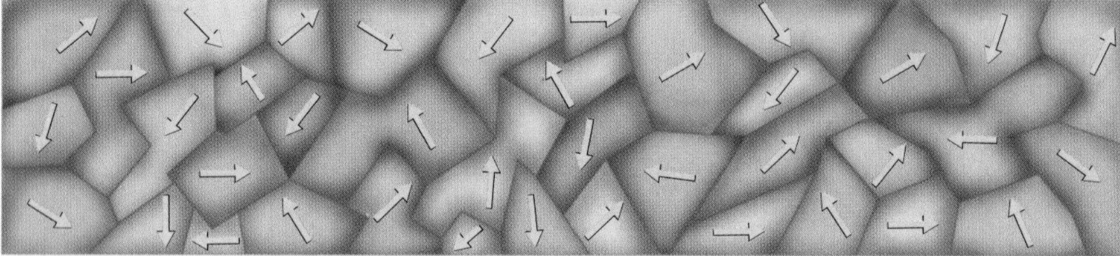

Magnetized Iron

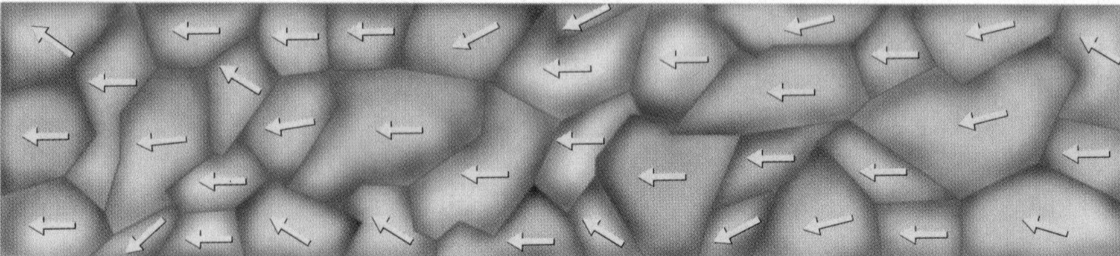

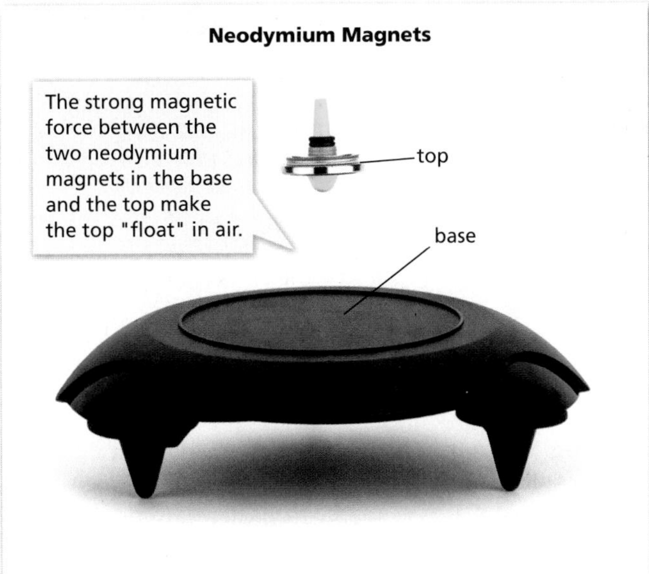

Neodymium Magnets
The strong magnetic force between the two neodymium magnets in the base and the top make the top "float" in air.
top
base

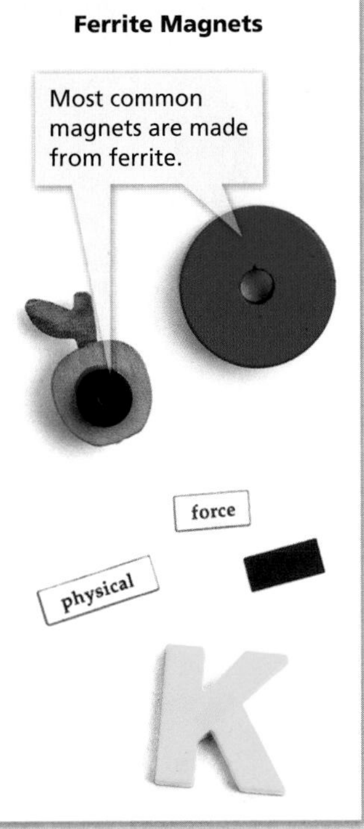

Ferrite Magnets
Most common magnets are made from ferrite.
force
physical

Magnetic Materials A material can be a strong magnet if its magnetic domains align. A material that shows strong magnetic properties is said to be a **ferromagnetic material**. The word *ferromagnetic* comes from the Latin *ferrum*, which means "iron." So a ferromagnetic material behaves like a piece of iron when it is placed in a magnetic field. In nature, iron, nickel, cobalt, and gadolinium are common ferromagnetic materials. Others include the rare elements samarium and neodymium, which can be made into extremely strong magnets as you can see in Figure 9.

Some magnets are made from several different metals. A combination of several metals is called an alloy. For example, the magnetic alloy alnico is made of aluminum, nickel, iron, and cobalt. Powerful magnets are also made of alloys of platinum and cobalt, and alloys of cobalt and neodymium.

Today, the most commonly used magnets are not made from alloys, but rather from a material called ferrite. Ferrite is a mixture of substances that contain ferromagnetic elements. Ferrite is a brittle material that chips easily, like some dishes. However, ferrite magnets are usually stronger and less expensive than metal magnets of similar size. Figure 9 shows some ferrite magnets.

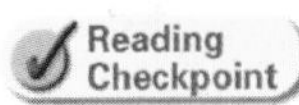
What are some common ferromagnetic materials found in nature?

FIGURE 9
Magnets of Different Materials
Modern magnets come in a variety of shapes and are made from many different materials.

For: Links on magnetic materials
Visit: www.SciLinks.org
Web Code: scn-1412

Help Students Read L1

Relating Text and Figures Refer to the Content Refresher in this chapter, which provides the guidelines for the Relating Text and Figures strategy.

Have students keep their books closed as you read aloud the paragraphs under the subheading *Alignment of Domains*. Then, have students open their books to the passage you read. Tell them to reread the passage and study Figure 8 carefully. Ask: **What parts of the text makes more sense now that you can see the figure?** *(Sample answer: Now I understand better the difference in the arrangement of domains in magnetized material and unmagnetized material.)* **What new information did you learn by looking at the figure?** *(Sample answer: The domains are all differently shaped, and the north poles of the domains point in all different directions in unmagnetized material.)*

For: Links on magnetic materials
Visit: www.SciLinks.org
Web Code: scn-1412

Download a worksheet that will guide students' review of Internet sources on magnetic materials.

Monitor Progress L2

Writing Have students write a paragraph explaining what causes a material to have magnetic properties. Ask them also to name one ferromagnetic material.

Answers

Figure 8 Most of the domains in magnetized iron are arranged in the same direction. Most of the domains in unmagnetized iron are arranged in random directions.

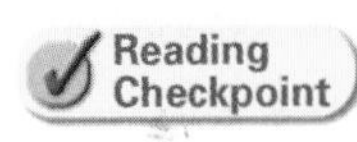
The domains point in random directions.

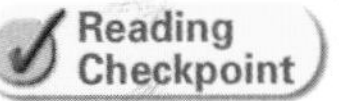
Iron, nickel, cobalt, gadolinium, neodymium, and samarium.

Differentiated Instruction

English Learners/Beginning L1
Comprehension: Modified Cloze
Distribute a simplified paragraph about the inside of a magnet, but leave some words blank. Model how to fill in the blanks, using a sample sentence on the board. Provide students with the correct answers as choices. **learning modality: verbal**

English Learners/Intermediate L2
Comprehension: Modified Cloze
Distribute the same paragraph in the Beginning strategy, but include some additional terms as incorrect answer choices. After students complete the paragraph, have them work together to write definitions for the answer choices not used. **learning modality: verbal**

Making and Changing Magnets

Teach Key Concepts L2

Making, Destroying, and Breaking Magnets

Focus Explain to students that magnets can be made and destroyed, and making and destroying magnets is common.

Teach Ask: **What are two ways a magnet can be made?** *(By placing an unmagnetized material in a strong magnetic field and by rubbing the material with one pole of the magnet)* **What is the difference between a temporary magnet and a permanent magnet?** *(A temporary magnet is made from a material that easily loses its magnetism, while a permanent magnet is made from material that keeps its magnetism for a long time.)* **What are two ways a magnet can be destroyed?** *(A magnet can be destroyed if it is dropped or heated.)*

Apply Demonstrate how to make a temporary magnet by rubbing a paper clip with one pole of a bar magnet. Then show students how that paper clip will attract another paper clip. Ask: **What did the magnetic field of the bar magnet cause to occur in the paper clip?** *(It caused some magnetic domains in the paper clip to line up in the same direction.)* **learning modality: visual**

Use Visuals: Figure 11 L1

A Magnet Cut in Half

Focus Tell students that breaking a magnet in half does not destroy the magnet.

Teach Have students look at Figure 11 and read the caption. Ask: **What happens if you break a magnet in two?** *(The result is two smaller magnets.)* **Why does breaking a magnet in half result in two smaller magnets?** *(In a magnet, many domains are lined up in one direction, producing strong magnetic forces at the poles. If the magnet is broken in half, the domains will still be lined up in the same way in the smaller pieces.)*

Apply Explain that this breaking process can continue until the magnets are extremely small. Ask: **Into how small a piece can a magnetic material be broken and still retain its magnetic properties?** *(A piece the size of an atom)* **learning modality: verbal**

All in One Teaching Resources

- Transparency N7

FIGURE 10
Temporary Magnets
A metal paper clip can be magnetized and temporarily attract another paper clip.
Relating Cause and Effect *How can a paper clip be attracted to another paper clip?*

Making and Changing Magnets

A magnet can be made from ferromagnetic material. However, no magnet can last forever. **Magnets can be made, destroyed, or broken apart.**

Making Magnets You know that magnetite exists in nature. But people make the magnets you use every day. Some unmagnetized materials can be magnetized. A magnet can be made by placing an unmagnetized ferromagnetic material in a strong magnetic field or by rubbing the material with one pole of a magnet.

Suppose, for example, that you want to magnetize a steel paper clip. Steel contains iron. So you can magnetize the paper clip by rubbing in one direction with one pole of a magnet. The magnetic field of the magnet causes some domains in the paper clip to line up in the same direction as the domains in the magnet. The more domains that line up, the more magnetized the paper clip becomes.

Some materials, such as the steel in a paper clip or pure iron, are easy to magnetize, but lose their magnetism quickly. A magnet made from a material that easily loses its magnetism is called a **temporary magnet.** Other materials, such as those in strong magnets, are hard to magnetize, but tend to stay magnetized. A magnet made from a material that keeps its magnetism for a long time is called a **permanent magnet.**

Destroying Magnets Like a temporary magnet, a permanent magnet can also become unmagnetized. One way for a magnet to become unmagnetized is to drop it or strike it hard. If a magnet is hit hard, its domains can be knocked out of alignment. Heating a magnet will also destroy its magnetism. When an object is heated, its particles vibrate faster and more randomly. These movements make it more difficult for all the domains to stay lined up. Above a certain temperature, every ferromagnetic material loses its magnetic properties. The temperature depends on the material.

Breaking Magnets What happens if you break a magnet in two? Do you have a north pole in one hand and a south pole in the other? The answer is no—you have two smaller magnets. Each smaller magnet has its own north pole and south pole. If you break those two halves again, you have four magnets.

Now that you know about domains, you can understand why breaking a magnet in half does not result in two pieces that are individual poles. Within the original magnet shown in Figure 11, many north and south poles are facing each other. Many of the magnet's domains are lined up in one direction. This produces a strong magnetic force at the magnet's north and south poles. If the magnet is cut in half, the domains in the two halves will still be lined up in the same way. So the shorter pieces will still have strong ends made up of many north or south poles.

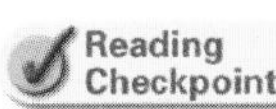

What is a temporary magnet?

FIGURE 11
Magnet Pieces
Each piece of a magnet retains its magnetic properties after it is cut in half.

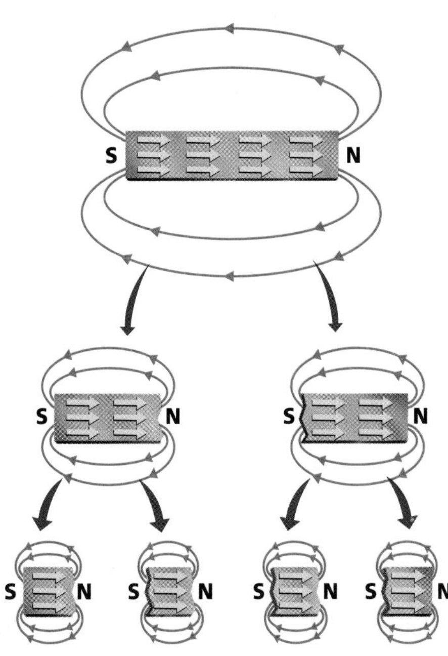

Section 2 Assessment

Target Reading Skill Asking Questions Work with a partner to check the answers in your graphic organizer.

Reviewing Key Concepts

1. a. Listing What particles are found in an atom?
   b. Identifying Which particle is responsible for a material's magnetic properties?
   c. Relating Cause and Effect How is a magnetic field produced in an atom?
2. a. Defining What is a magnetic domain?
   b. Explaining How are domains arranged in materials that are magnetized and in ones that are not?
   c. Applying Concepts What happens to the domains in iron filings that line up with the magnetic field of a bar magnet?
3. a. Reviewing How can magnets be changed?
   b. Comparing and Contrasting How are temporary and permanent magnets alike? How are they different?

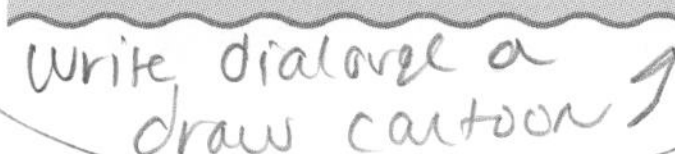

Writing Dialogue You are discussing magnets with another person. That person thinks that breaking a magnet will destroy the magnet's magnetic properties. Write a conversation you might have with the other person as you try to explain why the person's idea is incorrect.

write dialogue or draw cartoon

Lab zone Chapter Project

Keep Students on Track Check that each group has completed or is well on its way to completing a design for a magnetic sculpture. Ask students what materials they plan to use, and provide materials or suggest places to obtain needed materials. Ask questions such as the following: What kinds of magnets are you using in your sculpture? How many magnets are you using?

Writing in Science

Writing Mode Writing dialogue

Scoring Rubric

4 Exceeds criteria
3 Meets criteria
2 Meets some criteria; fails to explain completely and/or accurately what occurs when a magnet is broken
1 Includes serious errors or is incomplete

Monitor Progress L2

Answers

Figure 10 Placing a paper clip in a magnetic field causes its domains to be arranged in the same direction, making it a temporary magnet that attracts other clips.

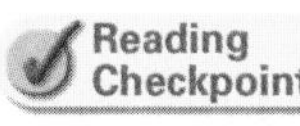

A magnet made from a material that easily loses its magnetism

Assess

Reviewing Key Concepts

1. a. Protons, neutrons, and electrons **b.** Electron **c.** A spinning electron produces a magnetic field that makes the electron behave like a tiny magnet in the atom.
2. a. A grouping of atoms with their magnetic fields lined up in the same direction **b.** In magnetized materials, all or most domains are arranged in the same direction. In unmagnetized materials, most domains point in random directions. **c.** The magnet's magnetic field causes most domains in the filings to line up with the magnetic field of the bar magnet.
3. a. A magnet can lose some or all of its magnetism if it is hit hard or heated above a certain temperature. It can also be broken into smaller magnets. **b.** Both are made of ferromagnetic materials. Temporary magnets are made of materials that are magnetized easily but lose their magnetism quickly. Permanent magnets are made of materials that are harder to magnetize but tend to keep their magnetism longer.

Reteach L1

Call on students to explain domains and how they are arranged in magnetized and unmagnetized materials.

Performance Assessment L2

Skills Check Have each student make a flowchart that explains how a temporary magnet can be made. Make sure students mention magnetic domains.

All in One Teaching Resources

- Section Summary: *Inside a Magnet*
- Review and Reinforce: *Inside a Magnet*
- Enrich: *Inside a Magnet*

Design and Build a Magnetic Paper Clip Holder

L3

Prepare for Inquiry

Key Concept

Combining the magnetic fields of magnets produces a stronger magnet.

Skills Objectives

After this lab, students will be able to:

- design a magnetic paper clip holder
- evaluate the design and performance of the magnetic paper clip holder
- troubleshoot the magnetic paper clip holder for problems and redesign it

Prep Time 10 minutes
Class Time 40 minutes

Advance Planning

Collect two bar magnets for each student or group and an assortment of other magnets of various types, shapes, and sizes. In addition, you'll need a box of paper clips and a roll of masking tape for each student or group. To make the base and strapping for the holder, each student or group will need modeling clay and string. Rubber bands might be useful in building a holder. Students might also request a foam or wooden base.

All in One Teaching Resources

- Lab Worksheet: *Design and Build a Magnetic Paper Clip Holder*

Guide Inquiry

Introduce the Procedure

Using two bar magnets, review with students the two polar ends of magnets. Review how unlike poles attract and like poles repel. Then, have students read the entire procedure, and answer any questions they have. Ask: **Why do you think you need to do three trials for each magnet and then find the average for the three?** *(To make sure you get a true reflection of the strength of the magnet and not a fluke on just one trial)* **What materials do you think you might need to make the holder?** *(Sample answer: A base might be useful, such as one made of foam or wood.)*

Lab zone **Technology Lab**
• Tech & Design •

Design and Build a Magnetic Paper Clip Holder

Problem

Many objects that you use in your daily life contain magnets. Can you design and build a magnetic paper clip holder?

Skills Focus

designing the solution, evaluating the design, troubleshooting

Materials

- 2 bar magnets
- masking tape
- container of 150 regular size paper clips
- an assortment of types, shapes, and sizes of magnets, including two bar magnets
- modeling clay, string, and other materials approved by your teacher

Procedure

PART 1 Research and Investigate

1. Copy the data table into your notebook.
2. Place one pole of a bar magnet into a container of paper clips. Slowly lift the magnet and count how many paper clips are attached to it. Record the number of paper clips in your data table. Return the paper clips to the container.
3. Repeat Step 2 two more times.
4. Calculate the average number of paper clips you lifted in the three trials.

Data Table	
Type of magnet	Number of paper clips

5. Use the other pole of the bar magnet and repeat Step 2.
6. Repeat Step 2 again using the poles of each of the other magnets to pick up the paper clips.
7. Repeat Step 2 using 3 or 4 different combinations of magnets. For example, you can tape two magnets together, as shown in the photo.

PART 2 Design and Build

8. Examine your data. Use it to design a magnetic paper clip holder that
   - holds at least 150 paper clips
   - allows easy access to the paper clips *(Hint:* The holder could sit on a desk or hang suspended from an object)
   - is made of materials approved by your teacher
   - is built following the Safety Guidelines in Appendix A
9. Draw a sketch of your paper clip holder and include a list of materials you'll need. Obtain your teacher's approval of your design. Then build your holder.

Sample Data Table	
Type of Magnet	**Number of Paper clips**
Bar Magnet—north pole	12
Bar Magnet—north pole	13
Bar Magnet—north pole	11
Ceramic Magnet—south pole	9
Ceramic Magnet—south pole	8
Ceramic Magnet—south pole	8

PART 3 Evaluate and Redesign

10. Test your holder. Does the device meet the criteria listed in Step 8? Compare the design and performance of your holder with the holders of some of your classmates.
11. Based on what you learned, redesign your holder. After you receive your teacher's approval, build and test your redesigned holder.

Analyze and Conclude

1. **Inferring** Why did you test each magnet three times in Part 1?
2. **Drawing Conclusions** What conclusions did you draw from the data you collected in Part 1?
3. **Designing a Solution** How did you use the data you collected to design your paper clip holder?
4. **Troubleshooting** Describe one problem you faced while designing or building your holder. How did you solve the problem?
5. **Working With Design Constraints** What limitations did the criteria of holding at least 150 paper clips place on your design? How did you solve those limitations?
6. **Evaluating the Impact on Society** Describe how a device that uses magnets affects your life on a daily basis.

Communicate

Write a letter to a friend that describes how you combined magnets to build a practical paper clip holder.

Go Online PHSchool.com

For: Data sharing
Visit: PHSchool.com
Web Code: cgd-4034

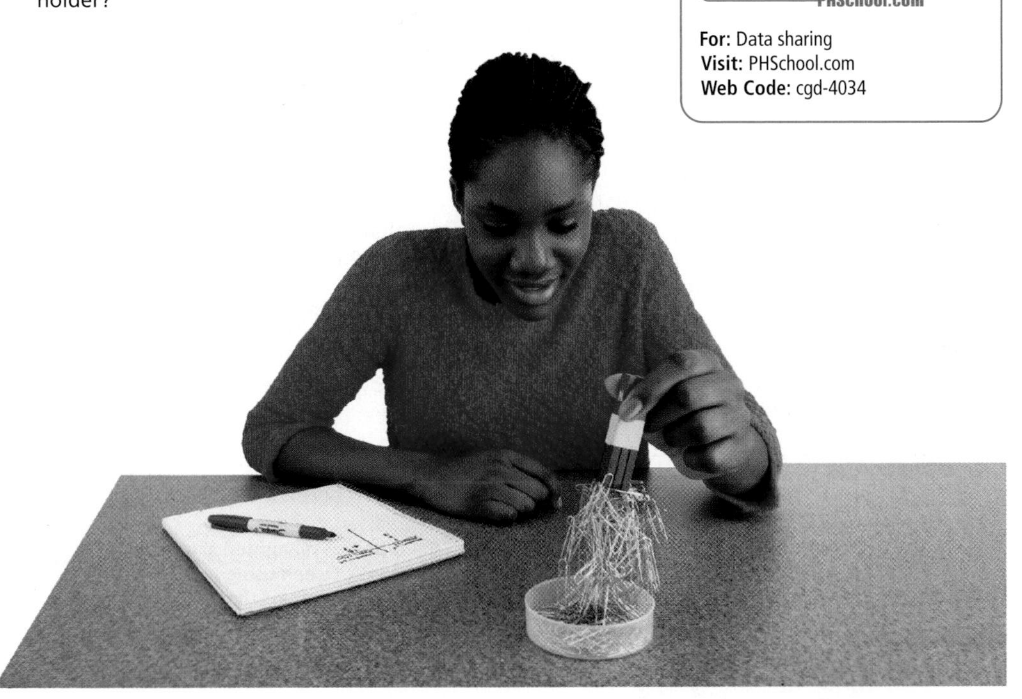

Expected Outcome

Students should discover that combinations of magnets are more powerful than any single magnet.

Analyze and Conclude

1. Sample answer: Testing three times ensures that a mistake or an odd result does not skew the data.

2. Sample answer: Different magnets have different strengths. Generally, combining magnets results in a stronger magnetic field.

3. The combination of magnets that picked up the most paper clips has the strongest magnetic field and was used in the holder design.

4. Sample answer: One problem was exposing enough of the surface of the magnets while securing them in place on a modeling clay base. To solve this problem, the clay base was reshaped.

5. Sample answer: The design constraint of holding that many paper clips meant that the design had to include a way of holding several magnets in place. That problem was solved using tape and string.

6. Sample answer: Magnets are used on a purse clasp to keep its contents from falling out.

Extend Inquiry

Communicate Students' letters will vary. An excellent letter will clearly and logically explain how to combine magnets to produce a more powerful magnet, including how to align the poles of a bar magnet. Students should also explain why combining magnets produces a more powerful magnetic field.

Troubleshooting the Experiment

- Combining magnets for greater strength will work with traditional bar magnets and will also work with ceramic magnets.
- If students work with disk magnets, advise them that they may get better results by combining magnets by unlike poles. Combining bar magnets, by contrast, works best when like poles are combined—one magnet on top of the other, both oriented the same way.
- As you check the students' drawings made in Part 2, suggest ways in which students can improve their designs. Help students find simple materials they request for use in their holders.

For: Data sharing
Visit: PHSchool.com
Web Code: cgd-4034

Students can share data online.

Section 3 Magnetic Earth

Objectives

After this lesson, students will be able to

N.1.3.1 Explain how Earth is like a bar magnet.

N.1.3.2 Describe the effects of Earth's magnetic field.

Target Reading Skill

Building Vocabulary Explain that using vocabulary strategies such as writing a meaningful sentence helps students define key-concept words.

Answers

Sample answers:

Christopher Columbus used a **compass** to navigate in 1492. **Magnetic declination** is that angle between two imaginary lines from geographic North Pole and magnetic north pole. The **Van Allen belts** are doughnut-shaped regions above Earth's surface. The sun sends out a stream of electrically charged particles called the **solar wind**. The **magnetosphere** is shaped by the solar wind. An example of an **aurora** is the Northern Lights.

Preteach

Build Background Knowledge L2

Using a Compass

Have students recall their experiences using a compass. Ask: **Has anyone ever used a compass while camping or taking a hike?** *(Sample answer: We used a compass at scout camp.)* **What is a compass used for?** *(Sample answer: To tell you which way is north. To help you navigate.)* **Which direction does a compass needle always point?** *(To the north)* **Why?** *(Some students may suggest that the North Pole is magnetic.)* Explain that in this section students will learn why a compass needle points north.

Section 3 Integrating Earth Science

Magnetic Earth

Reading Preview

Key Concepts

- How is Earth like a bar magnet?
- What are the effects of Earth's magnetic field?

Key Terms

- compass
- magnetic declination
- Van Allen belts
- solar wind
- magnetosphere
- aurora

Target Reading Skill

Building Vocabulary Using a word in a sentence helps you think about how best to explain the word. After you read the section, reread the paragraphs that contain definitions of Key Terms. Use all the information you have learned to write a meaningful sentence using the Key Term.

Lab zone Discover Activity

Can You Use a Needle to Make a Compass?

1. Magnetize a large needle by rubbing it several times in the same direction with one end of a strong bar magnet. Push the needle through a ball of foam or tape it to a small piece of cork.
2. Place a drop of dishwashing soap in a bowl of water. Then float the foam or cork in the water. Adjust the needle until it floats horizontally.
3. Allow the needle to stop moving. Note the direction it points.
4. Use a local map to determine the direction in which it points.

Think It Over

Observing In what direction did the needle point? If you repeat the activity, will it still point in the same direction? What does this tell you about Earth?

When Christopher Columbus sighted land in 1492, he didn't know what he had found. He was trying to find a shortcut from Europe to India. Where he landed, however, was on an island in the Caribbean Sea just south of the present-day United States. He had no idea that such an island even existed.

In spite of his error, Columbus had successfully followed a course west to the Americas without the help of an accurate map. Instead, Columbus used a compass for navigation. A **compass** is a device that has a magnetized needle that spins freely. A compass needle usually points north. As you read, you'll find out why.

◀ Columbus navigated across the Atlantic Ocean using a compass similar to one of these.

Lab zone Discover Activity

Skills Focus Observing L2

Materials large needle, strong bar magnet, dish, water, dishwashing soap, cork or foam ball

Time 15 minutes

Tips Caution students to handle the needle carefully. Students should rub the needle in only one direction. Magnetized objects in the room may attract the needle. Use a compass to verify that the needle points north.

Expected Outcome The needle will point north.

Think It Over Sample answer: The needle pointed north. Yes. The needle will always point north because Earth has a magnetic field.

FIGURE 12
Earth's Magnetic Field
The magnetic field lines show the shape of Earth's magnetic field. **Observing** *What magnetic properties does Earth have?*

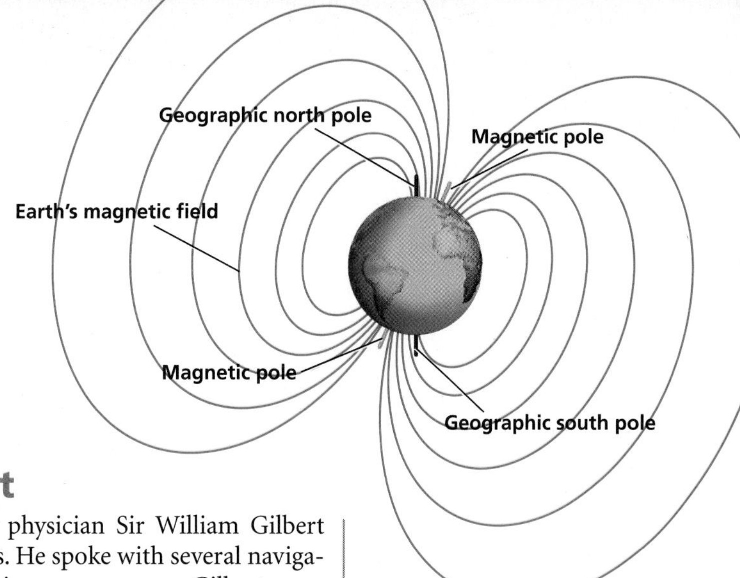

Earth as a Magnet

In the late 1500s, the English physician Sir William Gilbert became interested in compasses. He spoke with several navigators and experimented with his own compass. Gilbert confirmed that a compass always points in the same direction, no matter where it is. But no one knew why.

Gilbert hypothesized that a compass behaves as it does because Earth acts as a giant magnet. Although many educated people of his time laughed at this idea, Gilbert turned out to be correct. **Just like a bar magnet, Earth has a magnetic field surrounding it and two magnetic poles.**

The fact that Earth has a magnetic field explains why a compass works as it does. The poles of the magnetized needle on the compass align themselves with Earth's magnetic field.

Earth's Core Gilbert thought that Earth's center, or core, contains magnetic rock. Scientists now think that this is not the case, since the material inside Earth's core is too hot to be solid. Also, the temperature is too high for the material to be magnetic. Earth's magnetism is still not completely understood. But scientists do know that the circulation of molten material in Earth's core is related to Earth's magnetism.

Earth's Magnetic Poles You know that Earth rotates on its axis, around the geographic poles. But Earth also has magnetic poles. These magnetic poles are located on Earth's surface where the magnetic force is strongest. As you can see in Figure 12, the magnetic poles are not in the same place as the geographic poles. For example, the magnetic pole in the Northern Hemisphere is located in northern Canada about 1,250 kilometers from the geographic North Pole.

Instruct

Earth as a Magnet

Teach Key Concepts L2

Earth Has a Magnetic Field

Focus Tell students that Earth itself has magnetic properties.

Teach Ask: **How is Earth like a bar magnet?** *(Earth has a magnetic field surrounding it and two magnetic poles.)* **Are Earth's magnetic poles in the same place as its geographic poles?** *(No.)* **To which pole does a compass needle point?** *(The magnetic pole in the north)*

Apply Have students observe a compass. Ask: **Why does a compass needle point north?** *(It is magnetized; it points north because it aligns with Earth's magnetic field.)* **learning modality: verbal**

All in One Teaching Resources

- Transparency N8

Magnetism

Show the Video Field Trip to help students better understand Earth's magnetic field. Discussion question: **How far does Earth's magnetic field extend into space?** *(It extends thousands of kilometers into space.)*

Independent Practice L2

All in One Teaching Resources

- Guided Reading and Study Worksheet: *Magnetic Earth*

Student Edition on Audio CD

Differentiated Instruction

Less Proficient Readers L1

Answering Questions Select a passage from the text, such as the subsection Earth's Magnetic Field. Read the passage aloud to students as they follow along in their books. After reading, ask some questions about the passage. If they don't know the answers, challenge them to find the answers in the passage. **learning modality: verbal**

Gifted Students L3

Communicating Have interested students research what Earth scientists understand about how Earth's core creates Earth's magnetic field as well as what causes the magnetic field to reverse directions. Ask students to make a presentation to the class of their findings. **learning modality: verbal**

Monitor Progress L2

Oral Presentation Have students explain why a compass needle always points north.

Answer

Figure 12 Earth has a magnetic field surrounding it and two magnetic poles.

Math Analyzing Data

Math Skill Interpreting data

Focus Tell students that a data table is useful for organizing data so that the data can be interpreted or graphed.

Teach Ask: **What is the subject of the data table?** *(The movement of the magnetic north pole)* **What period of time do the data represent?** *(1948 through 2001, or 53 years)* **Is the time between the years of reading the same in each case?** *(No. The years between readings are different in every case.)*

Answers

1. The average speed of the pole's movement is increasing.

2. Between 1948 and 2001, the pole has moved 857 km *(150 km + 120 km + 120 km + 180 km + 287 km = 857 km).*

3. Sample answer: The average speed increased by 23.0 km/yr from 1994 to 2001 *(41.0 km/yr − 18.0 km/yr = 23.0 km/yr).* That is an increase of 3.3 km/yr per year *(23.0 km/yr ÷ 7 yr = 3.3 km/yr/yr).* There are 9 years between 2001 and 2010. Therefore, a good prediction is that the average speed of the pole's movement in 2010 will be 29.7 km/yr *(3.3 km/yr/yr × 9 yr = 29.7 km/yr).*

Earth's Magnetic Field

Teach Key Concepts

L2

Earth Magnetizes Materials

Focus Explain that Earth's magnetic field is strong, and Earth can make magnets just as other strong magnets do.

Teach Ask: **How can a magnetic field make a magnet?** *(A magnet can be made by placing an unmagnetized ferromagnetic material in a strong magnetic field.)*

Apply Ask: **When molten material from underground rises to the surface, how is the iron in the material affected by Earth's magnetic field?** *(As it solidifies, the iron in the molten material lines up in the direction of Earth's magnetic field.)* **What have scientists learned by studying the rock that has hardened from molten material?** *(Scientists have learned that Earth's magnetic field has completely reversed direction every million years or so.)* **learning modality: verbal**

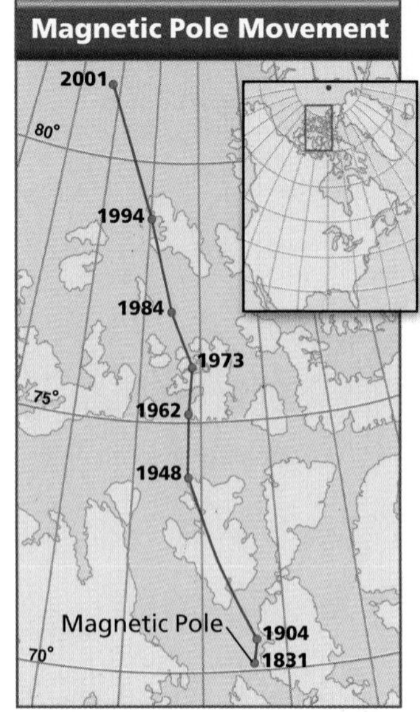

FIGURE 13
The location of Earth's magnetic poles does not stay the same.

Magnetic Declination If you use a compass, you have to account for the fact that Earth's geographic and magnetic poles are different. Suppose you could draw a line between you and the geographic North Pole. The direction of this line is geographic north. Then imagine a second line drawn between you and the magnetic pole in the Northern Hemisphere. The angle between these two lines is the angle between geographic north and the north to which a compass needle points. This angle is known as **magnetic declination**. So, magnetic declination differs depending on your location on Earth.

The magnetic declination of a location on Earth today is not the same as it was 10 years ago. The magnetic declination of a location changes. Earth's magnetic poles do not stay in one place as the geographic poles do. Figure 13 shows how the location of Earth's magnetic pole in the Northern Hemisphere has drifted over time.

Earth's Magnetic Field

You learned that a material such as iron can be made into a magnet by a strong magnetic field. **Since Earth produces a strong magnetic field, Earth itself can make magnets out of ferromagnetic materials.**

Earth as a Magnet Maker Suppose you leave an iron bar lying in a north-south direction for many years. Earth's magnetic field may attract the domains strongly enough to cause them to line up in the same direction. When the domains in the iron bar align, the bar becomes a magnet. This can happen to some everyday objects. So even though no one has tried to make metal objects such as file cabinets in your school into magnets, Earth might have done so anyway!

Math Analyzing Data

Movement of Earth's Magnetic Poles

Earth's magnetic poles move slowly over time. The data in the table show the position of Earth's magnetic north pole in specific years.

1. **Interpreting Data** What is the trend in the speed of the pole's movement?
2. **Calculating** What is the total distance the pole has traveled over the time shown?
3. **Predicting** Using this data, predict the average speed of the pole's movement between 2001 and 2010. Explain.

Magnetic North Pole Movement

Year of Reading	Distance Moved Since Previous Reading (km)	Average Speed (km/yr)
1948	420	9.5
1962	150	10.7
1973	120	10.9
1984	120	10.9
1994	180	18.0
2001	287	41.0

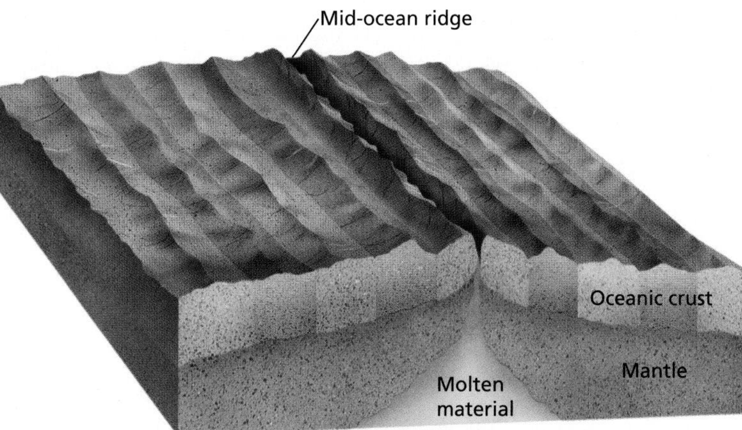

FIGURE 14
Earth's Magnetic Stripes
When molten material hardens into the rock of the ocean floor, the direction of Earth's magnetic field at that time is permanently recorded. **Applying Concepts** *How can scientists use this rock record to study changes in Earth's magnetic field?*

Earth Leaves a Record Earth's magnetic field also acts on rocks that contain magnetic material, such as rock on the ocean floor. Rock is produced on the ocean floor from molten material that seeps up through a long crack in the ocean floor known as a mid-ocean ridge. When the rock is molten, the iron it contains lines up in the direction of Earth's magnetic field. As the rock cools and hardens, the iron is locked in place. This creates a permanent record of the magnetic field.

As scientists studied such rock, they discovered that the direction and strength of Earth's magnetic field have changed over time. Earth's magnetic field has completely reversed direction every million years or so.

The different colored layers in Figure 14 indicate the directions of Earth's magnetic field over time. Notice that the patterns of bands on either side of the ridge are mirror images. This is because the sea floor spreads apart from the mid-ocean ridge. So rocks farther from the ridge are older than rocks near the ridge. Scientists can determine when the rock was formed by looking at the rock's magnetic record.

Why does Earth's magnetic field change direction? No one knows. Scientists hypothesize that changes in the motion of molten material in Earth's core may cause changes in Earth's magnetic field. But scientists cannot explain why changes in the molten material take place.

Reading Checkpoint **What evidence shows that Earth's magnetic field changes?**

Lab zone Skills Activity

Measuring

1. Use a local map to locate geographic north relative to your school. Mark the direction on the floor with tape or chalk.
2. Use a compass to find magnetic north. Again mark the direction.
3. Use a protractor to measure the number of degrees between the two marks.

Compare the directions of magnetic and geographic north. Is magnetic north to the east or west of geographic north?

Lab zone Teacher **Demo**

Earth Magnetizes Iron L2

Materials metal filing cabinet or other large object that has been in one place for a long time, such as a metal locker; compass

Time 5 minutes

Focus Tell students that Earth's magnetic field magnetizes everyday objects.

Teach Hold the compass parallel to the ground and move it slowly from the top of the filing cabinet or metal locker down to the bottom. If the needle turns and points in a different direction than north, then the filing cabinet or locker is magnetized. Allow students to move the compass around the cabinet or locker and watch for deflection of the needle.

Apply Ask: **What is the process by which this filing cabinet become magnetized?** *(Earth's magnetic field caused the domains to line up in the same direction).* **learning modality: visual**

All in One Teaching Resources

- Transparency N9

Lab zone Skills Activity

Skills Focus Measuring L2

Materials Local map, tape or chalk, compass, protractor

Time 10 minutes

Tips If possible, do this activity outdoors, away from power lines or other magnetic materials.

Expected Outcome Students should find that the compass needle points at an angle to the left, or west, of geographic north.

Extend Have students identify the direction the compass illustration points on a map of the local area and compare it to magnetic north. Encourage students to identify landmarks in each direction. **learning modality: logical/mathematical**

Monitor Progress L2

Drawing Have students make captioned sketches to explain why a compass does not point to geographic north.

Students can keep their drawings in their portfolios. Portfolio

Answers

Figure 14 By studying the direction of the iron in a rock, scientists can determine the direction of Earth's magnetic field at the time the rock solidified from molten material.

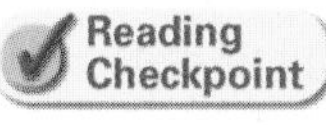

Reading Checkpoint The magnetic record in rock on the ocean floor shows that Earth's magnetic field has completely reversed direction every million years or so.

Integrating Earth Science L2

Evidence of Movements of Earth's Plates

Focus Tell students that the surface of Earth is composed of huge plates that move very slowly.

Teach Ask: **How is a permanent record of Earth's magnetic field made in rocks?** *(Before rocks harden, the iron in the rocks lines up in the direction of Earth's magnetic field.)* Explain that Earth scientists have studied rocks from all over the world, and the record in rocks of Earth's magnetic field is evidence that these plates have moved greatly over time.

Apply Ask: **Once a rock hardens, can the iron in the rock change directions?** *(Not easily. The rock's domains are very rigid and difficult to move.)* **If the iron in a rock is lined up in a different direction than the direction of Earth's magnetic field, what might that show about the rock?** *(The rock has moved from the position where the molten material originally hardened.)* **learning modality: verbal**

The Magnetosphere

Teach Key Concepts L2

Solar Wind and Auroras

Focus Tell students that Earth's magnetic field affects both atoms in materials on Earth and atomic particles in Earth's atmosphere.

Teach Ask: **What are the Van Allen belts?** *(They are doughnut-shaped regions above Earth's surface that contain electrons and protons traveling at very high speeds.)* **How do these charged particles reach the Van Allen belts?** *(They come from the stream of charged particles flowing from the sun, or the solar wind.)* **What is the magnetosphere?** *(The region of Earth's magnetic field shaped by the solar wind)*

Apply Ask: **Where do particles in the solar wind dip down toward Earth's surface?** *(Near the poles)* Refer to Figure 16, and emphasize that auroras occur near the magnetic poles. Ask: **What caused this aurora to occur?** *(Electrically charged particles in solar wind dipped down towards Earth's surface. When they got close to the surface, they interacted with atoms in the atmosphere and caused a glowing region, or an aurora.)* **learning modality: verbal**

All in One Teaching Resources

- Transparency N10

Lab zone Try This Activity

Spinning in Circles

Which way will a compass point?

1. Place a bar magnet in the center of a sheet of paper.
2. Place a compass about 2 cm beyond the north pole of the magnet. Draw a small arrow showing the direction of the compass needle.
3. Repeat Step 2, placing the compass at 20 to 30 different positions around the magnet.
4. Remove the magnet and observe the pattern of arrows you drew.

Drawing Conclusions What does your pattern of arrows represent? Do compasses respond only to Earth's magnetic field?

The Magnetosphere

Earth's magnetic field extends into space. Space is not empty. It contains electrically charged particles. **Earth's magnetic field affects the movements of electrically charged particles in space.** Those charged particles also affect Earth's magnetic field.

Between 1,000 and 25,000 kilometers above Earth's surface are two doughnut-shaped regions called the **Van Allen belts.** They are named after their discoverer, J. A. Van Allen. These regions contain electrons and protons traveling at very high speeds. At one time it was feared that these particles would be dangerous for spacecraft passing through them, but this has not been the case.

Solar Wind Other electrically charged particles in space come from the sun. Earth and the other objects in our solar system experience a solar wind. The **solar wind** is a stream of electrically charged particles flowing at high speeds from the sun. The solar wind pushes against Earth's magnetic field and surrounds the field, as shown in Figure 15. The region of Earth's magnetic field shaped by the solar wind is called the **magnetosphere**. The solar wind constantly reshapes the magnetosphere as Earth rotates on its axis.

Although most particles in the solar wind cannot penetrate Earth's magnetic field, some particles do. They follow Earth's magnetic field lines to the magnetic poles. At the poles, the magnetic field lines dip down to Earth's surface.

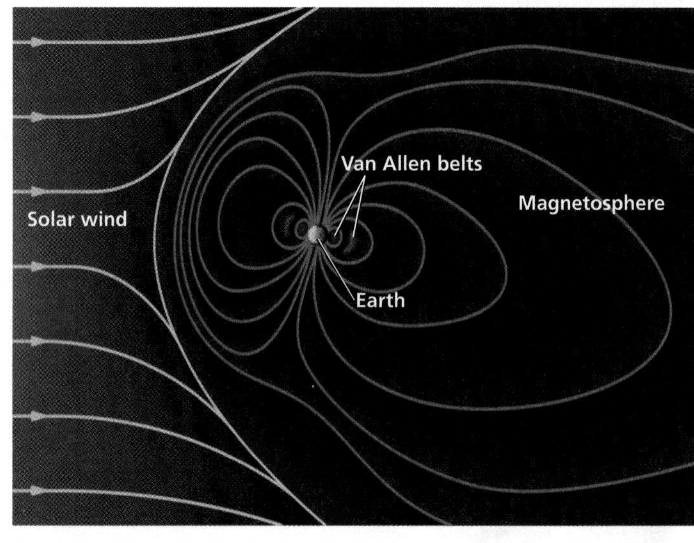

FIGURE 15
Earth's Magnetosphere
The solar wind causes Earth's magnetic field to stretch out on the side of Earth not facing the sun.
Relating Cause and Effect *What shapes the magnetosphere?*

Lab zone Try This Activity

Skills Focus Drawing conclusions L2

Materials bar magnet, sheet of paper, compass

Time 10 minutes

Tips Use a bar magnet that is much larger than the compass to give the most accurate results.

Expected Outcome Students will draw 20–30 small arrows, the pattern of which represents the bar magnet's magnetic field. Compasses respond both to Earth's magnetic field and to magnetic material near them.

Extend Students can repeat the activity using a horseshoe magnet. **learning modality: visual**

FIGURE 16
Aurora
A band of colored light called an aurora occasionally appears in the night sky near the magnetic poles.

Auroras When high-speed, charged particles get close to Earth's surface, they interact with atoms in the atmosphere. This causes some of the atoms to give off light. The result is one of Earth's most spectacular displays—a curtain of shimmering bright light in the atmosphere. A glowing region in the atmosphere caused by charged particles from the sun is called an **aurora**. In the Northern Hemisphere, an aurora is called the Northern Lights, or aurora borealis. In the Southern Hemisphere, it is called the Southern Lights, or aurora australis.

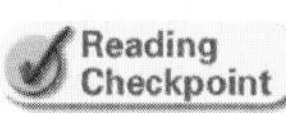 **What causes an aurora?**

For: More on Earth's magnetic field
Visit: PHSchool.com
Web Code: cgd-4013

Section 3 Assessment

Target Reading Skill Building Vocabulary Use your sentences to help answer the questions.

Reviewing Key Concepts

1. a. Reviewing How are Earth and a bar magnet similar?
   b. Describing How do Earth's magnetic properties explain how a compass works?
   c. Interpreting Diagrams Look at Figure 12. How do the positions of the geographic and magnetic poles compare?
2. a. Identifying What are two effects of Earth's magnetic field?
   b. Explaining How can scientists use rocks to learn about Earth's magnetic field?
   c. Relating Cause and Effect What causes the part of Earth's magnetic field called the magnetosphere to exist?

Lab zone At-Home Activity

House Compass With a family member, explore your home with a compass. Use the compass to discover magnetic fields in your house. Try metal objects that have been in the same position over a long period of time. Explain to your family member why the compass needle moves away from north near some objects.

Lab zone At-Home Activity

House Compass L1 Students should explain to the family member that Earth's magnetic field can magnetize a ferromagnetic material left in a certain position for many years. Some students may find that the top and bottom of a filing cabinet are opposite poles. This is due to magnetic lines that are not parallel to Earth's surface but are at an angle to Earth's surface.

Lab zone Chapter Project

Keep Students on Track A few days before presentations are to begin, ask a volunteer group to "exhibit" its sculpture for the rest of the class. This may give groups having trouble with the project a concrete idea about how to proceed. Ask groups still working on their sculptures what help they need to complete the project.

For: More on Earth's magnetic field
Visit: PHSchool.com
Web Code: cgd-4013

Download a worksheet that will guide students' review of Internet resources on Earth's magnetic field.

Monitor Progress L2

Answers

Figure 15 The solar wind shapes the magnetosphere.

Reading Checkpoint An aurora is caused by charged particles from the sun entering Earth's magnetic field and interacting with atoms in the atmosphere.

Assess

Reviewing Key Concepts

1. a. Like a bar magnet, Earth has a magnetic field surrounding it and two magnetic poles. **b.** A compass has a magnetized needle that aligns with Earth's magnetic field. **c.** The magnetic poles are not in the same place as the geographic poles.

2. a. Earth's magnetic field can magnetize a ferromagnetic material left in a certain position for many years. Earth's magnetic field lines up iron in molten rocks. **b.** By examining the pattern of magnetic material, scientists can study the magnetic history of Earth. When rock is molten, the iron it contains lines up in the direction of Earth's magnetic field. When the rock hardens, the iron is locked in place. This creates a permanent record of the magnetic field. **c.** The solar wind creates the magnetosphere as it pushes against and shapes Earth's magnetic field.

Reteach L1

Call on students to define the key terms *magnetic declination*, *magnetosphere*, and *aurora* and explain what causes each.

Performance Assessment L2

Drawing Have each student make a drawing of Earth and its magnetic field. Drawings should include magnetic field lines and the approximate locations of Earth's geographic and magnetic poles.

All in One Teaching Resources

- Section Summary: *Magnetic Earth*
- Review and Reinforce: *Magnetic Earth*
- Enrich: *Magnetic Earth*

Study Guide

Interactive Textbook

- Complete student edition
- Section and chapter self-assessments
- Assessment reports for teachers

Help Students Read

Building Vocabulary

Words in Context Help students learn the meaning of new words or phrases by examining context. Tell students to look for familiar words or phrases that surround a new term—these are clues to the new term's meaning. Have students reread the paragraph in which the key term *magnetic domain* is defined. Ask: **Which word in the same sentence as *domain* could you substitute for *domain* in the next sentence and still have it make sense?** *(Grouping)*

Word/Part Analysis Have students look up the word *sphere* in a dictionary. They will discover that *sphere* means "globe or ball." Then, ask: **What does *magnetosphere* mean, given the word parts that make it up?** *(A magnetosphere is a magnet globe or ball.)* Explain that the magnetosphere is a "ball-shaped" magnetic field around Earth.

Connecting Concepts

Concept Maps Help students develop one way to show how the information in this chapter is related. Have students brainstorm to identify key concepts, key terms, details, and examples. Write each suggestion on a self-sticking note and attach it at random on chart paper or on the board.

Tell students that this concept map will be organized in hierarchical order and to begin at the top with key concepts. Ask students these questions to guide them to categorize the information on the self-sticking notes: **What are the properties of a magnet? What are magnetic domains? How is Earth like a magnet?**

Prompt students by using connecting words or phrases, such as "causes," "includes," and "forms," to indicate the basis for the organization of the map. Explain that the phrases should help form a sentence between or among a set of concepts.

Answer

Accept logical presentations by students.

All in One Teaching Resources

- Key Terms Review: *Magnetism*
- Connecting Concepts: *Magnetism*

Chapter 1 Study Guide

1 What Is Magnetism?

Key Concepts

- Magnets attract iron and similar materials that contain iron. They attract or repel other magnets. In addition, one part of a magnet will always point north when allowed to swing freely.
- Magnetic poles that are unlike attract each other and magnetic poles that are alike repel each other.
- Magnetic field lines spread out from one pole, curve around the magnet, and return to the other pole.

Key Terms

magnet
magnetic pole
magnetic force
magnetic field
magnetic field lines

2 Inside a Magnet

Key Concepts

- A spinning electron produces a magnetic field that makes the electron behave like a tiny magnet in an atom.
- In a magnetized material, all or most of the magnetic domains are arranged in the same direction.
- Magnets can be made, destroyed, or broken apart.

Key Terms

atom
element
nucleus
proton
neutron
electron
magnetic domain
ferromagnetic material
temporary magnet
permanent magnet

3 Magnetic Earth

Key Concepts

- Just like a bar magnet, Earth has a magnetic field surrounding it and two magnetic poles.
- Since Earth produces a strong magnetic field, Earth itself can make magnets out of ferromagnetic materials.
- Earth's magnetic field affects the movements of electrically charged particles in space.

Key Terms

compass
magnetic declination
Van Allen belts
solar wind
magnetosphere
aurora

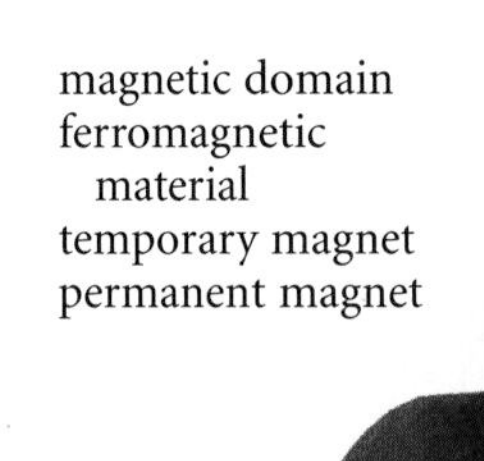

28 ◆ N

Review and Assessment

Go Online PHSchool.com
For: Self-Assessment
Visit: PHSchool.com
Web Code: cga-4010

Organizing Information

Concept Mapping Copy the concept map about magnetism onto a separate sheet of paper. Then complete it and add a title. (For more on concept maps, see the Skills Handbook.)

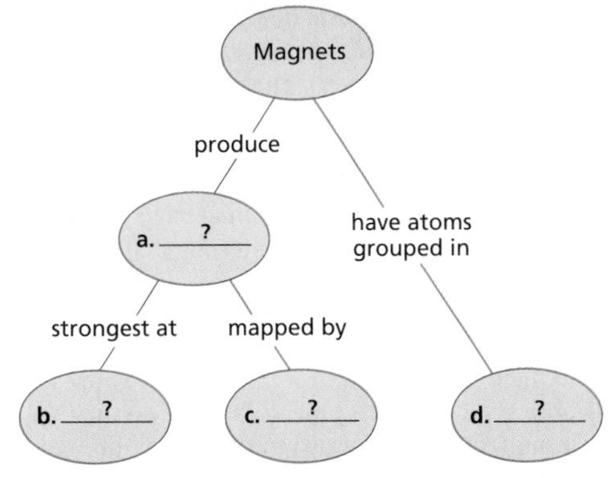

Reviewing Key Terms

Choose the letter of the best answer.

1. The area of a magnet where the magnetic force is strongest is a
   a. magnetic pole.
   b. magnetic field.
   c. magnetic field line.
   d. magnetosphere.
2. The negatively charged particles within atoms are
   a. electrons. **b.** nuclei.
   c. protons. **d.** orbits.
3. An example of a ferromagnetic material is
   a. plastic.
   b. copper.
   c. wood.
   d. iron.
4. A compass works because its magnetic needle
   a. contains atoms.
   b. contains charged particles.
   c. repels magnets.
   d. spins freely.
5. A stream of electrically charged particles flowing from the sun is called the
   a. Van Allen belt.
   b. magnetosphere.
   c. solar wind.
   d. magnetic field.

If the statement is true, write *true*. If it is false, change the underlined word or words to make the statement true.

6. Magnetic field lines map out the magnetic field around a magnet.
7. In an atom, the electrons and protons are located in the nucleus.
8. A ferromagnetic material is a material like iron that has strong magnetic properties.
9. A magnet that keeps its magnetism for a long time is called a temporary magnet.
10. The region of Earth's magnetic field shaped by the solar wind is called the aurora.

Writing in Science

Research Report You are a geologist reporting about Earth's magnetic field. In your report, explain what causes the field and give information on how scientists study it.

Magnetism
Video Preview
Video Field Trip
▶ Video Assessment

Go Online PHSchool.com
For: Self-Assessment
Visit: PHSchool.com
Web Code: cga-4010

Students can take a practice test online that is automatically scored.

All in One Teaching Resources

- Transparency N11
- Chapter Test
- Performance Assessment Teacher Notes
- Performance Assessment Student Worksheet
- Performance Assessment Scoring Rubric

***ExamView*® Computer Test Bank CD-ROM**

Review and Assessment

Organizing Information

a. magnetic fields
b. the poles
c. magnetic field lines
d. magnetic domains

Reviewing Key Terms

1. a **2.** a **3.** d **4.** d **5.** c
6. true
7. neutrons
8. true
9. permanent magnet
10. magnetosphere

Writing in Science

Writing Mode Description

Scoring Rubric

4 Exceeds criteria; is well-written and interesting and provides accurate details
3 Meets criteria
2 Meets some criteria; fails to describe completely and/or accurately the cause of auroras or what will be seen
1 Includes scant information and/or serious errors

Video Assessment

Magnetism

Show the Video Assessment to review chapter content and as a prompt for the writing assignment. Discussion questions: **Where is Earth's magnetic field the strongest?** *(At the two poles)* **What do rock samples from the ocean floor tell scientists about what's happened to Earth's magnetic field over geologic time?** *(Scientists are able to tell how many times the planet's magnetic field has changed by studying rock samples.)*

Checking Concepts

11. Magnetic field lines spread out from one pole, curve around the magnet, and return to the other pole. Arrows point from the north pole toward the south pole. Closely spaced field lines indicate strength, while lines spaced far apart indicate weakness. Diagrams should have field lines spaced so as to indicate field strength and with arrows showing field direction.

12. An atom is made up of a nucleus that contains protons and neutrons and an outer region in which electrons move.

13. Atoms in materials that can be used as magnets have unpaired electrons. Atoms in materials that cannot be used as magnets have electrons that exist in pairs.

14. In a magnetic material, all or most of the domains are arranged in the same direction.

15. In a magnet, many domains are lined up in one direction, producing strong magnetic effects at the two poles. If the magnet breaks in half, the domains in the two halves will still be lined up the same way.

16. A material becomes a magnet when the domains of the material are lined up to point in the same direction.

17. Earth acts like a magnet because it produces a magnetic field and has magnetic poles.

18. An aurora is a glowing region in the atmosphere caused by charged particles from the sun. When high-speed, charged particles get close to the atmosphere, they interact with atoms. This causes some atoms to give off light.

Review and Assessment

Checking Concepts

11. Explain how magnetic field lines are used to represent the field of a magnet. Draw a diagram that shows magnetic field lines around a magnet.

12. Describe the structure of an atom.

13. How do the atoms differ in materials that can be used as magnets and materials that cannot?

14. Describe the magnetic domains in a magnetized material.

15. Explain why you are not left with one north pole and one south pole if you break a magnet in half. Draw a diagram to support your answer.

16. How does a material become a magnet?

17. How does Earth act like a magnet?

18. What is an aurora? How is it produced?

Thinking Critically

19. **Applying Concepts** Examine the diagram below. Is the magnetic pole on the left a north or south pole? Are the two poles like or unlike?

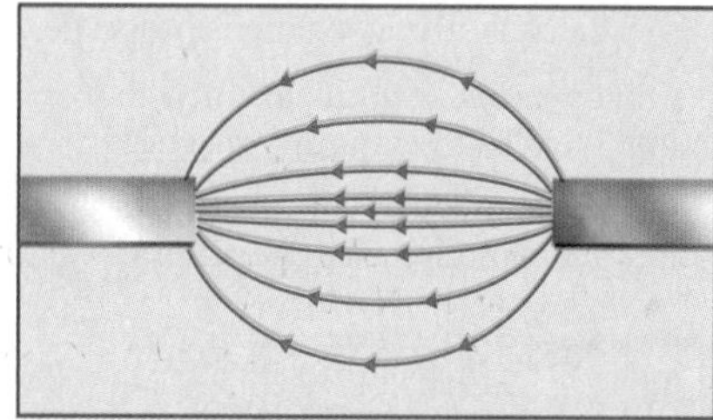

20. **Applying Concepts** The north pole of a bar magnet is held next to one end of an iron rod. Is the other end of the iron rod a north pole or a south pole? Why?

21. **Inferring** A compass points north until a bar magnet is brought next to it. The compass needle is then attracted or repelled by the magnet. What inference can you make about the strengths of the magnetic fields of Earth and the bar magnet?

22. **Problem Solving** Cassia borrowed her brother's magnet. When she returned it, it was barely magnetic. What might Cassia have done to the magnet?

23. **Drawing Conclusions** Why might an inexperienced explorer get lost using a compass?

24. **Relating Cause and Effect** What might happen to a metal pair of scissors if rubbed in one direction with the north pole of a magnet?

Applying Skills

Use the illustration to answer Questions 25–27.

The illustration shows two pairs of magnets.

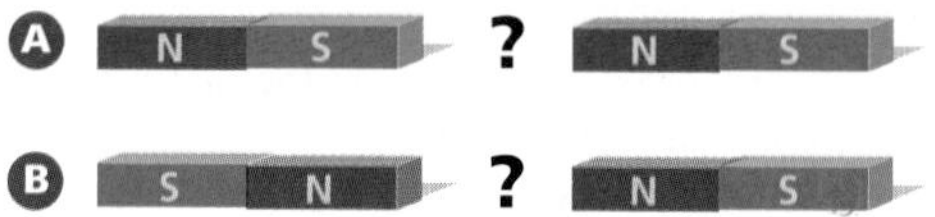

25. **Interpreting Diagrams** Which pair of magnets will have a force of attraction between them? Which pair will have a force of repulsion between them? Explain your choices.

26. **Predicting** Suppose the left-side magnet in pair A traded places with the left-side magnet in pair B. Make a sketch using magnetic field lines to show how the new pairs would look. Predict if the pairs will attract or repel. Explain.

27. **Problem Solving** If the poles of the magents were not identified, how could you identify them without using a compass?

Lab zone Chapter Project

Performance Assessment Present your sculpture to the class. Use a diagram of your sculpture to show the materials you used to create it and to show how the materials are connected to each other. Explain how you included any materials that were not originally magnetic.

Lab zone Chapter Project

L3

Performance Assessment Talk with each group before its presentation. Offer encouragement, and make suggestions about how to present the magnetic sculpture. Assess the presentations on how well the sculpture meets the criteria of using only magnets to hold it together, how creative the art is, and how informative the diagram is, as well as on the coherence of the presentation.

Standardized Test Prep

Test-Taking Tip

Interpreting a Diagram

Some questions ask you to interpret a diagram. Examine the diagram in detail, paying attention to labels, titles, and arrows. Study the diagram of the magnetic field of an iron bar for Question 3 and answer the sample question.

Sample Question

The distance between the magnetic field lines on the diagram indicates that the magnetic field is

A strongest where the lines are farthest apart.
B strongest where the lines are closest together.
C weakest where the lines are closest together.
D uniform.

Answer

The correct answer is **B.** The distance between the magnetic field lines on a magnetic field diagram indicate the strength of the magnetic field, which is strongest where the lines are closest together.

Choose the letter of the best answer.

1. Maglev trains use magnets to elevate trains so that they never touch the tracks. The poles of the magnets on the trains facing the poles of the magnets on the tracks must be
A the same, so they attract each other.
B the same, so they repel each other.
C opposites, so they repel each other.
D opposites, so they attract each other.

2. In lab, Claudio rubs the north pole of a bar magnet against a wooden coffee stirrer, iron nail, and plastic spoon. After rubbing each item for 2 minutes, Claudio tries to pick up one steel paper clip using each object. The variable tested in this experiment was
F the magnetic strength of the bar magnet.
G time.
H the magnetic properties of selected materials.
J the amount of rubbing.

Use the diagram below to answer Question 3.

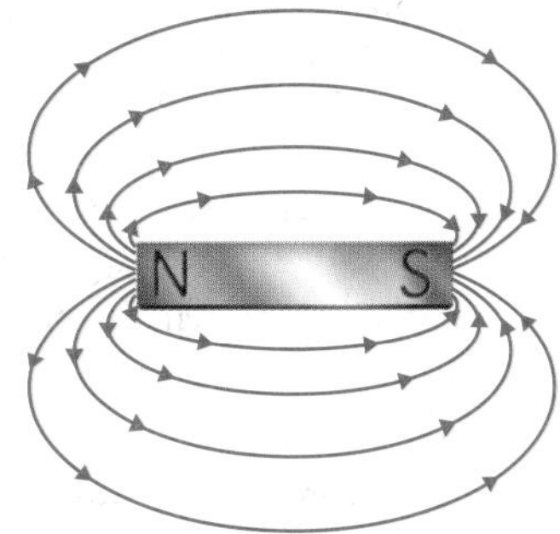

3. If the bar magnet in the above diagram were cut in half, which diagram below *best* represents the magnetic field of the two new pieces?

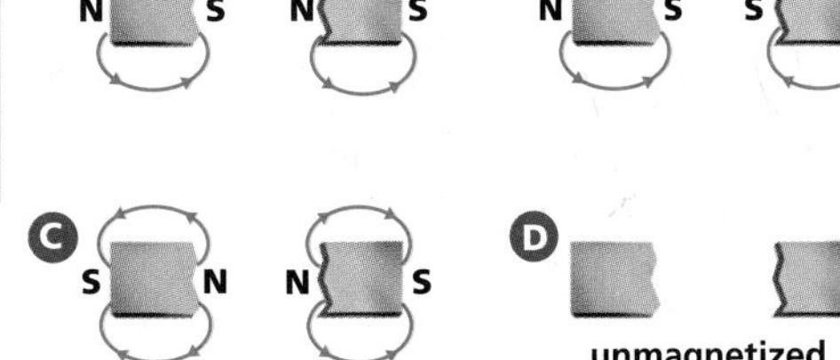

4. Which of the following statements *best* describes why compasses point north?
F Compasses, like all magnets, always point to the geographic North Pole.
G The magnetized compass needle aligns itself with Earth's magnetic field.
H Compass needles point toward the sun.
J The compass needle is repelled by Earth's geographic South Pole.

Constructed Response

5. A bar magnet picks up one paper clip. A second paper clip clings to the first paper clip but does not directly touch the magnet. Explain why the second paper clip clings to the first without touching the bar magnet.

Thinking Critically

19. Arrows point to the left. Therefore, the magnetic pole on the left is a south magnetic pole. The two poles are unlike because magnetic field lines leave the north magnetic pole and enter the south magnetic pole.

20. The other end of the iron rod becomes a north pole. The magnetic field of the bar magnet causes most of the domains in the iron rod to align, creating a south pole in the end of the rod nearest the bar magnet's north pole. At the same time, the far end of the iron rod becomes a north pole.

21. The strength of Earth's magnetic field at Earth's surface is less than the strength of the nearby bar magnet.

22. Cassia could have dropped the magnet or exposed it to heat.

23. The explorer might not know about magnetic declination. If the explorer follows the compass direction exactly, he or she will wind up off course.

24. The scissors might become magnetized.

Applying Skills

25. Pair A will have a force of attraction because the unlike poles are near each other. Pair B will have a force of repulsion because like poles are near each other.

26. The drawing for the new pair A will show lines starting from each north pole but not connecting to the other magnet. The pair will repel because they are like poles. The drawing for the new pair B will show lines starting from the north pole on the right and connecting to the south pole on the left. The magnets will attract because they are unlike poles.

27. Sample answer: You could tie a string to the middle of each magnet and let it swing freely. The magnet's north (seeking) pole would point toward Earth's magnetic pole in the Northern Hemisphere.

Standardized Test Prep

1. B **2.** H **3.** A **4.** G

5. A magnet can be made by placing an unmagnetized ferromagnetic material in a strong magnetic field. When the bar magnet picks up the first paper clip, the first paper clip becomes a temporary magnet. The first paper clip then attracts the second paper clip.

Chapter at a Glance

PRENTICE HALL

Technology | **Local Standards**

Chapter **Project** *Cause for Alarm*

All in One Teaching Resources

- Chapter Project Teacher Notes, pp. 98–99
- Chapter Project Student Overview, pp. 100–101
- Chapter Project Student Worksheets, pp. 102–103
- Chapter Project Scoring Rubric, p. 104

Video Preview

Electric Charge and Static Electricity

3–4 periods
1 1/2–2 blocks

N.2.1.1 Explain how electric charges interact.
N.2.1.2 Explain what an electric field is.
N.2.1.3 Describe how static electricity builds up and transfers.

Video Field Trip

Electric Current

3–4 periods
1 1/2–2 blocks

N.2.2.1 Explain how an electric current is produced.
N.2.2.2 Explain how conductors are different from insulators.
N.2.2.3 Describe what causes electric charges to flow in a circuit.
N.2.2.4 Explain how resistance affects current.

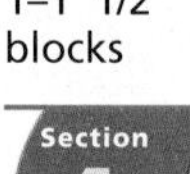

Batteries

2–3 periods
1–1 1/2 blocks

N.2.3.1 Describe what the first battery was made of.
N.2.3.2 Explain how an electrochemical cell works.

Electric Circuits

2–3 periods
1–1 1/2 blocks

N.2.4.1 Explain what Ohm's law is.
N.2.4.2 Describe the basic features of an electric circuit.
N.2.4.3 Identify how many paths currents can take in series and parallel circuits.

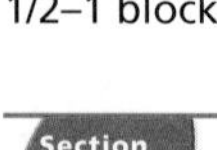

Electric Power

1–2 periods
1/2–1 block

N.2.5.1 Explain how to calculate electric power.
N.2.5.2 Identify the factors used to determine how people pay for electrical energy.

Electrical Safety

1–2 periods
1/2–1 block

N.2.6.1 Describe measures that help protect people from electrical shocks and short circuits.

Review and Assessment

All in One Teaching Resources

- Key Terms Review, p. 159
- Transparency N28
- Performance Assessment Teacher Notes, p. 170
- Performance Assessment Scoring Rubric, p. 171
- Performance Assessment Student Worksheet, p. 172
- Chapter Test, pp. 173–176

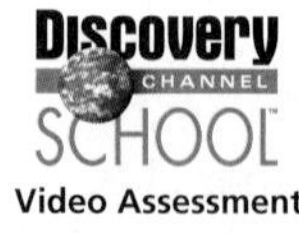

Video Assessment

Go Online PHSchool.com

Test Preparation

Test Preparation Blackline Masters

Chapter Activities Planner

For more activities

Student Edition	Inquiry	Time	Materials	Skills	Resources
Chapter Project, p. 33	Open-ended	2–3 weeks	All in One Teaching Resources p. 98	Applying concepts, designing a solution, evaluating the design, redesigning	Lab zone Easy Planner All in One Teaching Resources Support pp. 98–99
Section 1					
Discover Activity, p. 34	Guided	10 minutes	Empty aluminum can, balloon	Inferring	Lab zone Easy Planner
Skills Activity, p. 35	Directed	10 minutes	Tissue paper, hole punch, plastic comb	Drawing conclusions	Lab zone Easy Planner
Try This Activity, p. 38	Directed	10 minutes	2 foam plates, scissors, tape, aluminum pie plate	Inferring	Lab zone Easy Planner
At-Home Activity, p. 41	Directed			Communicating	Lab zone Easy Planner
Skills Lab, pp. 42–43	Directed	Prep: 20 minutes; Class: 30 minutes	Foam cup, plastic foam plate, pencil, aluminum foil, wool fabric, paper, scissors	Observing, predicting, classifying	Lab zone Easy Planner Lab Activity Video All in One Teaching Resources Skills Lab: *The Versorium,* pp. 113–116
Section 2					
Discover Activity, p. 44	Guided	15 minutes	1 m bell wire, wire cutters and strippers, metric ruler, magnetic compass, electrical tape, 1 1.5-volt bulb and socket, D-cell and holder, modeling clay	Inferring	Lab zone Easy Planner
Try This Activity, p. 49	Directed	10 minutes	250-mL beakers, funnel, ring stand, clear tubing of various lengths and widths, stopwatch	Making models	Lab zone Easy Planner
Skills Lab, pp. 52–53	Directed	Prep: 10 minutes; Class: 30 minutes	D-cell, masking tape, flashlight bulb in a socket, thick lead from mechanical pencil, uninsulated copper wire the same length as the pencil lead, rubber tubing, 1 wire (10–15 cm long), 2 wires (20–30 cm long), 2 alligator clips	Predicting, observing	Lab zone Easy Planner Lab Activity Video All in One Teaching Resources Skills Lab: *Constructing a Dimmer Switch,* pp. 124–126
Section 3					
Discover Activity, p. 54	Guided	15 minutes	Penny, vinegar, scissors, paper towel, aluminum foil, salt, mixing cup, stirring rod, voltmeter	Observing	Lab zone Easy Planner
At-Home Activity, p. 57	Guided			Observing, communicating	Lab zone Easy Planner
Consumer Lab, pp. 58–59	Guided	Prep: 15 minutes; Class: 40 minutes	Cardboard tube, flashlight bulb, paper clip, scissors, D-cell, aluminum foil, duct tape, 2 lengths of wire (about 10 cm) with the insulation stripped off about 2 cm at each end, 1 length of wire (15–20 cm) with the insulation stripped off at each end	Making models, predicting, designing	Lab zone Easy Planner Lab Activity Video All in One Teaching Resources Consumer Lab: *Build a Flashlight,* pp. 134–137
Section 4					
Discover Activity, p. 60	Guided	15 minutes	4 light bulbs with sockets, 2 dry cells with holders, several lengths of insulated wire, alligator clips	Observing	Lab zone Easy Planner
Skills Activity, p. 61	Directed	10 minutes		Calculating	Lab zone Easy Planner
Skills Activity, p. 65	Directed	15 minutes	Dry cell, 3 light bulbs, insulated wire, switch	Predicting	Lab zone Easy Planner
Section 5					
Discover Activity, p. 67	Guided	15 minutes	Light bulb in socket, hand generator, 1 m insulated copper wire	Posing questions	Lab zone Easy Planner
Skills Activity, p. 68	Directed	10 minutes	Household appliances such as toaster, microwave oven, mixer, blender	Observing	Lab zone Easy Planner
Section 6					
Discover Activity, p. 71	Guided	15 minutes	Dry cell, light bulb, 2 alligator clips, very fine steel wool (00 or 000 grade)	Developing hypotheses	Lab zone Easy Planner
At-Home Activity, p. 73	Directed			Observing, communicating	Lab zone Easy Planner

Section 1 Electric Charge and Static Electricity

3–4 periods, 1 1/2–2 blocks

ABILITY LEVELS
- L1 Basic to Average
- L2 For All Students
- L3 Average to Advanced

Local Standards

Objectives

N.2.1.1 Explain how electric charges interact.
N.2.1.2 Explain what an electric field is.
N.2.1.3 Describe how static electricity builds up and transfers.

Key Terms

• electric force • electric field • static electricity • conservation of charge
• friction • conduction • induction • static discharge

Preteach

Build Background Knowledge

Students explain what causes "static cling."

Discover Activity *Can You Move a Can Without Touching It?* L1

Targeted Print and Technology Resources

All in One Teaching Resources

- L2 Reading Strategy Transparency N12: Previewing Visuals

PresentationExpress™ CD-ROM

Instruct

Electric Charge Use Figure 1 to have students explain the three ways that electric charges interact.

Electric Force Ask leading questions for a discussion about the push and pull of charged objects.

Static Electricity Have students analyze the buildup of charge in Figure 3.

Transferring Charge Have students identify the ways in which objects are charged.

Static Discharge Ask students to describe where the charged areas are when lightning occurs.

Skills Lab *The Versorium* L3

Targeted Print and Technology Resources

All in One Teaching Resources

- L2 Guided Reading, pp. 107–110
- L2 Transparencies N13, N14, N15, N16
- L3 Skills Lab: *The Versorium*, pp. 113–116

Lab Activity Video/DVD
Skills Lab: *The Versorium*

www.SciLinks.org Web Code: scn-1421

Video Field Trip

Student Edition on Audio CD

Assess

Section Assessment Questions

Have students use their completed graphic organizers to answer the questions.

Reteach

Use the photographs in Figure 3 to reteach the three methods by which electrons can be transferred.

Targeted Print and Technology Resources

All in One Teaching Resources

- Section Summary, p. 106
- L1 Review and Reinforce, p. 111
- L3 Enrich, p. 112

Section 2 Electric Current

 *3–4 periods, 1 1/2–2 blocks*

ABILITY LEVELS
L1 Basic to Average
L2 For All Students
L3 Average to Advanced

Objectives

N.2.2.1 Explain how an electric current is produced.
N.2.2.2 Explain how conductors are different from insulators.
N.2.2.3 Describe what causes electric charges to flow in a circuit.
N.2.2.4 Explain how resistance affects current.

Key Terms

• electric current • electric circuit • conductor • insulator • voltage • voltage source • resistance

Local Standards

Preteach

Build Background Knowledge

Use the analogy of drinking milkshakes through straws to introduce the concept of electric current.

 *How Can Current Be Measured?* 

Targeted Print and Technology Resources

 **Teaching Resources**

L2 Reading Strategy Transparency N17: Outlining

PresentationExpress™ CD-ROM

Instruct

Flow of Electric Charges Have students analyze the flow of charges through wires with different currents.

Conductors and Insulators Ask students to identify the conductor and the insulator that make up an electric cord.

Voltage Use the analogy shown in Figure 10 to clarify concepts related to voltage.

Resistance Ask leading questions for a discussion about the resistance in circuits.

 *Constructing a Dimmer Switch* 

Targeted Print and Technology Resources

All in One Teaching Resources

L2 Guided Reading, pp. 119–121
L2 Transparency N18
L2 Skills Lab: *Constructing a Dimmer Switch,* pp. 124–126

Lab Activity Video/DVD
Skills Lab: *Constructing a Dimmer Switch*

PHSchool.com Web Code: cgd-4022

Student Edition on Audio CD

Assess

Section Assessment Questions

Have students use their completed outlines to answer the questions.

Reteach

Have students create a concept map using the terms *electric current, electrical potential, voltage, resistance, ohms, amperes,* and *volts.*

Targeted Print and Technology Resources

All in One Teaching Resources

• Section Summary, p. 118
L1 Review and Reinforce, p. 122
L3 Enrich, p. 123

Section 3 Batteries

 *2–3 periods, 1–1 1/2 blocks*

ABILITY LEVELS
- L1 Basic to Average
- L2 For All Students
- L3 Average to Advanced

Objectives

N.2.3.1 Describe what the first battery was made of.
N.2.3.2 Explain how an electrochemical cell works.

Local Standards

Key Terms

• chemical energy • chemical reaction • electrochemical cell • electrode • electrolyte • terminal • battery • wet cell • dry cell

Preteach

Build Background Knowledge

Students relate experiences they've had with batteries.

Can You Use a Penny as an Energy Source? L1

Targeted Print and Technology Resources

All in One Teaching Resources
- L2 Reading Strategy: Building Vocabulary

PresentationExpress™ CD-ROM

Instruct

The First Battery Ask students what the major difference was between Galvani's hypothesis and Volta's hypothesis.

Electrochemical Cells Have students explain whether a flashlight battery is a wet cell or a dry cell.

Build a Flashlight 

Targeted Print and Technology Resources

All in One Teaching Resources
- L2 Guided Reading, pp. 129–131
- L2 Transparencies N19, N20
- L2 Consumer Lab: *Build a Flashlight*, pp. 134–137

Lab Activity Video/DVD
Consumer Lab: *Build a Flashlight*

PHSchool.com Web Code: cgd-4034

Student Edition on Audio CD

Assess

Section Assessment Questions

Have students use their definitions of key terms to answer the questions.

Reteach

Use Figure 14 to reinforce concepts related to batteries.

Targeted Print and Technology Resources

- Section Summary, p. 128
- L1 Review and Reinforce, p. 132
- L3 Enrich, p. 133

Section 4 Electric Circuits

 *2–3 periods, 1–1 1/2 blocks*

ABILITY LEVELS
- L1 Basic to Average
- L2 For All Students
- L3 Average to Advanced

Objectives

N.2.4.1 Explain what Ohm's law is.

N.2.4.2 Describe the basic features of an electric circuit.

N.2.4.3 Identify how many paths currents can take in series and parallel circuits.

Key Terms

• Ohm's law • series circuit • ammeter • parallel circuit • voltmeter

Local Standards

Preteach

Build Background Knowledge

Students relate their experiences with electric circuits.

 *Do the Lights Keep Shining?* 

Targeted Print and Technology Resources

All in One Teaching Resources

L2 Reading Strategy Transparency N21: Comparing and Contrasting

PresentationExpress™ CD-ROM

Instruct

Ohm's Law Have students manipulate the equation for Ohm's law to find voltage and current.

Features of a Circuit Ask students to identify features of a circuit in Figure 17.

Series Circuits Have students use their fingers to trace the path current can take in the series circuit diagram in Figure 18.

Parallel Circuits Have students use their fingers to trace the path current can take in the parallel circuit diagram in Figure 19.

Targeted Print and Technology Resources

All in One Teaching Resources

L2 Guided Reading, pp. 140–143

L2 Transparencies N22, N23, N24

PHSchool.com Web Code: cgp-4023

Student Edition on Audio CD

Assess

Section Assessment Questions

Have students use their completed Venn diagrams to answer the questions.

Reteach

Hold up drawings of circuits on cards, and ask students to identify the type of circuit shown.

Targeted Print and Technology Resources

All in One Teaching Resources

• Section Summary, p. 139

L1 Review and Reinforce, p. 144

L3 Enrich, p. 145

Section 5 Electric Power

 *1–2 periods, 1/2–1 block*

ABILITY LEVELS
L1 Basic to Average
L2 For All Students
L3 Average to Advanced

Objectives

N.2.5.1 Explain how to calculate electric power.

N.2.5.2 Identify the factors used to determine how people pay for electrical energy.

Key Term

- power

Local Standards

Preteach

Build Background Knowledge

Students think of ways that people can save money on their electric bills.

 *How Can You Make a Bulb Burn More Brightly?* L1

Targeted Print and Technology Resources

All in One Teaching Resources

L2 Reading Strategy Transparency N25: Asking Questions

 **PresentationExpress™ CD-ROM**

Instruct

Electric Power Have students explain why a 100-watt light bulb is brighter than a 40-watt light bulb.

Paying for Electrical Energy Have students explain how power and time make up the amount of energy shown on an electric bill.

Targeted Print and Technology Resources

All in One Teaching Resources

L2 Guided Reading, pp. 148–149

L2 Transparency N26

PHSchool.com Web Code: cgp-4022

Student Edition on Audio CD

Assess

Section Assessment Questions

Have students use the questions and answers in their completed graphic organizer to answer the questions.

Reteach

Call on students to explain the formula for power and the formula for energy use.

Targeted Print and Technology Resources

All in One Teaching Resources

- Section Summary, p. 147

L1 Review and Reinforce, p. 150

L3 Enrich, p. 151

Section 6 Electrical Safety

ABILITY LEVELS
L1 Basic to Average
L2 For All Students
L3 Average to Advanced

 *1–2 periods, 1/2–1 block*

Local Standards

Objectives

N.2.6.1 Describe measures that help protect people from electrical shocks and short circuits.

Key Terms

• short circuit • grounded • third prong • fuse • circuit breaker

Preteach

Build Background Knowledge

Students describe ways to avoid getting shocked when using electrical devices.

 *How Can You Blow a Fuse?* L2

Targeted Print and Technology Resources

 **Teaching Resources**

L2 Reading Strategy Transparency N27: Using Prior Knowledge

 **PresentationExpress™ CD-ROM**

Instruct

Personal Safety Ask students to explain why the current is high when there is a short circuit through a human body.

Breaking a Circuit Have students explain the difference between a fuse and a circuit breaker.

Targeted Print and Technology Resources

All in One Teaching Resources

L2 Guided Reading, pp. 154–156

www.SciLinks.org Web Code: scn-1425

 **Student Edition on Audio CD**

Assess

Section Assessment Questions

Have students use their completed graphic organizers to answer the questions.

Reteach

Call on volunteers to define the key terms *short circuit, grounded, third prong, fuse,* and *circuit breaker.*

Targeted Print and Technology Resources

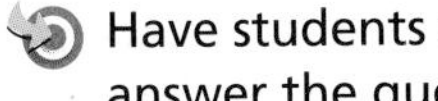 **Teaching Resources**

• Section Summary, p. 153

L1 Review and Reinforce, p. 157

L3 Enrich, p. 158

Chapter 2 Content Refresher

Section 1 Electric Charge and Static Electricity

Charges and Charging Charge is a fundamental property of subatomic particles. An electron or proton doesn't "become" charged; rather, it simply *is* charged as part of its nature. The two types of charges are arbitrarily designated as positive and negative. The law of conservation of electric charge states that the net amount of electric charge produced in any process is zero. That is, whenever there is a negative charge produced in a system, there is always an equal positive charge in the same system, or in the vicinity.

Static electricity was once called the "amber effect," because long ago humans discovered that when amber (petrified tree resin) was rubbed with a cloth, the amber would attract leaves or dust. The word *electricity* derives from the Greek word for amber, *elektron*. Charging by rubbing is another term for charging by friction. In the case of both charging by friction and charging by conduction, one material gives up electrons and the other material accepts the electrons. Which way the transfer proceeds depends on the materials involved. Certain materials lose electrons more easily than others. For instance, glass loses electrons more easily than wool. So, rubbing a glass rod with wool cloth produces a positively charged glass rod and a negatively charged piece of wool. But wool loses electrons more easily than rubber. So, rubbing a rubber rod with wool cloth produces a negatively charged rubber rod and a positively charged piece of wool.

Address Misconceptions

Many students may think that charging by friction involves most or all of the atoms in the rubbing objects. In reality, only a very small fraction of atoms of a substance give up electrons. For a strategy for overcoming this misconception, see **Address Misconceptions** in the section *Electric Charge and Static Electricity.*

Section 2 Electric Current

The Movement of Electrons An electric current is the movement of charges through a material. A common analogy is the flow of water through a closed system, in which the water flows from one place through a hose and back to the starting place. An electric current is similar but not precisely the same. A major difference is that in the flow of water, the water molecules actually flow from beginning to end, whereas in an electric current, the electrons may not. Instead, free electrons are pulled in a direction because of potential difference, or voltage. The electrons drift from atom to atom. As a free electron drifts, it may join the electron cloud of an atom nearby. The atom then has an extra electron, and gives up an electron that moves on to another atom. This process occurs throughout a circuit as the voltage results in a drift of free electrons toward the positive end of the circuit. Each individual electron moves at a relatively slow pace. For example, at room temperature an electron moves through a wire at about 1 mm per second. This speed is much less than the speed of current, which is comparable to the speed of light. At that pace, it would take over 15 minutes for an electron to travel 1 m. Thus, it is not the movement of electrons from one end of a circuit to another that produces electric current. Rather, voltage throughout the circuit causes the movement of electrons, which produces current.

Electric current is traditionally symbolized with the capital letter *I*. This symbol was derived from the German word *Intensität*, which means "intensity." Thus, the measure of current is a measure of how intense or how concentrated the flow of charges is in a circuit.

Address Misconceptions

Many students may think that metals are the only good conductors. Although many metals are good conductors, other materials conduct current as well. For a strategy for overcoming this misconception, see **Address Misconceptions** in the section *Electric Current.*

Section 3 Batteries

Typical Batteries One way to classify batteries is to distinguish between wet cells and dry cells. Another way is to distinguish between primary cells, which cannot be recharged, and secondary cells, with can be recharged. The most common primary cells are the familiar round dry cells, including AAA, AA, and D cells. These cells are carbon-zinc dry cells. A carbon rod down the middle of the battery serves as the positive electrode, and a zinc layer just inside the covering serves as the negative electrode. The electrolyte is an ammonium chloride paste. Another common primary cell is the little "button" battery used in watches, hearing aids, and calculators. The most common of these is the mercury cell, in which the electrodes are zinc and mercury and the electrolyte is potassium hydroxide. Secondary cells include the auto battery—called a lead-acid cell—as well as several types of rechargeable dry cells. These include the nickel-cadmium (NiCad) cell, the nickel metal hydride (NiMH) cell, and the nickel-iron (Edison) cell. Secondary cells can be recharged when a direct current from an outside voltage source reverses the chemical action inside the cell.

Section 4 Electric Circuits

Series and Parallel Circuits In a series circuit, the total resistance of the circuit is the sum of the several resistances in the circuit. Therefore, adding more resistors—including light bulbs, heaters, or any other electrical devices—to the circuit increases the total resistance. Increasing the total resistance decreases the current because (rearranging Ohm's law), $I = V \div R$. Increasing the resistance increases the divisor in the equation. If the voltage doesn't change, the result is a smaller quotient—a decreased current.

Homes, on the other hand, are wired with parallel circuits in which resistance decreases with each added branch. A good analogy for understanding why this decrease occurs is to think of a pipe draining a reservoir of water. The water flows down the pipe because of the potential energy caused by gravity. Suppose a second pipe the same size is added to drain the reservoir. The potential energy is the same for both pipes. But adding a second pipe doubles the flow of water and reduces the resistance to that flow. Similarly, adding a branch to a parallel circuit gives current another path to follow and thus reduces the overall resistance.

Section 5 Electric Power

Using Resistance to Produce Heat For most wires, resistance is kept to a minimum through the use of a good conductor. Copper is a good conductor, and for that reason copper is used as the conductor in most wires. When charges flow through a wire, heat is produced because of the collisions between the moving electrons and the atoms of the wire. As the current increases in a wire, the heat produced also increases. This principle is used in the safety device called a fuse, which has a metal strip that melts when heat increases to an unsafe level.

Many other devices besides fuses also depend on transforming electrical energy into thermal energy. A 100-W light bulb uses that amount of power because the current through the bulb's high-resistance filament heats the filament enough to make it glow. A heater or toaster contains a heating element that does not conduct electric current as efficiently as copper wire. Instead, the heating element dissipates the energy running through it as heat, a desirable product in these devices.

Section 6 Electrical Safety

Circuit Breakers One type of circuit breaker has both a magnetic component (a solenoid) and a thermal component (a bimetallic strip). A bimetallic strip—a strip composed of two different layers of metals—holds a switch closed. The closed switch completes the circuit. The reason that two metals are used is that one expands more quickly than the other when both are heated at the same rate. The electric current in the circuit passes through the bimetallic strip. If the current becomes too high for the circuit, one metal strip expands more than the other. The result is that the bimetallic strip bends as one side becomes longer than the other. When the strip bends, it moves into a notch on the arm of the switch and opens the contact points of the switch. The result is a break in the circuit. Once the bimetallic strip cools, the circuit breaker can be reset and the electric circuit is closed again.

Help Students Read

Identifying Supporting Evidence

Following a Chain of Reasoning

Strategy Help students understand the structure of the text they are reading. One way is to use a graphic organizer as a device for identifying supporting evidence for hypotheses that are presented in the text. Before students begin, choose a subsection in this chapter, such as the *Voltage* section.

Example

1. Have students look for the hypothesis of the subsection. Write the hypothesis on the board, leaving enough room around it to add supporting evidence. This will be the center of your graphic organizer.
2. As students read, have them call out the supporting evidence for the hypothesis.
3. Write the supporting evidence on the board around the center of your graphic organizer. Draw "spokes" from each piece of evidence to the hypothesis.
4. After reading the subsection and completing the graphic organizer, ask students if they think the text provided sufficient supporting evidence for the hypothesis. Suggest to students that a graphic organizer such as this one can be used to help understand a concept.

Interactive Textbook

- Complete student edition
- Video and audio
- Simulations and activities
- Section and chapter activities

Chapter 2

Electricity

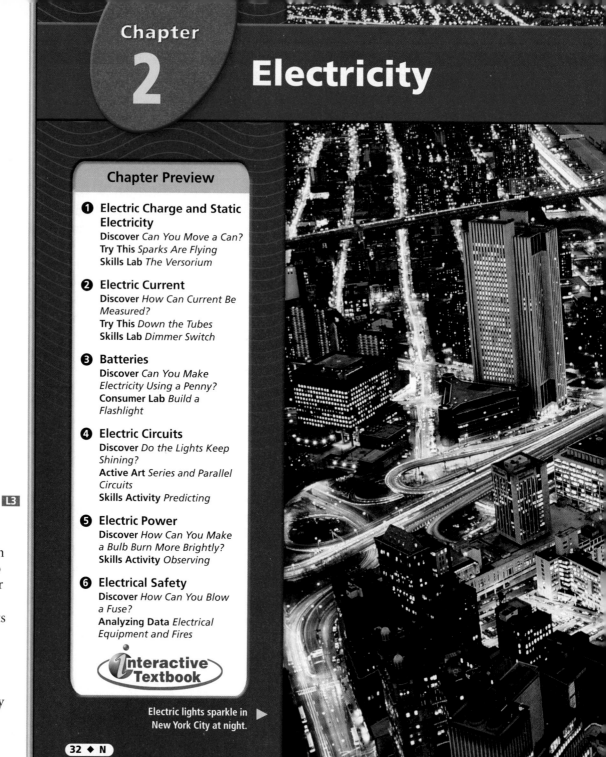

Chapter Preview

Interactive Textbook

Electric lights sparkle in New York City at night. ▶

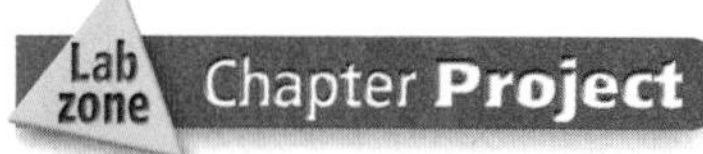

L3

Objectives

Students will design and build an alarm circuit that will light a bulb in response to some event. After completing this Chapter Project, students will be able to

- apply concepts related to electric circuits
- design a solution to the problem of constructing an alarm circuit
- evaluate the design through tests of the alarm circuit
- redesign the alarm circuit to address any problems
- communicate results to the class

Skills Focus

Applying concepts, designing a solution, evaluating the design, redesigning, communicating

Project Time Line 2–3 weeks

All in One Teaching Resources

- Chapter Project Teacher Notes
- Chapter Project Overview
- Chapter Project Worksheet 1
- Chapter Project Worksheet 2
- Chapter Project Scoring Rubric

Developing a Plan

Students will individually design and build an alarm circuit. Students begin by brainstorming possible events to which their detectors will respond. Then they plan the circuits and draw diagrams of their designs. Once you have approved their designs, they construct their alarm circuits. Students should conduct several tests of their designs, and then redesign as necessary. Finally, students will demonstrate their alarms and present a circuit diagram to the class at the conclusion of the project.

Possible Materials

Provide a wide variety of materials from which students can choose, and encourage students to suggest and use other materials as well. Each student will need one or two 1.5-volt dry cells, about 3 m of insulated wire, and a light bulb and socket. Make sure to select bulbs that require only 1.5 volts for a single battery, or 3 volts for two batteries connected in series. In addition, students may need aluminum foil, paper clips, screws, washers, nails, metal cans, electrical tape, basins or bowls, water, or salt.

Discovery Channel School

Electricity

▶ Video Preview
Video Field Trip
Video Assessment

Chapter Project

Cause for Alarm

In this chapter, you will learn about electric charges and how they are involved in electricity. You will also learn about types of circuits and how to use electric current safely. As you work on this chapter project, you will choose an event, such as the opening or closing of a door or window, and design a circuit that alerts you when the event happens.

Your Goal To construct an alarm circuit that will light a bulb in response to some event

For your project to be complete, your circuit must

- be powered by one or two D-cells
- have a switch that detects your chosen event
- turn on a light when the switch is closed
- follow the safety guidelines in Appendix A

Plan It! Brainstorm with your classmates about ways to make two pieces of a conductor come in contact. Then, design a detector switch to complete a circuit when the event happens. Submit the design for approval. When your teacher has approved your design, build the alarm circuit and demonstrate it to the class.

Electricity

Show the Video Preview to introduce the Chapter Project and overview the chapter content. Discussion question: **How does a lightning rod work?** *(Lightning rods are made of highly conductive metal that provides a low resistance path for electric current. When lightning strikes, a wire attached to the lightning rod carries the current safely to the ground.)*

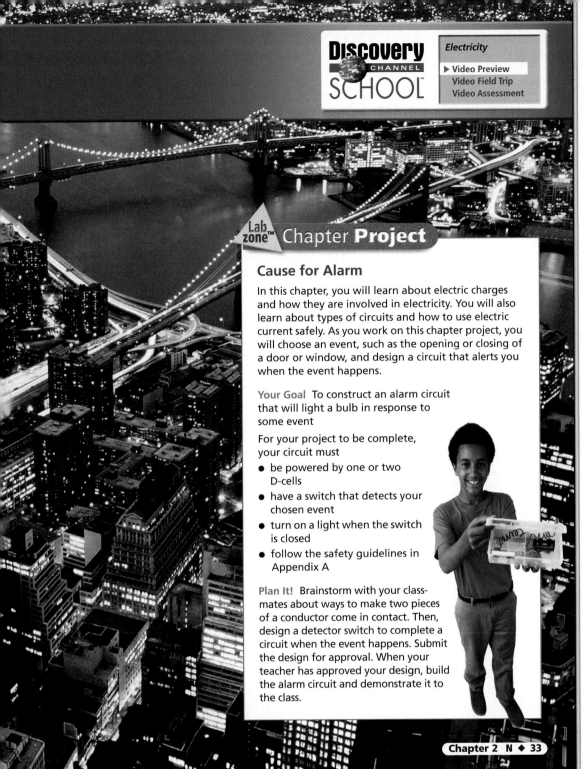

Performance Assessment

The Chapter Project Scoring Rubric will help you evaluate how well students complete the Chapter Project. You may want to share the scoring rubric with your students so they are clear about what will be expected of them. Students will be assessed on

- how well they plan and build the alarm circuit
- how well they conduct experiments to test and revise their circuits
- how clear they make the description and diagram of the alarm circuit
- how effectively they present the alarm circuit and the circuit diagram to the class

Students can keep their plans, descriptions and circuit diagrams in their portfolios.

Portfolio

Possible Shortcuts

- In order to reduce the amount of time for presentations, have students work in groups.
- Use a few generic setups consisting of a light bulb or buzzer, one or two dry cells, and about 3 meters of wire. Have individual students connect their detector switches to the wire.

Launching the Project

To introduce the project, tape an uninsulated end of a piece of wire to a penny. Connect the other end of the wire to a light bulb. Connect the light bulb to a dry cell. Tape the other pole of the dry cell to an empty metal can. Ask: **What will happen if I drop the penny in the can?** *(The bulb will light.)*

Section 1

Electric Charge and Static Electricity

Objectives

After this lesson, students will be able to

N.2.1.1 Explain how electric charges interact.

N.2.1.2 Explain what an electric field is.

N.2.1.3 Describe how static electricity builds up and transfers.

Target Reading Skill

Previewing Visuals Explain that looking at the visuals before they read helps students activate prior knowledge and predict what they are about to read.

Answers

Sample questions and answers:

What are three ways that static electricity can be transferred? *(Charging by friction, charging by conduction, and charging by induction.)* **Why does an object become charged?** *(An object becomes charged when electrons are transferred from one location to another.)*

All in One Teaching Resources

- Transparency N12

Preteach

Build Background Knowledge

L2

Experience With Static Electricity

Before class, rub together a piece of polyester fabric and nylon socks so that they stick together. Show students the fabric and sock sticking to each other. Ask: **Would you expect to find glue or some other form of matter between these two fabrics?** *(No)* **What do you think holds these fabrics together?** *(Students might suggest "static cling" or some kind of electricity.)* Explain that students will learn more about the forces that hold two fabrics together as they explore electric charges.

Section 1

Electric Charge and Static Electricity

Reading Preview

Key Concepts

- How do electric charges interact?
- What is an electric field?
- How does static electricity build up and transfer?

Key Terms

- electric force
- electric field
- static electricity
- conservation of charge
- friction
- conduction
- induction
- static discharge

Target Reading Skill

Previewing Visuals Before you read, preview Figure 4. Then write two questions that you have about the diagram in a graphic organizer like the one below. As you read, answer your questions.

Transferring Static Electricity

Q.	What are three ways static electricity can be transferred?
A.	
Q.	

Lab zone Discover Activity

Can You Move a Can Without Touching It?

1. Place an empty aluminum can on its side on the floor.
2. Blow up a balloon. Then rub the balloon back and forth on your hair several times.
3. Hold the balloon about 2 to 3 centimeters away from the can.
4. Slowly move the balloon farther away from the can. Observe what happens.
5. Move the balloon to the other side of the can and observe what happens.

Think It Over

Inferring What happens to the can? What can you infer from your observation?

You're in a hurry to get dressed for school, but you can't find one of your socks. You quickly head for the pile of clean laundry. You've gone through everything, but where's your matching sock? The dryer couldn't have really destroyed it, could it? Oh no, there it is. It's sticking to the back of your blanket. What makes clothes and blankets stick together? The explanation has to do with tiny electric charges.

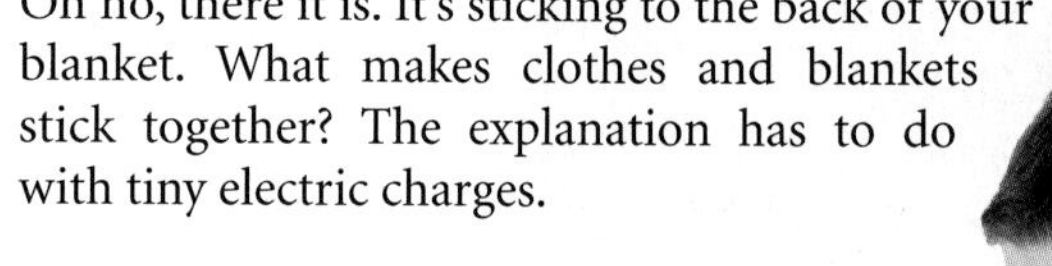

Why do these clothes stick together? ▶

Lab zone Discover Activity

Skills Focus Inferring L1

Materials empty aluminum can, balloon

Time 10 minutes

Tips Make sure students rub the balloon vigorously. Avoid doing this activity on a damp or rainy day.

Expected Outcome The can follows the balloon in either direction.

Think It Over Sample answer: The can follows the balloon in either direction. Some force is attracting the can to the balloon.

Positive charges repel each other

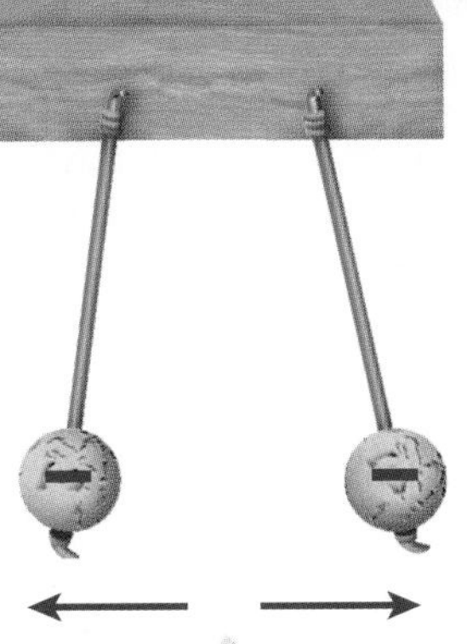
Negative charges repel each other

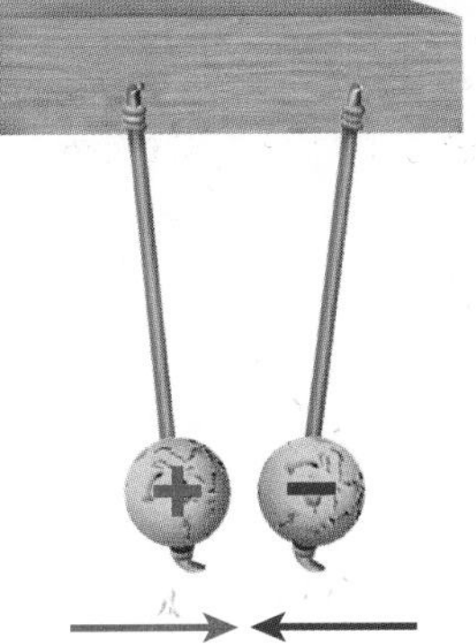
Positive and negative charges attract each other

FIGURE 1
Repel or Attract?
The two types of charge, positive and negative, react to one another in specific ways.
Interpreting Diagrams *Which combinations of charges repel each other?*

Electric Charge

Recall that the charged parts of atoms are electrons and protons. When two protons come close together, they push one another apart. In other words, the protons repel each other. But if a proton and an electron come close together, they attract one another.

Why do protons repel protons but attract electrons? The reason is that they have different types of electric charge. Electric charge is a property of electrons and protons. Protons and electrons have opposite charges. The charge on a proton is called positive (+), and the charge on a electron is called negative (–). The names *positive* and *negative* were given to charges by Benjamin Franklin in the 1700s.

The two types of electric charges interact in specific ways, as you see in Figure 1. **Charges that are the same repel each other. Charges that are different attract each other.** Does this sound familiar to you? This rule is the same as the rule for interactions between magnetic poles. Recall that magnetic poles that are alike repel each other, and magnetic poles that are different attract each other. This interaction between magnetic poles is called magnetism. The interaction between electric charges is called electricity.

There is one important difference between electric charges and magnetic poles. Recall that magnetic poles cannot exist alone. Whenever there is a south pole, there is always a north pole. In contrast, electric charges can exist alone. In other words, a negative charge can exist without a positive charge.

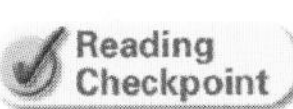
Reading Checkpoint **What is one important difference between magnetism and electricity?**

Lab zone Skills Activity

Drawing Conclusions

1. Tear tissue paper into small pieces, or use a hole punch to cut circles.
2. Run a plastic comb through your hair several times.
3. Place the comb close to, but not touching, the tissue paper pieces. What do you observe?

What can you conclude about the electric charges on the comb and the tissue paper?

Instruct

Electric Charge

Teach Key Concepts L2

Types of Electric Charge

Focus Tell students that there are two types of charge, positive charge and negative charge.

Teach Have students recall their understanding of magnetic poles. Ask: **What is the rule about the attraction or repulsion of like and unlike magnetic poles?** *(Like poles repel, and unlike poles attract.)* Explain that electric charges are similar. Ask: **How do the two types of electric charges interact?** *(Charges that are alike repel each other. Charges that are unlike attract each other.)*

Apply Have students examine the three ways electric charges interact shown in Figure 1. Ask students to point their two index fingers downward to represent the suspended objects in one of the diagrams. Then ask them to model with their index fingers the three interactions shown in the figure, as you read the annotations. Students will spread their fingers out to model positive charges repelling and negative charges repelling, and bring their fingers together to model positive and negative charges attracting. **learning modality: kinesthetic**

All in One Teaching Resources
- Transparency N13

Independent Practice L2

All in One Teaching Resources
- Guided Reading and Study Worksheet: *Electric Charge and Static Electricity*

Student Edition on Audio CD

Lab zone Skills Activity

Skills Focus Drawing conclusions L2

Materials tissue paper, hole punch, plastic comb

Time 10 minutes

Tips Avoid performing this activity on a damp or rainy day. The tissue paper should be attracted to the comb.

Expected Outcome Students should conclude that the comb and tissue paper are unlike—the tissue paper is neutral (it has no charge).

Extend Have students find out what happens if they run a comb through their hair several times and then hold it a short distance from their hair. **learning modality: kinesthetic**

Monitor Progress L2

Writing Have students write a paragraph that describes the types of electric charges and the kinds of interactions between them.

Answers

Figure 1 Positive charges repel each other, and negative charges repel each other.

Reading Checkpoint Magnetic poles cannot exist alone, but electric charges can exist alone.

Electric Force

Teach Key Concepts

L2

Attraction or Repulsion

Focus Tell students that charged objects exert a force through a region called an electric field.

Teach Ask: **What is an electric field?** *(A region around a charged object where the charged object's electric force is exerted on other charged objects)* Explain that an electric field can be represented by electric field lines. Ask: **How is the strength of an electric field represented by field lines?** *(The closer the lines, the stronger the field that the lines represent.)*

Apply Ask: **Suppose a negatively charged object is placed in the electric field of a positively charged object—will it be attracted or repelled?** *(The negatively charged object will be attracted to the positively charged object.)* **learning modality: verbal**

All in One Teaching Resources

- Transparency N14

L1

Electric Field Exerts a Force

Materials inflated balloon, wool cloth, faucet

Time 5 minutes

Focus Tell students that an electric field around a charged object is where the object's electric force is exerted.

Teach Vigorously rub the balloon with the wool cloth, and then turn on the faucet so that water flows in a steady narrow stream. Bring the charged balloon near the stream of water. Have students observe how the water bends toward the balloon.

Apply Ask: **What causes the water to bend toward the balloon?** *(The water is attracted to the balloon because it must have an opposite charge.)* **learning modality: visual**

FIGURE 2
Electric Charges and Fields
The lines in each diagram represent an electric field. The stronger the field, the closer together the lines are.

A The electric field around a positive charge points outward.

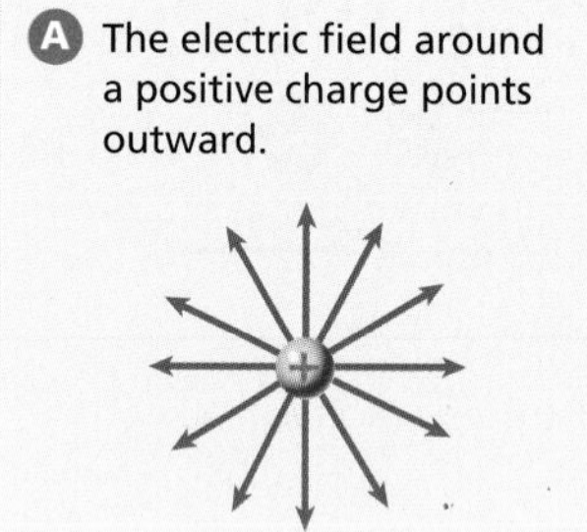

B The electric field around a negative charge points inward.

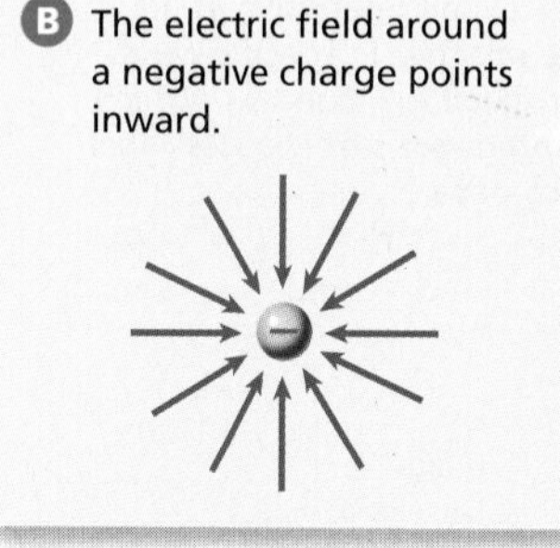

C The electric fields around charged particles are combined when they are brought near each other.

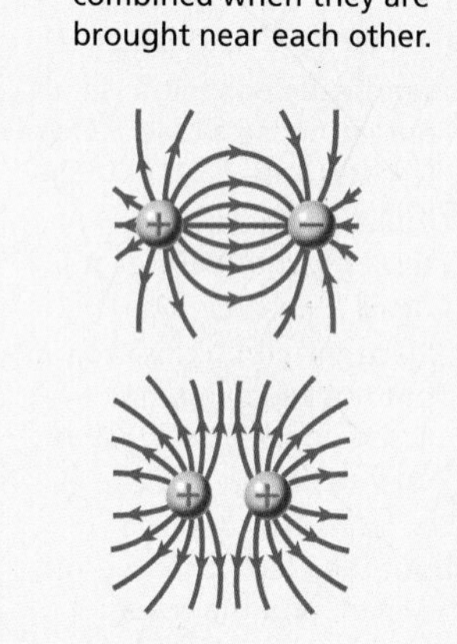

Electric Force

You may think of force as a push or pull on an object. For example, the force of gravity pulls objects toward the ground. You have learned that magnetic force is the attraction or repulsion between magnetic poles. In electricity, **electric force** is the attraction or repulsion between electric charges.

Electric Field Just as magnetic poles exert their forces over a distance, so do electric charges. Recall that a magnetic field extends around a magnet. Similarly, an **electric field** extends around a charged object. **An electric field is a region around a charged object where the object's electric force is exerted on other charged objects.**

When one charged object is placed in the electric field of another charged object, it is either pushed or pulled. It is pushed away if the two objects have the same charge. It is pulled toward the other charged object if their charges are different.

Electric Field Around a Single Charge An electric field is invisible, just like a magnetic field. You may recall using magnetic field lines to represent a magnetic field. In a similar way, you can use electric field lines to represent the electric field. Electric field lines are drawn with arrows to show the direction of the electric force. The electric force always points away from positive charges, as shown in Figure 2A. Notice in Figure 2B that the electric force always points toward negative charges.

The strength of an electric field is related to the distance from the charged object. The greater the distance, the weaker the electric field is. The strength of an electric field is represented by how close the electric field lines are to each other. The electric field is strongest where the lines are closest together. Since the strength of the electric field is greatest near the charged object, that's where the lines appear closest together. Farther from the charged object, the lines appear more spread out because the magnetic field is weaker.

Electric Field Around Multiple Charges When there are two or more charges, the shape of the electric field of each charge is altered. The electric fields of each individual charge combine by repelling or attracting. Figure 2C shows the interaction of the electric fields from two pairs of charges.

What is electric force?

Differentiated Instruction

Gifted and Talented

L3

Researching Fabric Softeners Have students investigate why sheets of fabric softener added to the dryer with clothes reduce "static cling." Have them prepare a presentation for the class complete with labeled diagrams that show the processes involved. **learning modality: verbal**

Special Needs

L1

Modeling How Objects Are Charged Place three blue marbles in a jar. Explain that the jar is an atom, and the blue marbles are protons. Give students six red marbles, and tell them the red marbles are electrons. Then have students model how to make the atom neutral, negatively charged, and positively charged by adding marbles. **learning modality: kinesthetic**

Static Electricity

Most objects normally have no overall charge, which means that they are neutral. Each atom has an equal number of protons and electrons. So each positive charge is balanced by a negative charge. As a result, there is no overall electric force on an atom.

Some objects, however, can become charged. Protons are bound tightly in the center of an atom, but electrons can sometimes leave their atoms. In materials such as silver, copper, gold, and aluminum, some electrons are held loosely by the atoms. These electrons can move to other atoms. As you see in Figure 3, an uncharged object becomes charged by gaining or losing electrons. If an object loses electrons, it is left with more protons than electrons. Therefore, the object has an overall positive charge. If an object gains electrons, it has more electrons than protons and has an overall negative charge.

The buildup of charges on an object is called **static electricity.** *Static* means "not moving or changing." **In static electricity, charges build up on an object, but they do not flow continuously.**

For: Links on static electricity
Visit: www.SciLinks.org
Web Code: scn-1421

Rubbing the balloon allows more electrons to move onto the balloon. The balloon gains a negative charge.
The negative charges of the balloon attract the positive charges in the girl's hair.

FIGURE 3
Charging by Friction
Rubbing two objects together may produce a buildup of static electricity.
Relating Cause and Effect *In what two ways can an uncharged object become charged?*

Static Electricity

Teach Key Concepts

L2

A Buildup of Charges

Focus Tell students that objects can become charged as electrons move from atom to atom.

Teach Ask: **What does it mean that most objects are neutral?** *(Most objects normally have no overall charge.)* **How does an uncharged object become charged?** *(By gaining or losing electrons)* **What is the buildup of charges on an object called?** *(Static electricity)*

Apply Have students analyze the buildup of charges in Figure 3. Ask: **What causes the uncharged balloon to become charged?** *(Rubbing the balloon on the student's sweater)* **Why does the balloon become negatively charged?** *(Electrons move from the sweater to the balloon.)* **Why is the student's hair attracted to the balloon?** *(Positive charges in the hair are attracted to negative charges in the balloon.)* **learning modality: visual**

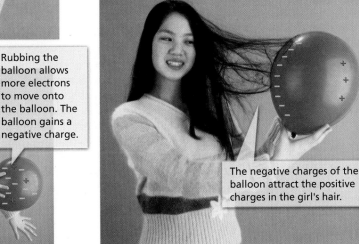

For: Links on static electricity
Visit: www.SciLinks.org
Web Code: scn-1421

Download a worksheet that will guide students' review of Internet sources on static electricity.

Monitor Progress

L2

Oral Presentation Call on students to describe an electric field around a single charge and an electric field around multiple charges.

Answers

Figure 3 An uncharged object can be charged by gaining electrons or by losing electrons.

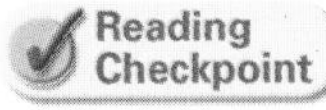

The attraction or repulsion between charges

Transferring Charge

Teach Key Concepts L2

Three Methods of Transfer

Focus Tell students that charges can be transferred from object to object by three methods.

Teach Ask: **What is the law of conservation of charge?** *(Charges are neither created nor destroyed. If one object gives up electrons, another object gains those electrons.)* Emphasize that this law of conservation of charge holds true for all three methods of transfer.

Apply Ask: **Suppose a positively charged object touches an uncharged object and gains electrons. By which method was the uncharged object charged?** *(Charging by conduction)* **Is there a way in which the uncharged object could have been charged without touching the charged object?** *(Yes, by induction)* **learning modality: verbal**

Address Misconceptions L2

Relatively Few Electrons Transfer

Focus Many students may think that charging by friction involves most or all of the atoms in the rubbing objects. Explain that only a very small fraction of atoms of a substance give up electrons.

Teach Ask: **Do all the atoms in a substance give up electrons when another object rubs against it?** *(Many students will think that all atoms are involved.)* Explain that even if a billion atoms give up electrons, an object is normally made up of many trillions of atoms. In fact, only about one in a trillion atoms loses electrons during the process of charging by friction.

Apply Have students look again at Figure 3. Ask: **What method of transfer is shown?** *(Charging by friction)* **Do most of the sweater's atoms lose electrons in the process?** *(No. Only a small fraction of atoms lose electrons.)* **learning modality: verbal**

Transferring Charge

An object becomes charged only when electrons are transferred from one location to another. Charges are neither created nor destroyed. This is a rule known as the law of **conservation of charge.** If one object gives up electrons, another object gains those electrons. **There are three methods by which charges can be transferred to build up static electricity: charging by friction, by conduction, and by induction.**

Charging by Friction When two uncharged objects rub together, some electrons from one object can move onto the other object. The object that gains electrons becomes negatively charged, and the object that loses electrons becomes positively charged. Charging by **friction** is the transfer of electrons from one uncharged object to another by rubbing. In Figure 4, when the girl's socks rub the carpet, electrons move from the carpet onto her sock. This causes an overall negative charge on the sock. Clothing that sticks together when it is taken out of the dryer is another example of charging by friction.

Charging by Conduction When a charged object touches another object, electrons can be transferred between the objects. Electrons transfer from the object that has the more negative charge to the one that has the more positive charge. For example, a positively charged object will gain electrons when it touches an uncharged object. Charging by **conduction** is the transfer of electrons from a charged object to another object by direct contact. In Figure 4, charges are transferred from the girl's feet to the rest of her body because of charging by conduction.

Charging by Induction In charging by friction and by conduction, electrons are transferred when objects touch one another. In charging by induction, however, objects do not touch when the charges transfer. Charging by **induction** is the movement of electrons to one part of an object that is caused by the electric field of a second object. The electric field around the charged object attracts or repels electrons in the second object. In Figure 4, for example, the negative charges in the girl's fingertip produce an electric field that repels the electrons on the surface of the doorknob. The electrons on the doorknob move away from the finger. This movement produces an induced positive charge on the doorknob.

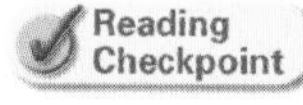

What is the difference between charging by induction and charging by conduction?

Lab zone Try This Activity

Sparks Are Flying

Lightning is the result of static electricity. You can make your own lightning.

1. Cut a strip 3 cm wide from the middle of a foam plate. Fold the strip to form a W. Tape it to the center of an aluminum pie plate as a handle.

2. Rub a second foam plate on your hair. Place it upside down on a table.
3. Use the handle to pick up the pie plate. Hold the pie plate about 30 cm over the foam plate and drop it.
4. Now, very slowly, touch the tip of your finger to the pie plate. Be careful not to touch the foam plate. Then take your finger away.
5. Use the handle to pick up the pie plate again. Slowly touch the pie plate again.

Inferring What did you observe each time you touched the pie plate? How can you explain your observations?

38 ◆ N

Lab zone Try This Activity

Skills Focus Inferring L2

Materials 2 foam plates, scissors, tape, aluminum pie plate

Time 10 minutes

Tips You may want to prepare the plates in advance. Perform this activity on a dry day, and, if possible, in the dark.

Expected Outcome Students should observe that each time they touch the pie plate, a spark is seen. The spark is a transfer of a tiny amount of electrons , and is safe. Sample answer: When the pie plate is first put onto the foam, electrons in the foam repel electrons in the plate. Touching the plate causes a spark as electrons jump from plate to hand. Touching it again causes a spark as electrons jump back from hand to plate. **learning modality: kinesthetic**

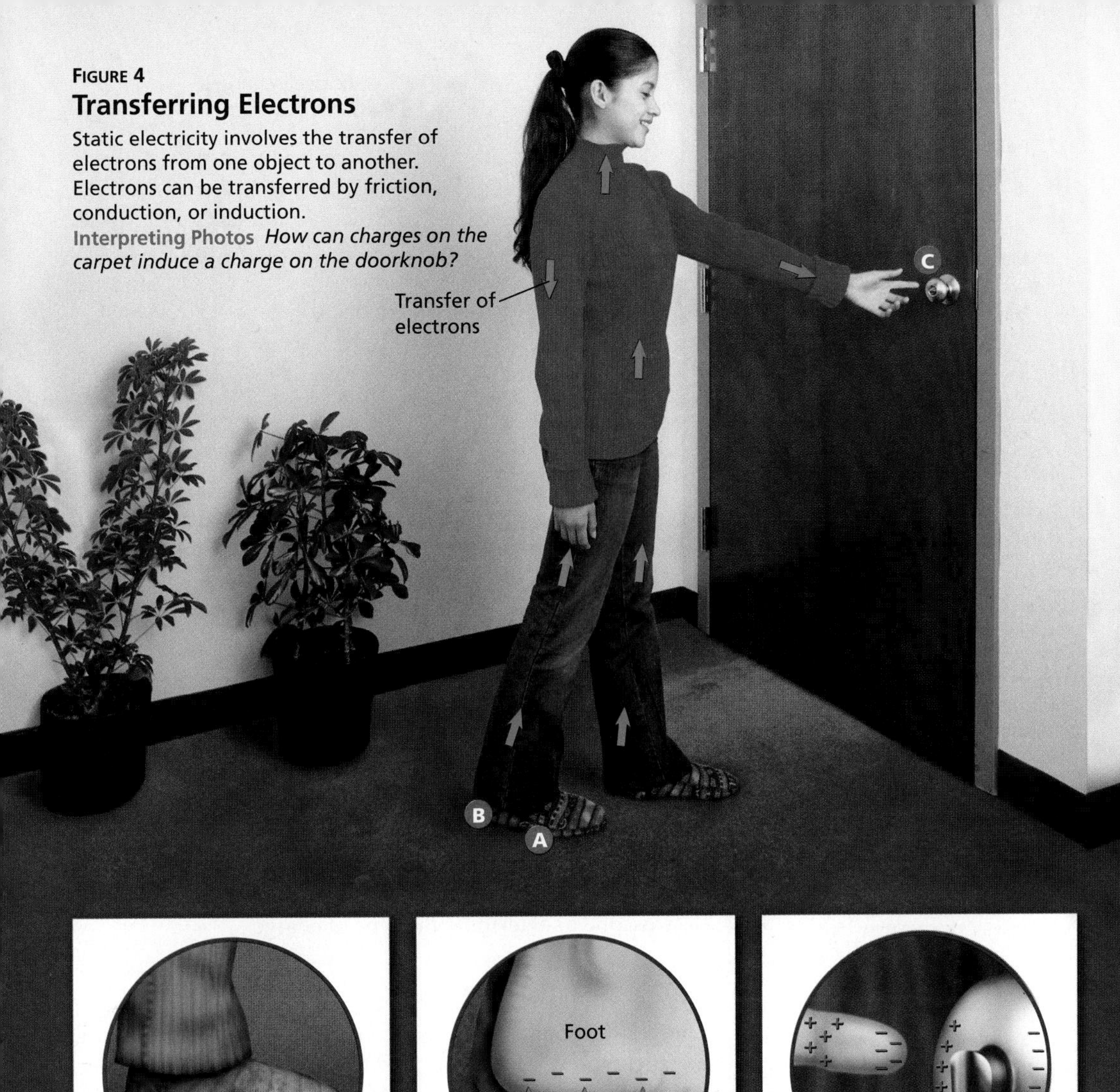

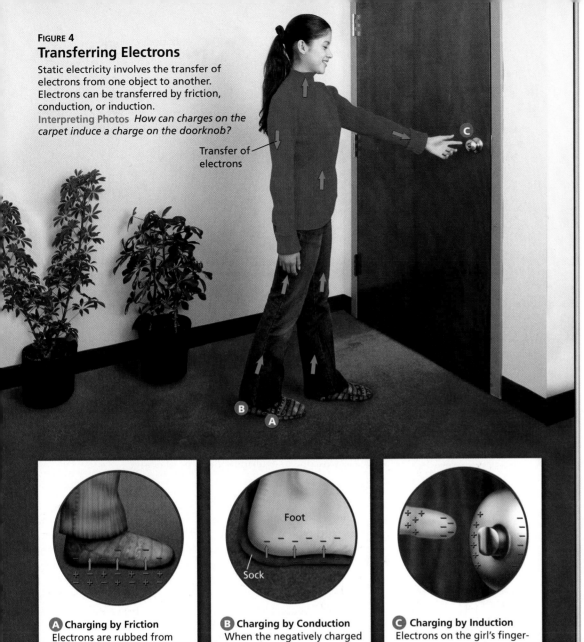

FIGURE 4
Transferring Electrons
Static electricity involves the transfer of electrons from one object to another. Electrons can be transferred by friction, conduction, or induction.
Interpreting Photos *How can charges on the carpet induce a charge on the doorknob?*

A Charging by Friction
Electrons are rubbed from the carpet to the girl's sock. The charges are distributed evenly over the sock.

B Charging by Conduction
When the negatively charged sock touches the skin, electrons are transferred by direct contact. Electrons are then distributed throughout the girl's body.

C Charging by Induction
Electrons on the girl's fingertip produce an electric field that repels negative charges and attracts positive charges on the doorknob. An overall positive charge is induced on the edge of the doorknob.

N ◆ 39

Use Visuals: Figure 4 L2

Transferring Electrons

Focus Ask: **What are three methods by which electrons can be transferred to build up static electricity?** *(Charging by friction, charging by conduction, and charging by induction)*

Teach As students look at the images in the figure, question them about the transfer of electrons by each of the three methods. Ask: **By what method did electrons move from the carpet to the girl's sock?** *(Charging by friction)* **Which object lost electrons, and which gained electrons?** *(The carpet lost electrons, and the socks gained electrons.)* **By what method were electrons transferred to her foot?** *(Charging by conduction)* **Which object lost electrons and which gained electrons?** *(The sock lost electrons, and the foot gained electrons.)* **By what method did the doorknob become positively charged?** *(Charging by induction)* **What caused the edge of the doorknob to become positively charged?** *(The girl's fingertip was negative, and its electric field repelled negative charges and attracted positive charges in the doorknob.)*

Apply Have students predict what the girl will likely feel as her hand gets closer to the doorknob. *(Sample answer: The shock of static electricity.)* **learning modality: visual**

All in One Teaching Resources
- Transparency N15

Monitor Progress L2

Skills Check Ask students to make a compare/contrast table listing and describing the three methods by which charges can be transferred to build up static electricity.

Students can keep their tables in their portfolios. Portfolio

Answers

Figure 4 Electrons are transferred from the carpet to the girl's sock by friction. Then, electrons are transferred to the skin on her foot by conduction and are distributed over the surface of the girl's body. When the electrons on her fingertip come close to the doorknob, their electric field induces a positive charge on the doorknob's edge.

Reading Checkpoint Charging by conduction occurs by direct contact, while charging by induction occurs without direct contact.

All in One Teaching Resources
- Transparency N16

Static Discharge

Teach Key Concepts L2

The Loss of Static Electricity

Focus Tell students that static electricity on an objects doesn't last forever.

Teach Ask: **What is static discharge?** *(The loss of static electricity as electric charges transfer from one object to another)* Explain that lightning is an example of static discharge as electrons transfer from an area of negative charge to an area of positive charge.

Apply Ask: **When lightning occurs, what is the area of negative charge and what is the area of positive charge?** *(The bottom of storm clouds is an area of negative charge, while the surface of Earth is an area of positive charge.)* **learning modality: verbal**

Electricity

Show the Video Field Trip to let students experience the dramatic static discharge of lightning. Discussion question: **Describe how the top and bottom of a thundercloud become oppositely charged.** *(Fast-moving winds cause water crystals in thunderclouds to be in constant motion, resulting in lots of tiny collisions. These collisions cause some particles to lose electrons. The electrons gather at the bottom of the cloud so that the bottom of the cloud has a negative charge, while the top of the cloud acquires a positive charge.)*

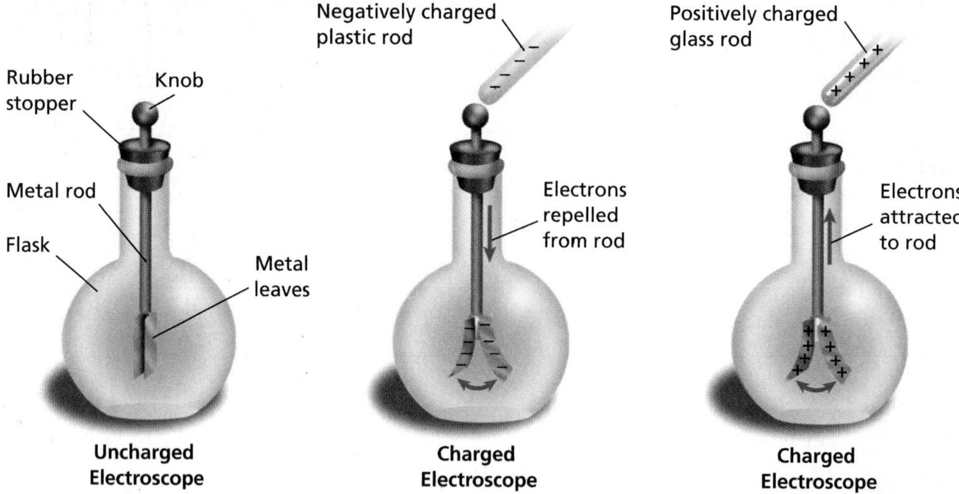

FIGURE 5
An Electroscope
An electroscope can be used to detect the presence of a charge, but it does not tell you whether the charge is positive or negative. **Relating Cause and Effect** *Why do the leaves of the electroscope move apart when a charged object touches the knob?*

Detecting Charge Electric charge is invisible, but it can be detected by an instrument called an electroscope. A typical electroscope, shown in Figure 5, consists of a metal rod with a knob at the top and two thin metal leaves at the bottom. When the electroscope is uncharged, its metal leaves hang straight down. When a charged object touches the knob, electric charge travels by conduction into or out of the leaves. Since the charge on both leaves is the same, the leaves repel each other and spread apart. The leaves move apart in response to either negative charge or positive charge. Therefore, you cannot use an electroscope to determine the type of charge.

Static Discharge

Charges that build up as static electricity on an object don't stay there forever. Electrons tend to move, returning the object to its neutral condition. Consider what happens when two objects with opposite charges touch one another. **When a negatively charged object and a positively charged object are brought together, electrons transfer until both objects have the same charge.** The loss of static electricity as electric charges transfer from one object to another is called **static discharge.**

Often, a static discharge produces a spark. As electrons transfer between objects, they heat the air around the path they travel until it glows. The glowing air is the spark you see. The tiny spark you may have seen when you touch a doorknob or metal object is an example of static discharge.

Lightning is a dramatic example of static discharge. You can think of lightning as a huge spark. During thunderstorms, air swirls violently. Water droplets within the clouds become electrically charged. To restore a neutral condition in the clouds, electrons move from areas of negative charge to areas of positive charge and produce an intense spark. You see that spark as lightning.

Some lightning reaches Earth because negative charges at the bottom of storm clouds may cause the surface of Earth to become positively charged by induction. Electrons jump between the cloud and Earth's surface, producing a giant spark as they travel through the air. This is possible because of charging by conduction.

 **How is lightning formed?**

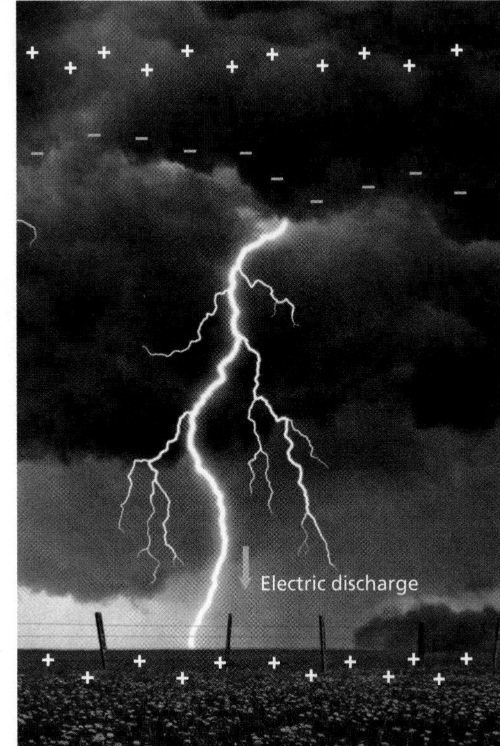

FIGURE 6
Static Discharge
Lightning is a spectacular discharge of static electricity. Lightning can occur within a cloud, between two clouds, or between a cloud and Earth.

Section 1 Assessment

Target Reading Skill **Previewing Visuals** Refer to your questions and answers about Figure 4 to help you answer Question 3 below.

Reviewing Key Concepts

1. a. **Identifying** What are the two types of electric charge?
   b. **Explaining** How do objects with the same charge interact? How do objects with opposite charges interact?
   c. **Comparing and Contrasting** How are electric charges similar to magnetic poles? How are they different?
2. a. **Defining** What is an electric field?
   b. **Interpreting Diagrams** What do the lines represent in an electric field diagram?
3. a. **Reviewing** What is static electricity?
   b. **Describing** How is static electricity transferred during charging by conduction?
   c. **Applying Concepts** What role does induction play when lightning strikes Earth?

Lab zone At-Home Activity

TV Attraction Rub a balloon against your hair and bring the balloon near one of your arms. Observe the hair on your arm; then put down the balloon. Then bring your other arm near the front of a television screen that is turned on. Ask a family member to explain why the hairs on your arms are attracted to the balloon and to the screen. Explain that this is evidence that there is static electricity present on both the balloon and the screen.

Lab zone At-Home Activity

TV Attraction L1 Tell students to avoid doing the activity on a humid day. Students should readily feel the hairs of their arm attracted to the television screen or observe that their hair is attracted. They may even feel very tiny sparks jump from the screen.

Lab zone Chapter Project

Keep Students on Track By this point, students should have chosen an event that will close a switch on the alarm circuit. For students who are having trouble, suggest an event, such as an object falling or a container filling with salt water.

Monitor Progress L2

Answers

Figure 5 Electrons move between the rod and the electroscope, leaving the electroscope charged either positively or negatively. Because the leaves have the same net charge, they repel each other.

Reading Checkpoint Lightning forms when electrons travel through the air between clouds and Earth.

Assess

Reviewing Key Concepts

1. a. Positive charge and negative charge **b.** Objects with like charge repel. Objects with unlike charge attract. **c.** Electric charges that are alike repel each other. Similarly, magnetic poles that are alike repel each other. Unlike charges attract each other, and poles that are unlike attract each other. However, electric charges can exist alone, while magnetic poles always exist in pairs.

2. a. An electric field is the region around a charged object in which the object's electric force is exerted on other charged objects. **b.** Electric field lines show the direction and strength of the electric force.

3. a. Static electricity is the buildup of charges on an object. **b.** During charging by conduction, electrons are transferred by direct contact from an object that has a greater negative charge to the one that has a greater positive charge.. **c.** Induction can cause the surface of Earth to become positively charged. Then, lighting can occur when electrons jump between negatively charged clouds and Earth's positively charged surface.

Reteach L1

Use Figure 3 to reteach the three methods by which electrons can be transferred.

Performance Assessment L2

Drawing Have students make a labeled drawing of how an electroscope works.

All in One Teaching Resources

- Section Summary: *Electric Charge and Static Electricity*
- Review and Reinforce: *Electric Charge and Static Electricity*
- Enrich: *Electric Charge and Static Electricity*

The Versorium

L3

Prepare for Inquiry

Key Concept

An uncharged object—the versorium—is attracted to a charged object.

Skills Objectives

After this lab, students will be able to:

- predict the behavior of both the aluminum tent and the paper tent
- observe the behavior of the aluminum tent and the paper tent
- classify the process that explains observed behaviors of materials

Prep Time 20 minutes
Class Time 30 minutes

Advance Planning

On the day of the lab, test the plastic foam plates and wool to be sure they develop adequate static charge. To save time, cut the 3-cm by 10-cm strips of aluminum foil and paper in advance. Buy wool fabric at fabric or craft stores.

Alternative Materials

Any set of materials that develops a static charge will work. Examples: wool fabric and balloon; plastic bag and plastic foam plate; acetate transparency and plastic foam plate; fur and balloon.

Safety

Be sure that students avoid pushing the sharpened pencil into their skin. Review the safety guidelines in Appendix A.

All in One Teaching Resources

- Lab Worksheet: *The Versorium*

Guide Inquiry

Introduce the Procedure

Balance a meter stick on a thumbtack on a table in front of the class, and rub a balloon on your sweater or hair. Ask: **What is the charge on the meter stick?** *(No charge)* Bring the balloon close to the meter stick, and students will observe that the meter stick is attracted to the balloon. Ask: **What causes the attraction?** *(Some students may know that the electric charge on the balloon is attracting oppositely charged particles on the meter stick.)*

Lab zone **Skills Lab**

The Versorium

Problem

A versorium is a device that was first described in 1600 by Sir William Gilbert. Why does a versorium turn?

Skills Focus

observing, predicting, classifying

Materials

- foam cup
- plastic foam plate
- pencil
- aluminum foil
- wool fabric
- paper
- scissors

Procedure

PART 1 Aluminum Foil Versorium

1. Cut a piece of aluminum foil approximately 3 cm by 10 cm.
2. Make a tent out of the foil strip by gently folding it in half in both directions.
3. Push a pencil up through the bottom of an inverted cup. **CAUTION:** *Avoid pushing the sharpened pencil against your skin.* Balance the center point of the foil tent on the point of the pencil as shown.
4. Make a copy of the data table.
5. Predict what will happen if you bring a foam plate near the foil tent. Record your prediction in the data table.
6. Predict what will happen if you rub the foam plate with wool fabric and then bring the plate near the foil tent. Record your prediction.
7. Predict what will happen if you bring the rubbed wool near the foil tent. Again record your prediction.
8. Test each of your three predictions and record your observations in the data table.

PART 2 Paper Tent Versorium

9. What might happen if you used a paper tent versorium instead of aluminum foil? Record your prediction for each of the three tests.
10. Test your prediction and record your observations in the data table.

Data Table

	Unrubbed Foam Plate	Rubbed Foam Plate	Rubbed Wool Fabric
Aluminum Tent: Prediction			
Aluminum Tent: Observation			
Paper Tent: Prediction			
Paper Tent: Observation			

Troubleshooting the Experiment

- Show students how to make the versorium. The tent has to turn freely.
- Remind students to slowly bring the plastic foam plate or wool fabric near—but not touching—the top of the tent.
- Humidity may affect the static charge.
- Demonstrate that the tent must be approached from the side.

Analyze and Conclude

1. **Inferring** At the beginning of the lab, is the foil negatively charged, positively charged, or uncharged? Use your observations to explain your answer.
2. **Predicting** Refer to the predictions you recorded in Steps 5, 6, and 7. Explain the reasoning behind those predictions.
3. **Observing** Did the behavior of the foil match each of your predictions in Steps 5, 6, and 7? Refer to your observations to explain your answer.
4. **Classifying** Did the effect of the foam plate differ in Steps 5 and 6? If so, identify which process—charging by friction, by conduction, or by induction—produced that change.
5. **Classifying** In Step 7, which process—charging by friction, by conduction, or by induction—explains the behavior of the foil when you brought the rubbed wool near it? Explain.
6. **Predicting** Explain the reasoning for your prediction about the paper tent versorium in Part B.
7. **Observing** Did the behavior of the paper tent match your prediction in Step 9? Refer to your observations to explain your answer.
8. **Drawing Conclusions** Were the procedures and results in Part 2 generally similar to those in Part 1? Explain your answer with reference to charging by friction, by conduction, or by induction.
9. **Controlling Variables** During this lab, why is it important to avoid touching the foam plate or the wool with other objects before testing them with the versorium?
10. **Communicating** Another student who did this lab says that the versorium can show whether an object has a positive or negative charge. Write an e-mail to that student giving your reasons for agreeing or disagreeing.

Design an Experiment

What other materials besides foam or wool might have an effect on the versorium? What other materials could you use to make the versorium tent? Design an experiment to test specific materials and see how they respond. *Obtain your teacher's permission before carrying out your investigation.*

Analyze and Conclude

1. Sample answer: Uncharged. If the foil had been charged, it would have been attracted to the unrubbed foam plate.
2. Students' predictions may vary. Students should support each prediction with reasoning that shows an understanding of how the wool and the foam plate both became charged by friction, as well as how the tent was either repelled or attracted to the charged materials and became charged by induction.
3. Sample answer: Yes. My observations matched my predictions.
4. Sample answer: Yes. In Step 6, the foam plate became negatively charged by friction when it was rubbed with wool.
5. Sample answer: Charging occurred by induction when the positively charged wool caused electrons in the foil to travel to the near end of the versorium. Thus, the negative end was attracted to the wool.
6. Sample answer: In Part 2, I predicted that the paper tent would be attracted to both. Even though electrons are not able to move freely in the paper, they might cluster on the sides of the paper molecules toward or away from the charged materials.
7. Sample answer: Yes. My observations in Step 10 matched my predictions.
8. Sample answer: Yes. The foam plate and wool became charged by friction, just as in Part 1. Because the paper tent was attracted to both the rubbed foam plate and the rubbed wool, it became charged by induction.
9. Sample answer: If allowed to touch other objects, the charged foam plate and charged wool will become uncharged because of transfer by conduction.
10. Sample e-mail: I disagree with your assertion. The device cannot detect the sign of the charge because induction causes the tent to be attracted equally to both positively charged and negatively charged objects.

Expected Outcome

The foam plate that is not rubbed with wool fabric should cause no change, because the plate is neutral. Both the foil tent and the paper tent should be attracted both to the rubbed foam plate and rubbed wool fabric. Friction charges the plate and the wool; the versorium tent is then charged by induction when charged material comes near.

Extend Inquiry

Design an Experiment Students may want to try materials such as inflated balloons, plastic rulers that have been rubbed with plastic sandwich bags, or objects charged with a Van de Graff generator, if available. Other materials for the versorium tent might be plastic, wood, or other metal foils.

Section 2
Electric Current

Objectives
After this lesson, students will be able to
N.2.2.1 Explain how an electric current is produced.
N.2.2.2 Explain how conductors are different from insulators.
N.2.2.3 Describe what causes electric charges to flow in a circuit.
N.2.2.4 Explain how resistance affects current.

Target Reading Skill
Outlining Explain that using an outline format helps students organize information by main topic, subtopic, and details.

Answer
Electric Current
- I. Flow of Electric Charges
  - A. What Is Electric Current?
  - B. Current in a Circuit
- II. Conductors and Insulators
  - A. Conductors
  - B. Insulators
- III. Voltage
  - A. Charges Need Energy to Flow
  - B. Voltage
  - C. Voltage Sources
- IV. Resistance
  - A. Current Depends on Resistance
  - B. Factors That Determine Resistance
  - C. Path of Least Resistance

All in One Teaching Resources
- Transparency N17

Preteach

Build Background Knowledge L2
A Current Through a Straw
Hold up a drinking straw and a straw-type coffee stirrer. Ask: **Is it easier to drink a milkshake through a narrow straw or a wide straw?** *(Through a wide straw)* Explain that a narrow straw is more resistant to the flow of the milkshake. Therefore, you have to suck harder to get the milkshake to flow through the straw. Tell students in this section they will learn about similar concepts involving the path of electric current.

Section 2
Electric Current

Reading Preview
Key Concepts
- How is an electric current produced?
- How are conductors different from insulators?
- What causes electric charges to flow in a circuit?
- How does resistance affect current?

Key Terms
- electric current
- electric circuit • conductor
- insulator • voltage
- voltage source • resistance

Target Reading Skill
Outlining As you read, make an outline about electric current. Use the red headings for the main ideas and the blue headings for the supporting ideas.

Lab zone Discover Activity
How Can Current Be Measured?
1. Obtain four pieces of wire with the insulation removed from both ends. Each piece should be about 25 cm long.
2. Wrap one of the wires four times around a compass as shown. You may use tape to keep the wire in place.
3. Build a circuit using the remaining wire, wrapped compass, two bulbs, and a D-cell as shown. Adjust the compass position so that the wire is aligned directly over the compass needle.
4. Make sure the compass is level. If it is not, place it on a piece of modeling clay so that the needle swings freely.
5. Observe the compass needle as you complete the circuit. Record the number of degrees the needle moves.
6. Repeat the activity using only one bulb, and again with no bulb. Record the number of degrees the needle moves.

Think It Over
Inferring Based on your observations of the compass, when did the compass needle move the most? How can you explain your observations?

Thousands of tomatoes ride along a conveyer belt through a giant machine. The conveyer belt carries the tomatoes through a cleaning station, a sorter, and into a lane to be packaged. You might be wondering what a huge conveyer belt of tomatoes could possibly have to do with electricity. Like the tomatoes, electric charges can be made to move in a confined path.

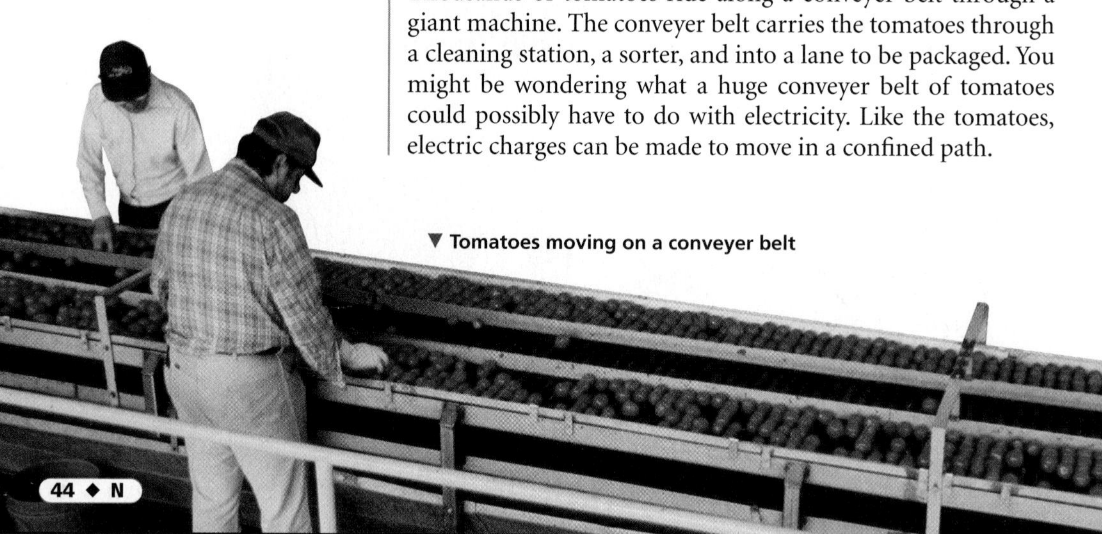

▼ Tomatoes moving on a conveyer belt

44 ◆ N

Lab zone Discover Activity
Skills Focus Inferring L2

Materials 1 m bell wire, wire cutters and strippers, metric ruler, magnetic compass, electrical tape, 1 1.5-volt bulb and socket, D-cell and holder, modeling clay

Time 15 minutes

Tips Remove the insulation from the ends of the wire. Demonstrate how to connect the batteries and then how to rewire the circuit in Step 6 each time a bulb and socket are removed.

Expected Outcome The compass needle deflects more as bulbs and sockets are removed from the circuit.

Think It Over Sample answer: The compass needle moved the most when no bulbs were present. Removing the bulbs may have increased the current.

Flow of Electric Charges

Lightning releases a large amount of electrical energy. However, the electric charge from lightning can't be used to power your TV, clock radio, video game, or kitchen lights because it only lasts for an instant. These electric devices need electric charges that flow continuously. They require electric current.

What Is Electric Current? Recall that static electric charges do not flow continuously. However, when electric charges are made to flow through a wire or similar material, they produce an electric current. **Electric current** is the continuous flow of electric charges through a material. The amount of charge that passes through the wire in a unit of time is the rate of electric current. The unit for the rate of current is the ampere, named for André Marie Ampère, an early investigator of electricity. The name of the unit is often shortened to *amp* or *A*. The number of amps describes the amount of charge flowing past a given point each second.

Compare to river current

FIGURE 7
Representing an Electric Current
Tomatoes moving on a conveyer belt are similar to charges moving in a wire, or electric current.
Interpreting Photos *Which characteristics of electric current are represented in the illustrations?*

Tomatoes on a conveyer belt are similar to electric current in a wire. Both the tomatoes and the current move in a confined path.

If the tomatoes move faster, more tomatoes pass the worker every second. Similarly, if current is increased in a wire, more charges pass by a point on the wire every second.

Instruct

Flow of Electric Charges

Teach Key Concepts L2

A Continuous Flow of Charges

Focus Explain that in static electricity, charges build up on an object, but the charges do not flow continuously. By contrast, an electric current is the continuous flow of electric charges through a material.

Teach Ask: **What is the rate of electric current?** *(The amount of charge that passes through a wire in a unit of time)* **What unit is used for rate of current?** *(The ampere, or amp)*

Apply Tell students that there is an electric current through two different wires, and the current through wire A is greater than the current through wire B. Ask: **What can you say about the electric charges flowing through each of the wires?** *(More charges are flowing past a given point per second in wire A than in wire B.)* **learning modality: verbal**

Independent Practice L2

All in One Teaching Resources

- Guided Reading and Study Worksheet: *Electric Current*

Student Edition on Audio CD

Differentiated Instruction

Less Proficient Readers L1
Identifying Supporting Ideas Have students listen to this section on the **Student Edition on Audio CD.** As they listen, they can identify supporting ideas and add them under the appropriate headings and subheadings in their section outlines. **learning modality: verbal**

Gifted and Talented L3
Communicating Have students find other real-world analogies to represent current and prepare a presentation to the class. Ask that they include a drawing or photograph to show to the class. **learning modality: verbal**

Monitor Progress L2

Writing Have students write a paragraph that explains how an electric current is like a conveyor belt.

Answer
Figure 7 The flow of electric charges and the rate of current are represented by the movement of tomatoes on a conveyor belt.

Use Visuals: Figure 8 L2

An Unbroken Path

Focus Tell students that for an electric current to exist, charges must be able to flow from one place to another with no gaps in the path.

Teach Have students study Figure 8 and read the caption. Ask: **What is an electric circuit?** *(A complete, unbroken path through which electric charges flow)* **Why is a racetrack like an electric circuit?** *(Both a racetrack and an electric circuit form a complete path, or closed loop.)* Emphasize that a closed loop is a path from the beginning of the circuit, through the circuit, and back to the beginning of the circuit.

Apply Ask: **What are some other examples of closed loops?** *(Sample answer: A jogging track; a roller coaster.)* **learning modality: visual**

Conductors and Insulators

Teach Key Concepts L2

Transfer of Charges Through Materials

Focus Tell students that electric charges do not flow through all materials equally well. Materials through which charges flow easily are called conductors, while materials through which charges do not flow easily are called insulators.

Teach Ask: **What is the difference between electrons in the atoms of conductors and the electrons in the atoms of insulators?** *(In a conductor, atoms contain electrons that are loosely bound and able to move through the conductor. In an insulator, the electrons are bound tightly to their atoms and do not flow easily.)* **What are some good conductors?** *(Metals, such as silver, copper, aluminum, and iron)* **What are some good insulators?** *(Rubber, glass, sand, plastic, and wood)*

Apply Show students an electric cord that is stripped at the end. Ask: **Which material is a conductor?** *(The inside metal part of the cord)* **Which is the insulator?** *(The outside covering of the cord)* **learning modality: visual**

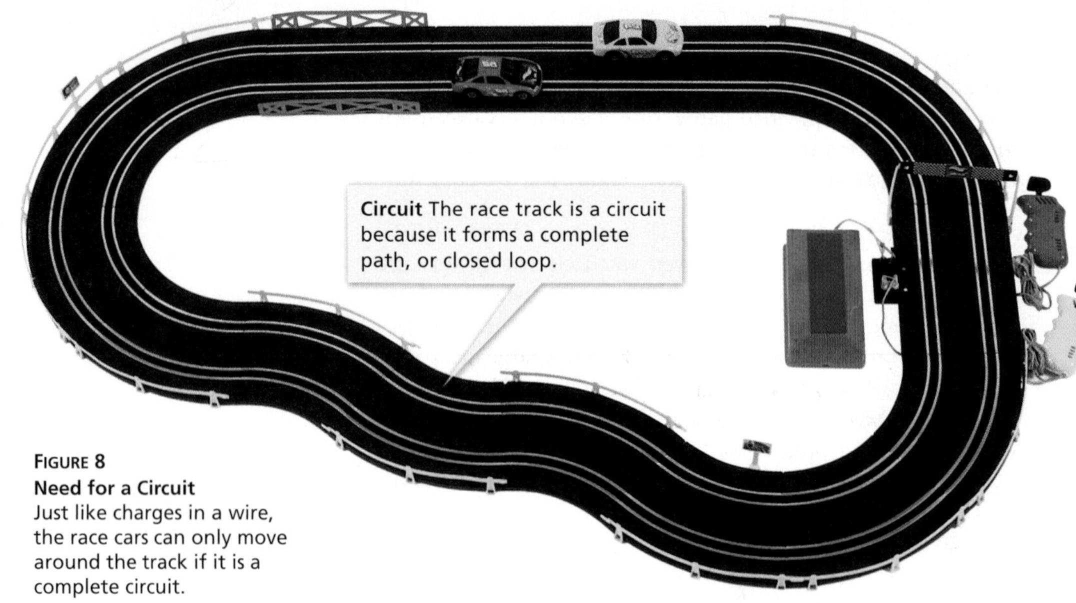

Circuit The race track is a circuit because it forms a complete path, or closed loop.

FIGURE 8
Need for a Circuit
Just like charges in a wire, the race cars can only move around the track if it is a complete circuit.

Current in a Circuit Electric current does not automatically exist in a material. Current requires a specific path to follow. **To produce electric current, charges must flow continuously from one place to another.** Current requires an electric circuit. An **electric circuit** is a complete, unbroken path through which electric charges can flow.

The cars on the racetrack in Figure 8 are like the charges in an electric circuit. If the racetrack forms a complete loop, the cars can move around the track continuously. However, if a piece of the racetrack is missing, the cars are unable to move around the loop. Similarly, if an electric circuit is complete, charges can flow continuously. If an electric circuit is broken, charges will not flow.

Electric circuits are all around you. All electrical devices, from toasters to radios to electric guitars and televisions, contain electric circuits. You will learn more about the characteristics of electric circuits in Section 4.

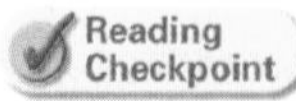

What is an electric circuit?

Conductors and Insulators

Charges flow easily through a circuit made of metal wires. But would charges flow in wires made of plastic? The answer is no. Electric charges do not flow easily through every material. **A conductor transfers electric charge well. An insulator does not transfer electric charge well.** Figure 9 shows materials that are good conductors and materials that are insulators.

Conductors Metals, such as silver, copper, aluminum, and iron, are good conductors. A **conductor** is a material through which charge can flow easily. In a conductor, atoms contain electrons that are bound loosely. These electrons, called conduction electrons, are able to move throughout the conductor. As these electrons flow through a conductor, they form an electric current. Conductors are used to carry electric charge.

Did you ever wonder why a light goes on the instant you flip the switch? How do the electrons get to your lamp from the electric company so fast? The answer is that electrons are not sent to your house when you flip a switch. They are already present inside the conductors that make up the circuit. When you flip the switch, electrons at one end of the wire are pulled, while those at the other end are pushed. The result is a continuous flow of electrons through all parts of the circuit as soon as the circuit is completed.

Insulators A material through which charges cannot flow easily is called an **insulator**. The electrons in an insulator are bound tightly to their atoms and do not move easily. Rubber, glass, sand, plastic, and wood are good insulators. Insulators are used to stop the flow of charges.

The rubber coating on an appliance cord is an example of an insulator. A cord carries charges from an electrical outlet to an appliance. So why don't you get a shock when you touch a cord? The inner wire is the conductor for the current. The rubber coating around the wire is an insulator. The cord allows charge to continue to flow to the appliance, but stops it from flowing into your hand and shocking you.

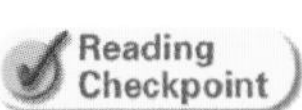
Reading Checkpoint **Why don't you get a shock from touching an extension cord?**

For: More on electric current
Visit: PHSchool.com
Web Code: cgd-4022

make a list
conductors

write a 3 p. essay on differences you infer from your lists between cond. + insulators

Conductors

Insulators

FIGURE 9
Conductors and Insulators
C

Classifying *In which category do metals belong?*

Address Misconceptions L1

Metals Aren't the Only Conductors

Focus Many students may think that metals are the only good conductors. Tell them that although many metals are good conductors, other materials conduct electric current as well.

Teach Explain that good conductors also include various liquids and gases. Tell students that they will learn later that charges flow easily through liquids and pastes in batteries.

Apply Turn on a fluorescent light. Explain that a fluorescent light bulb contains a gas through which charges flow freely. Ask: **If charges flow freely through the gas in this bulb, how would you classify the gas?** *(As a conductor, because a conductor is a material through which charges can easily flow)*
learning modality: verbal

For: More on electric current
Visit: PHSchool.com
Web Code: cgd-4022

Students can review electric currents in an online interactivity.

Monitor Progress L2

Oral Presentation Call on students at random to give one example of a conductor and one example of an insulator and to describe the difference between them.

Answers

Figure 9 Metals are good conductors.

Reading Checkpoint A complete, unbroken path through which electric charges can flow

Reading Checkpoint The coating on the cord is an insulator, which keeps charges from flowing into your body.

Voltage

Teach Key Concepts

L2

Potential Difference in a Circuit

Focus Explain to students that current is present in an electric circuit because there is a difference in electrical potential energy between two places in the circuit.

Teach Ask: **What causes a current in an electric circuit?** *(Voltage)* Tell students that the terms *voltage* and *potential difference* are two terms for the same concept. Explain that to have a current, there must be a force that causes the charges to flow. That force is voltage. Ask: **What maintains voltage in an electric circuit?** *(A voltage source)* **What are two examples of a voltage source?** *(Batteries and generators)*

Apply Use the analogy shown in Figure 10 to clarify concepts related to voltage. Ask: **What is the roller coaster motor like in an electric circuit?** *(A voltage source)* **What happens when the car reaches the top of the hill?** *(It moves down the hill.)* **Why does it move down the hill?** *(Potential energy at the top of the hill is higher than at the bottom of the hill.)* **What does this difference in potential energy represent in an electric circuit?** *(Voltage, or difference in electrical potential energy)* **learning modality: visual**

Help Students Read

Identifying Supporting Evidence Refer to the Content Refresher in this chapter, which provides the guidelines for identifying supporting evidence.

Have students read the subsection related to voltage. Ask: **What is the hypothesis for this subsection?** *(Sample answer: Voltage causes current in an electric circuit.)* Write the hypothesis on the board, leaving enough room around it to add supporting evidence. This will be the center of a graphic organizer. As students read, have them call out the supporting evidence for the hypothesis. Ask: **What is one piece of evidence that supports this hypothesis?** *(Sample answer: Charges in an electric circuit flow because of a difference in electrical potential energy.)* Write the supporting evidence on the board, drawing "spokes" from each piece of evidence to the hypothesis.

Lab zone Try This Activity

Down the Tubes

Use water to model voltage.

1. Set up a funnel, tubing, beaker, and ring stand as shown.

2. Have a partner start a stopwatch as you pour 200 mL of water into the funnel.
3. Stop the stopwatch when all of the water has flowed into the beaker.
4. Repeat steps 2 and 3 setting the funnel at different heights.

Making Models How did your model represent voltage? How did changing the height affect the model's "voltage"?

Voltage

Imagine you are on a roller coaster at an amusement park. Strapped in your seat, you wait anxiously as your car climbs to the top of the hill. Then, whoosh! Your car speeds down the steel track. Believe it or not, electric charges flow in much the same way as your roller coaster car moves on the track.

Charges Need Energy to Flow The roller coaster cars need energy to give you an exciting ride, but they have no energy when you first climb aboard. A motor provides energy to move a chain attached to the cars. The moving chain pulls the cars to the top of the hill. As they climb, the cars gain potential energy. Potential energy is the energy an object has as a result of its position, or height. The higher up the hill the chain carries the cars, the more potential energy the cars gain. Then, after reaching the hilltop, the cars rush down the hill. As they do, they move from a place of high potential energy—the hilltop—to a place of low potential energy—the bottom of the hill. It is the difference in potential energy between the hilltop and the bottom of the hill that allows the cars to speed down the hill.

In a similar way, charges in an electric circuit flow because of a difference in electrical potential energy. Think of the charges that make up the electric current as being like the roller coaster cars. The circuit is like the steel track. An energy source, such as a battery, is like the roller coaster motor. The battery provides the potential energy difference for the circuit. However, its potential energy is not related to height, as in the roller coaster. Instead it is related to the charges inside the battery.

Voltage Just as the roller coaster creates a difference in potential energy between two places, so does an electric circuit. The difference in electrical potential energy between two places in a circuit is called **voltage,** or potential difference. The unit of measure of voltage is the volt (V). **Voltage causes a current in an electric circuit.** You can think of voltage as the amount of force pushing an electric current.

Voltage Sources At the amusement park, if there were no way of pulling the roller coaster cars to the top of the first hill, there would be no ride. Recall that the ride has a source of energy, a motor. The motor moves the chain that takes the cars to the top of the hill. Once the cars reach the top of any hill, they gain a high potential energy.

Lab zone Try This Activity

Skills Focus Making models L1

Materials 2-mL beakers, funnel, ring stand, clear tubing of various lengths and widths, stopwatch

Time 15 minutes

Tips Have students work in pairs. Keep paper towels handy to clean up spills.

Expected Outcome The height of the tubing represents voltage or potential difference. The higher the funnel, the more potential energy the water has, or the higher the model's "voltage."

Extend Challenge students to find out what happens if they increase or decrease resistance by using tubing of different lengths and widths. **learning modality: kinesthetic**

An electric circuit also requires a source of energy, such as a battery, to maintain a voltage. A **voltage source** is a device that creates a potential difference in an electric circuit. Batteries and generators are examples of voltage sources. A voltage source has two terminals. The voltage between the terminals causes charges to move around the circuit.

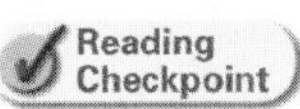
Reading Checkpoint
What does a voltage source do?

FIGURE 10
Voltage
Voltage in a circuit is similar to the difference in potential energy on a roller coaster. **Interpreting Diagrams** *From where do the cars get their energy?*

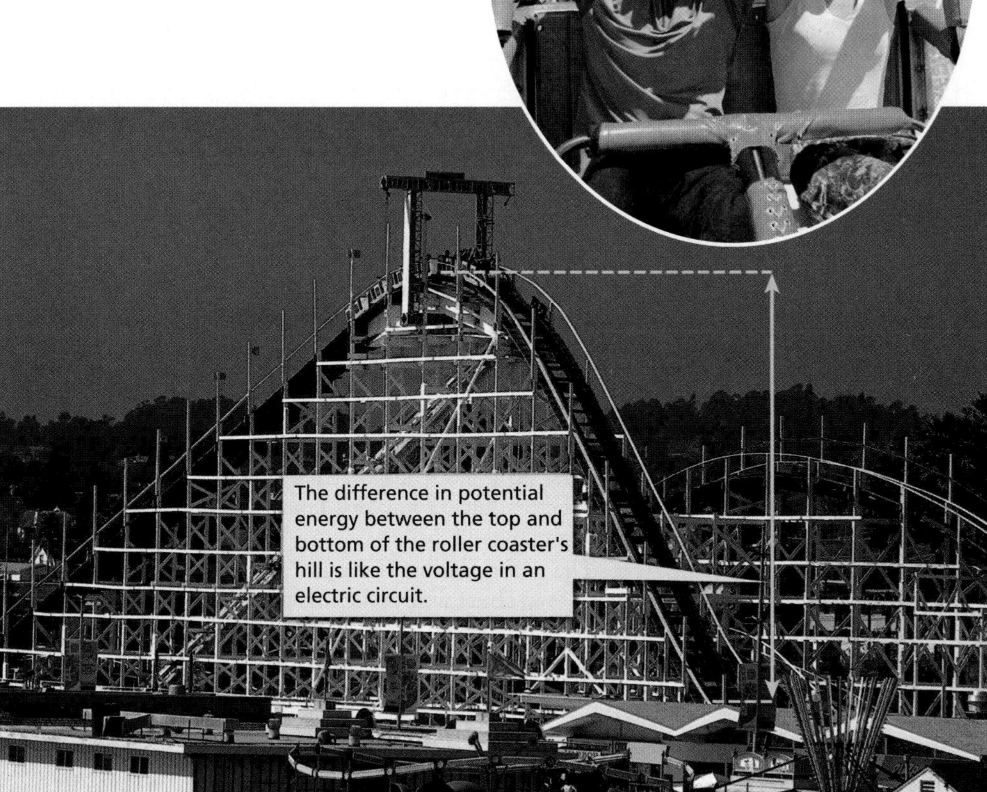
The difference in potential energy between the top and bottom of the roller coaster's hill is like the voltage in an electric circuit.

Lab zone
Build Inquiry
L2

Modeling Potential Difference

Materials plastic bottle with small hole in bottom and cap removed, flexible plastic tubing, basin, modeling clay

Time 15 minutes

Focus Tell students they can design and build a model that can represent what happens as voltage, or potential difference, increases.

Teach Divide the class into groups and provide each group with a set of materials. Challenge each group to design a model using the given materials and water that will show what happens as voltage increases. Give groups time to plan their models.

Apply Check student plans, and then allow them to test their models. A sample model might be to insert tubing through the bottom of the bottle, seal around the tubing with modeling clay, and fill the bottle with water. When the end of the plastic tube is at the same height as the top of the water bottle, no water flows, because there is no potential difference. As the bottle is raised or the end of the tubing is lowered, the water flows faster and faster—higher and higher potential difference. **learning modality: kinesthetic**

Monitor Progress L2

Writing Ask students to write a paragraph explaining why voltage is needed for current to flow.

Answers

Figure 10 The motor provides energy to the roller coaster cars.

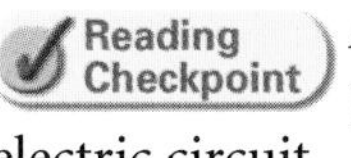
Reading Checkpoint
A voltage source creates a potential difference in an electric circuit.

Resistance

Teach Key Concepts

L2

The Difficulty of Flowing

Focus Explain that charges have more difficulty flowing through some materials than others.

Teach Ask: **What is resistance?** *(The measure of how difficult it is for charges to flow through a material.)* Write the term *Resistance* on the board, and ask: **What are the four factors that determine the resistance of any object?** *(The material, the length of the material, the diameter of the material, and the temperature of the material)* Write each factor on the board, and question students about the details of each.

Apply Ask: **If there is more resistance in a circuit, is there more or less current for a given voltage?** *(Less)* **Do longer wires have more or less resistance?** *(More)* **Therefore, does a longer wire have more or less current than a shorter wire, if the voltage is the same in both wires?** *(The longer wire has less current because it has more resistance.)* **learning modality: verbal**

All in One Teaching Resources

- Transparency N18

L1

The Path of Least Resistance

Materials latex glove, push pin, scissors, sink or basin

Time 10 minutes

Focus Tell students that you will model with water a path of least resistance.

Teach Fill the glove with water until the water is about 4–6 cm from the top of the wrist. Then tie the wrist. Hold the glove over the sink or basin with the fingers pointed upward, and put a single pinhole in one finger of the glove. Then snip the tip off a different finger. Ask students to predict what will happen if you turn the glove back over. Allow students to observe the water flowing out of the fingers of the glove.

Apply Ask: **Which path offered the least resistance? Why?** *(The path through the finger with the larger hole offered the path of least resistance, because the water could flow out of that hole more quickly.)* **learning modality: visual**

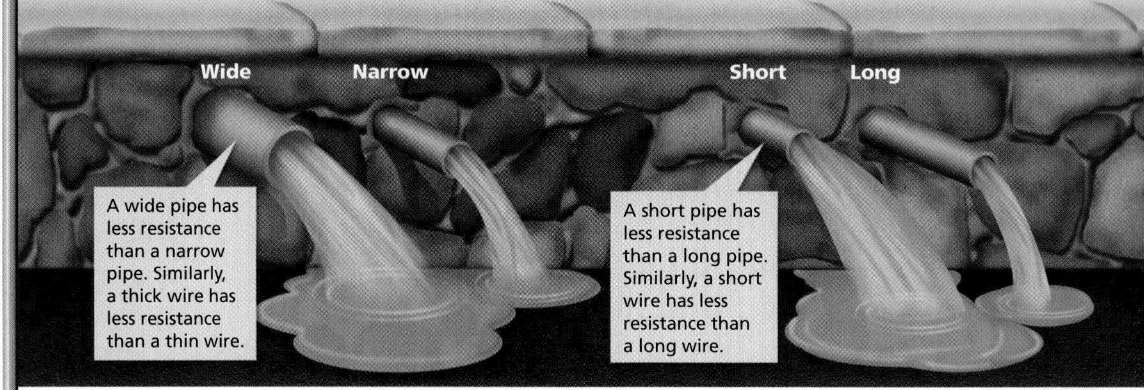

FIGURE 11
Resistance
Two factors that affect the resistance of water flowing in a pipe are diameter and length. The diameter and length of a wire also affect resistance in a circuit.
Inferring *If you reduce the resistance in a circuit, will there be more or less current?*

Resistance

In the example of the roller coaster, you only learned how the height difference, or "voltage," affected the cars' speed. But other factors affect how fast the cars move. For instance, if the roller coaster cars have rusty wheels, their speed will decrease because the wheels do not turn as well. Current in a circuit works in a similar way.

Current Depends on Resistance The amount of current that exists in a circuit depends on more than just the voltage. Current also depends on the resistance of the material. **Resistance** is the measure of how difficult it is for charges to flow through a material. **The greater the resistance, the less current there is for a given voltage.** The unit of measure of resistance is the ohm (Ω). The ohm is named for Georg Ohm, a German physicist who investigated resistance.

Factors That Determine Resistance There are four factors that determine the resistance of a wire, or any object. The first factor is the material from which the wire is made. Some materials, such as insulators, have electrons that are tightly held to their atoms. Insulators have a high resistance because it is difficult for charges to move. Other materials, such as conductors, have electrons that are loosely held to their atoms. Conductors have a low resistance because charges can move through them easily.

The second factor is length. Long wires have more resistance than short wires. The resistance of current in a wire can be compared to the resistance of water flowing through a pipe. Suppose water is being released from a reservoir held by a dam. As shown in Figure 11, less water flows from the reservoir through the long pipe than through the short pipe. The water in the long pipe slows down because it bumps into more of the pipe's inner wall.

Diameter is the third factor. In Figure 11, the pipe with the small diameter has less water flowing through it than the pipe with the large diameter. In the small-diameter pipe, there is less area through which the water can flow. Similarly, thin wires have more resistance than thick wires.

The fourth factor that determines the resistance of a wire is the temperature of the wire. The electrical resistance of most materials increases as temperature increases. As the temperature of most materials decreases, resistance decreases as well.

FIGURE 12
Which Path?
Charges flow through the wire, not the bird, because the wire offers less resistance.

Path of Least Resistance Perhaps you have heard it said that someone is taking the "path of least resistance." This means that the person is doing something in the easiest way possible. In a similar way, if electric charge can flow through either of two paths, more of the charge will flow through the path with lower resistance.

Have you seen a bird perched on an uninsulated electric fence? The bird doesn't get hurt because charges flow through the path of least resistance. Since the bird's body offers more resistance than the wire, charges flow directly through the wire without harming the bird.

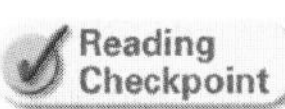

What is the "path of least resistance"?

Section 2 Assessment

Target Reading Skill **Outlining** Use your outline to help you answer the questions below.

Reviewing Key Concepts

1. a. **Reviewing** What happens when an electric current is produced?
   b. **Comparing and Contrasting** Contrast electric current and static electricity.
   c. **Relating Cause and Effect** Explain why electric current cannot exist if an electric circuit is broken.
2. a. **Defining** Define *conductor* and *insulator*.
   b. **Listing** List materials that make good conductors. List materials that are insulators.
   c. **Applying Concepts** If a copper wire in a working electric circuit is replaced by a piece of rubber tubing, will there be a current in the circuit? Explain.
3. a. **Listing** What are two examples of voltage sources?
   b. **Explaining** How does voltage cause charges to flow in a circuit?
   c. **Predicting** The electrical potential energy at one point in a circuit is greater than the electrical potential energy at another point. Will there be a current between the two points? Explain.
4. a. **Reviewing** What is resistance?
   b. **Summarizing** What are four factors that determine resistance?

Writing in Science

Analogies An analogy can help people understand new information by comparing it to something familiar. Write a paragraph that compares an electric circuit to skiing down a slope and riding the chairlift to the top.

Lab zone Chapter Project

Keep Students on Track By this point in the project, students should have begun to construct their alarm circuits. Each student should have designed a detector switch that closes when an event occurs. Talk to each student, and try to provide any materials they might need to complete the building of their circuits.

Writing in Science

Writing Mode Analysis

Scoring Rubric

4 Exceeds criteria; develops the analogy accurately and interestingly

3 Meets criteria

2 Meets some criteria; fails to fully develop the analogy

1 Fails to develop the analogy in an accurate way

Monitor Progress L2

Answers

Figure 11 More current

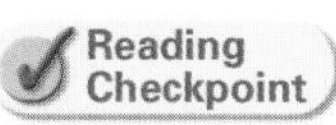

The path with lower resistance.

Assess

Reviewing Key Concepts

1. a. A continuous flow of charges travels through a material. **b.** An electric current is a continuous flow of charge. Although charges build up on an object in static electricity, the charges do not flow continuously. **c.** Charges cannot flow because the path is no longer complete.

2. a. A conductor is a material through which charges can flow easily. An insulator is a material through which charges cannot flow easily **b.** Sample answer: Silver, copper, aluminum, and iron are examples of good conductors. Rubber, sand, plastic, glass, and wood are examples of good insulators. **c.** There will be no current because rubber is an insulator.

3. a. Sample answer: Batteries and generators **b.** Voltage acts as a force that causes the charges to flow. **c.** Yes. A difference in electrical potential energy in a circuit causes charges to flow in the circuit, resulting in a current.

4. a. Resistance is the measure of how difficult it is for charges to flow through a material. **b.** Four factors that determine resistance are the material, the length of the material, the diameter of the material, and the temperature of the material.

Reteach L1

Have students create a concept map using the terms *electric current, electrical potential, voltage, resistance, ohms, amperes,* and *volts.*

Performance Assessment L2

Skills Check Ask each student to write two questions each about electric currents, conductors and insulators, voltage, and resistance. Then, divide the class into groups and have group members ask each other to answer their questions.

All in One Teaching Resources

- Section Summary: *Electric Current*
- Review and Reinforce: *Electric Current*
- Enrich: *Electric Current*

L2

Constructing a Dimmer Switch

Prepare for Inquiry

Key Concept
The brightness of a bulb is controlled by the amount of current in the circuit, which in turn depends on the voltage and the resistance in the circuit.

Skills Objectives
After this lab, students will be able to:
- predict how the brightness of the bulb will change
- observe the change in brightness of the bulb

Prep Time 10 minutes
Class Time 30 minutes

Advance Planning
Cut the copper wire and the rubber tubing to the same length as the pencil lead.

Alternative Materials
Any nonconductor, such as wood or plastic, can be substituted for the rubber tubing.

Safety
Caution students to be careful not to break the flashlight bulb. Review the safety guidelines in Appendix A.

All in One Teaching Resources
- Lab Worksheet: *Constructing a Dimmer Switch*

Guide Inquiry

Invitation
Ask students to think about sitting in a movie theater just as the show is about to begin. Ask: **When people are arriving, are the lights on or off?** *(On)* **During the show, are the lights on or off?** *(Off)* **Do the lights all go off suddenly?** *(No. They gradually get dimmer.)*

Lab zone Skills Lab

Constructing a Dimmer Switch

Problem
What materials can be used to make a dimmer switch?

Skills Focus
predicting, observing

Materials
- D-cell
- masking tape
- flashlight bulb in a socket
- thick lead from mechanical pencil
- uninsulated copper wire, the same length as the pencil lead
- rubber tubing, the same length as the pencil lead
- 1 wire, 10–15 cm long
- 2 wires, 20–30 cm long
- 2 alligator clips

Procedure
1. To make a device that can dim a light bulb, construct the circuit shown in the photo on the opposite page. To begin, attach wires to the ends of the D-cell.
2. Connect the other end of one of the wires to the bulb in a socket. Attach a wire with an alligator clip to the other side of the socket.
3. Attach an alligator clip to the other wire.
4. The pencil lead will serve as a resistor that can be varied—a variable resistor. Attach one alligator clip firmly to the tip of the pencil lead. Be sure the clip makes good contact with the lead. (*Note*: Pencil "lead" is actually graphite, a form of the element carbon.)
5. Predict how the brightness of the bulb will change as you slide the other alligator clip back and forth along the lead. Test your prediction.

Introduce the Procedure
Have students read through the entire procedure, and then answer any questions they have. Explain that pencil lead is not made of lead but graphite, a form of carbon.

Tell students that the drawing part of a pencil is called lead because people use to draw on paper with the metal lead before pencils were invented.

6. What will happen to the brightness of the bulb if you replace the lead with a piece of uninsulated copper wire? Adapt your pencil-lead investigation to test the copper wire.
7. Predict what will happen to the brightness of the bulb if you replace the pencil lead with a piece of rubber tubing. Adapt your pencil-lead investigation to test the rubber tubing.

Analyze and Conclude

1. **Controlling Variables** What variable did you manipulate by sliding the alligator clip along the pencil lead in Step 5?
2. **Observing** What happened to the brightness of the bulb when you slid the alligator clip along the pencil lead?
3. **Predicting** Explain your reasoning in making predictions about the brightness of the bulb in Steps 6 and 7. Were your predictions supported by your observations?
4. **Interpreting Data** Do you think that pencil lead has more or less resistance than copper? Do you think it has more or less resistance than rubber? Use your observations to explain your answers.
5. **Drawing Conclusions** Which material tested in this lab would make the best dimmer switch? Explain your answer.
6. **Communicating** Suppose you want to sell your dimmer switch to the owner of a theater. Write a product information sheet that describes your device and explains how it works.

More to Explore

The volume controls on some car radios and television sets contain resistors that can be varied, called rheostats. The sliding volume controls on a sound mixing board are rheostats as well. Homes and theaters may use rheostats to adjust lighting. Where else in your house would rheostats be useful? (*Hint*: Look for applications where you want to adjust a device gradually rather than just turn it on or off.)

Troubleshooting the Experiment

- Poor contact between alligator clips and the pencil lead can be improved by buffing the lead with sandpaper.
- To make a quantitative comparison of bulb brightness, students could use small pieces of paper through which they view the bulb. They can compare the brightness by how many pieces of paper they can see the bulb through. This procedure works best in a darkened room.

Expected Outcome

As students include more pencil lead in the circuit, the total resistance increases and current decreases, and so the bulb becomes dimmer. When students move the clips close together—making the circuit contain less pencil lead—the total resistance decreases and the bulb becomes brighter. Students will observe that the copper wire conducts well and the rubber tubing doesn't conduct at all.

Analyze and Conclude

1. Resistance. The amount of resistance increased as the length of pencil lead increased.

2. The bulb became dimmer as the length of lead in the circuit increased.

3. Sample answer: I reasoned that the brightness would increase in Step 6 because copper is an excellent conductor. I reasoned that the bulb would not light in Step 7 because rubber is an excellent insulator. My observations supported my predictions.

4. Sample answer: My tests showed that pencil lead has more resistance than copper and that rubber has such a high resistance that it did not conduct electric current at all.

5. Sample answer: Pencil lead. Copper wire would have to be very long to offer enough resistance, and rubber would not conduct current well enough.

6. Students' product information sheets should describe the dimmer device and explain how it works. Students also may explain how a dimmer switch could help a theater owner create pleasant, low-light conditions while trailers are being shown and moviegoers are moving in and out of their seats. A dimmer switch might also save money for the owner by decreasing their theaters' use of electrical energy.

Extend Inquiry

More to Explore Students should find that variable resistors are common and useful in household devices such as electric dryers, exercise treadmills, ceiling fans, and variable-speed tools.

Section 3 Batteries

Objectives

After this lesson, students will be able to

N.2.3.1 Describe what the first battery was made of.

N.2.3.2 Explain how an electrochemical cell works.

Target Reading Skill

Building Vocabulary Explain that knowing the definitions of key-concept words helps students understand what they read.

Answers

Sample definitions:

chemical energy the energy that chemical compounds store within the compounds; **chemical reaction** a process in which substances change into other substances with different properties than the original substances; **electrochemical cell** an electrical device that changes chemical energy into electrical energy; **electrode** a metal in an electrochemical cell that is covered with electrolyte; **electrolyte** a substance in an electrochemical cell through which current flows; **terminal** the electrode part that sticks up above the electrolyte; **battery** electrochemical cells in combination; **wet cell** an electrochemical cell that has liquid as its electrolyte; **dry cell** an electrochemical cell that has paste as its electrolyte

Preteach

Build Background Knowledge L2

Experience With Batteries

Ask: **What's inside a battery that you use in your portable CD player?** *(Sample answer: Some kind of chemical)* **Both a car battery and the batteries used in a flashlight are called batteries—what are the differences between them?** *(Sample answer: The car battery is much larger.)* **How do batteries provide the energy for devices?** *(Sample answer: Somehow, electrical energy is stored inside the battery.)* Explain that in this section students will learn what is inside batteries and how they provide electrical energy.

Section 3 Integrating Chemistry

Batteries

Reading Preview

Key Concepts

- What was the first battery made of?
- How does an electrochemical cell work?

Key Terms

- chemical energy
- chemical reaction
- electrochemical cell
- electrode • electrolyte
- terminal • battery
- wet cell • dry cell

Target Reading Skill

Building Vocabulary After you read the section, reread the paragraphs that contain definitions of Key Terms. Use the information you have learned to write a definition of each Key Term in your own words.

Lab zone Discover Activity

Can You Make Electricity Using a Penny?

1. Clean a penny with vinegar. Wash your hands.
2. Cut a 2-cm × 2-cm square from a paper towel and a similar square from aluminum foil.
3. Stir salt into a glass of warm water until the salt begins to sink to the bottom. Then soak the paper square in the salt water.
4. Put the penny on your desktop. Place the wet paper square on top of it. Then place the piece of aluminum foil on top of the paper.
5. Set a voltmeter to read DC volts. Touch the red lead to the penny and the black lead to the foil. Observe the reading on the voltmeter.

Think It Over

Observing What happened to the voltmeter? What type of device did you construct?

Using a headlamp for light ▼

When you finally step into camp, barely enough light is left to see the trees in front of you. But you must still set up your tent. You need more light. There are no generators or electric lines nearby. Where can you find enough electrical energy to produce some light? Fortunately, your headlamp contains a battery that provides electrical energy to its bulb. In this section, you'll find out how a battery produces electrical energy.

Lab zone Discover Activity

Skills Focus Observing L1

Materials penny, vinegar, scissors, paper towel, aluminum foil, salt, mixing cup, stirring rod, voltmeter

Time 15 minutes

Tips Make sure students mix the salt thoroughly with the water. The paper towel squares should be thoroughly soaked.

Expected Outcome The voltmeter will show a reading of about 3 volts when connected to the circuit.

Think It Over Sample answer: The voltmeter needle moved. The device is a type of battery, an energy source for an electric circuit.

The First Battery

Energy can be transformed from one form into another. For example, batteries transform chemical energy into electrical energy. **Chemical energy** is energy stored in chemical compounds.

Luigi Galvani The research that led to the development of the battery came about by accident. In the 1780s, an Italian physician named Luigi Galvani was studying the anatomy, or body structure, of a frog. He was using a brass hook to hold a leg muscle in place. As he touched one end of the hook to an iron railing, he noticed that the frog's leg twitched. Galvani hypothesized that there was some kind of "animal electricity" present only in living tissue. This hypothesis was later proven to be incorrect. However, Galvani's observations and hypothesis led to further research.

Alessandro Volta An Italian scientist named Alessandro Volta developed a different hypothesis to account for Galvani's observations. Volta argued that the electrical effect Galvani observed was actually a result of a chemical reaction. A **chemical reaction** is a process in which substances change into new substances with different properties. In this case, Volta hypothesized that a chemical reaction occurred between the two different metals (the iron railing and the brass hook) and the salty fluids in the frog's leg muscle.

To confirm his hypothesis, Volta placed a piece of paper that had been soaked in salt water in between a piece of zinc and a piece of silver. Volta found that if he connected wires to the silver and zinc, current was produced. Then he repeated the layers: zinc, paper, silver, zinc, and so on. When he added more layers, a greater current was produced. If you did the Discover activity, you did something similar to what Volta did.

Volta built the first electric battery by layering zinc, paper soaked in salt water, and silver. In 1800, he made his discovery public. Although his battery was much weaker than those made today, it produced a current for a relatively long period of time. Volta's battery was the basis of more powerful modern batteries.

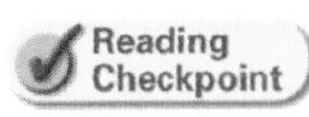

What is a chemical reaction?

FIGURE 13
The First Battery
Alessandro Volta demonstrates the first battery. **Interpreting Diagrams** *What materials made up Volta's battery?*

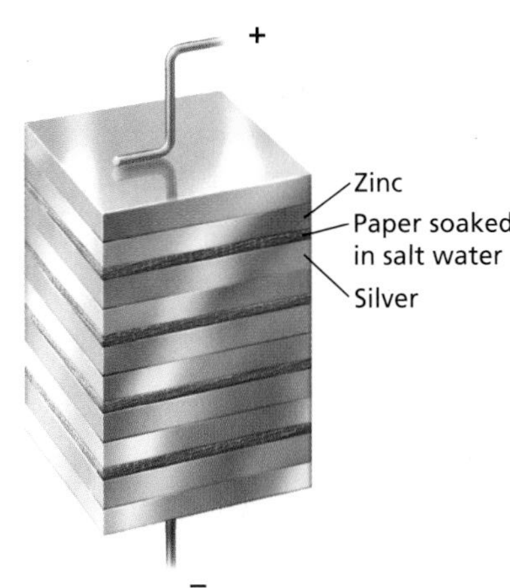

Instruct

The First Battery

Teach Key Concepts L2

Alessandro Volta

Focus Tell students that the first battery was developed in the late 1700s, at about the same time as the American Revolution was occurring.

Teach Ask: **Who developed the first battery?** *(Alessandro Volta)* **What was Volta's hypothesis about Galvani's observations?** *(A chemical reaction occurred between two metals and the salty fluids in the frog's leg muscle.)* **What materials did Volta's battery consist of?** *(Layers of zinc, paper soaked in saltwater, and silver)*

Apply Ask: **What was the major difference between Galvani's hypothesis and Volta's hypothesis?** *(Galvani believed that the frog itself produced the electrical effect he observed. Volta believed that chemical reaction took place between the metals and the frog.)* **learning modality: verbal**

Independent Practice L2

All in One Teaching Resources

- Guided Reading and Study Worksheet: *Batteries*

Student Edition on Audio CD

Differentiated Instruction

Less Proficient Readers L1

Communicating Have students use sketches, photographs, and short captions to create a visual display about uses of batteries. Tell students to draw ideas from the text and illustrations in the chapter. **learning modality: visual**

Special Needs L2

Observing Batteries For students who are visually impaired, provide an assortment of batteries of various sizes and shapes for them to handle. As students feel the batteries, point out the terminals and discuss what the electrolyte is in each kind of battery. **learning modality: kinesthetic**

Monitor Progress L2

Oral Presentation Call on students to describe the parts of Alessandro Volta's battery and explain how that battery produced an electric current.

Answers

Figure 13 Zinc, paper soaked in saltwater, and silver

Reading Checkpoint A process in which substances change into new substances with different properties.

Electrochemical Cells

Teach Key Concepts

Chemical Energy Into Electrical Energy

Focus Tell students that an electrochemical cell transforms chemical energy into electrical energy.

Teach Ask: **What is an electrode?** *(A metal in an electrochemical cell that is immersed in an electrolyte)* **What is an electrolyte?** *(A substance that conducts electric current)* **What does the chemical reaction between the electrolyte and the electrodes cause in the electrodes?** *(The chemical reaction causes one electrode to become negatively charged and the other electrode to become positively charged.)* **What are the two kinds of electrochemical cells?** *(Wet cell and dry cell)*

Apply Ask: **Is the battery you use to provide energy in a flashlight a wet cell or a dry cell?** *(Dry cell)* **What is the electrolyte in that kind of electrochemical cell?** *(Paste)* **learning modality: verbal**

All in One Teaching Resources

- Transparency N19

Build an Electrochemical Cell

Materials lemon, copper bar, zinc bar, connecting wires, galvanometer

Time 15 minutes

Focus Tell students that they will use the given materials to design and build an electrochemical cell.

Teach Divide the class into small groups, and challenge each group to design and build an electrochemical cell using a lemon. Ask: **What part of the cell might the lemon be?** *(The electrolyte)* Have groups determine how to use the other materials to build their cells.

Apply The cells each group builds may vary. A typical electrochemical cell would use the copper bar and the zinc bar as electrodes and the lemon as the electrolyte. Have students test their cells with the galvanometer. **learning modality: logical/mathematical**

FIGURE 14
An Electrochemical Cell
An electrochemical cell can make a complete circuit.

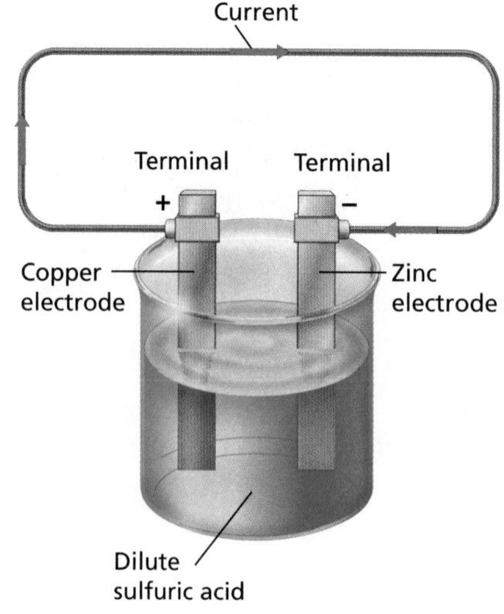

Electrochemical Cells

In Volta's setup, each pair of zinc and silver layers separated by paper soaked in salt water acted as an electrochemical cell. An **electrochemical cell** is a device that transforms chemical energy into electrical energy. An electrochemical cell consists of two different metals called **electrodes,** which are immersed in a substance called an electrolyte. An **electrolyte** is a substance that conducts electric current. Volta used silver and zinc as electrodes and salt water as his electrolyte.

A Simple Cell In the cell in Figure 14, the electrolyte is dilute sulfuric acid. Dilute means that the sulfuric acid has been mixed with water. One of the electrodes in this cell is made of copper and the other is made of zinc. The part of an electrode above the surface of the electrolyte is called a **terminal.** The terminals are used to connect the cell to a circuit.

Chemical reactions occur between the electrolyte and the electrodes in an electrochemical cell. These reactions cause one electrode to become negatively charged and the other electrode to become positively charged. Because the electrodes have opposite charges, there is a voltage between them. Recall that voltage causes charges to flow. If the terminals are connected by a wire, charge will flow from one terminal to the other. In other words, the electrochemical cell produces an electric current in the wire. Charges flow back through the electrolyte to make a complete circuit.

Batteries Several electrochemical cells can be stacked together to form a battery. A **battery** is a combination of two or more electrochemical cells in a series. Today, single cells are often referred to as "batteries." So the "batteries" you use in your flashlight are technically cells rather than batteries.

In a battery, two or more electrochemical cells are connected in series. This means the positive terminal of one cell is connected to the negative terminal of the next. The voltage of the battery is the sum of the voltages of the cells. You connect two cells in this way inside a flashlight. The total voltage of a battery is found by adding the voltages of the individual cells.

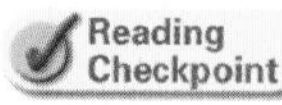

What is a battery?

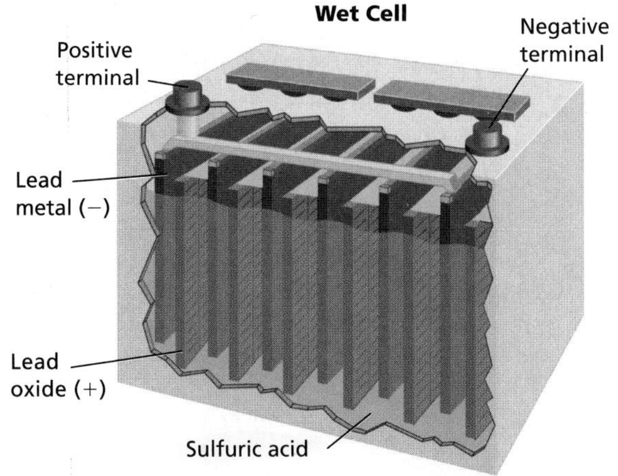

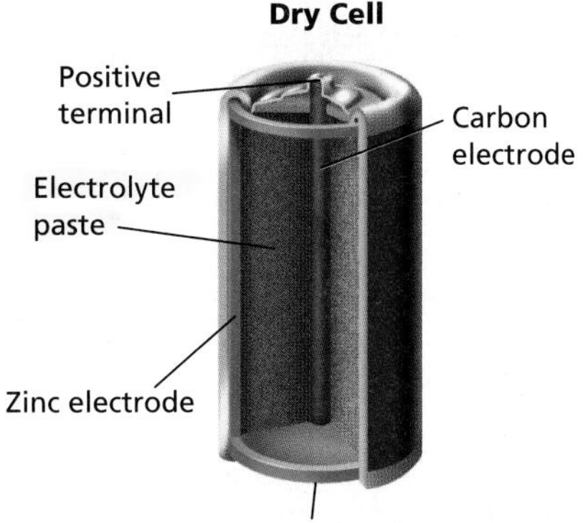

FIGURE 15
Wet and Dry Cells
The wet electrolyte in the car battery on the left is sulfuric acid. The diagram on the right shows the parts of a typical dry cell. The electrolyte is not really dry — it is a paste.

Wet Cells There are two kinds of electrochemical cells: wet cells and dry cells. An electrochemical cell in which the electrolyte is a liquid is a **wet cell.** Volta's battery consisted of wet cells because the electrolyte was salt water. The 12-volt automobile battery in Figure 15 consists of six wet cells. In this case, the electrolyte is sulfuric acid.

Dry Cells Flashlights and many other devices use dry cells. A **dry cell** is an electrochemical cell in which the electrolyte is a paste. Figure 15 shows the parts of a dry cell.

Section 3 Assessment

Target Reading Skill Building Vocabulary Use your definitions to help answer the questions.

Reviewing Key Concepts

1. a. **Describing** Describe the parts of Volta's battery and how they were arranged.
   b. **Explaining** What happened when Volta connected the parts of his cells in a circuit?
   c. **Relating Cause and Effect** What caused the event in Question b to happen?
   d. **Explaining** Explain how Volta used Galvani's observations to develop a relationship between chemical energy and electrical energy.
2. a. **Listing** What are the parts of an electrochemical cell?
   b. **Summarizing** Summarize how the parts of a cell interact to produce a current.
   c. **Predicting** Would a current be produced if both terminals had the same charge? Explain your answer.

Lab zone At-Home Activity

Reviving Old Cells Test a flashlight with two old D-cells and observe its brightness. Then ask a family member to remove the D-cells and place them in direct sunlight to warm up. After an hour or more, use the cells to test the flashlight. Compare the brightness of the bulb in the two tests. Explain what your observations indicate about the chemical reactions in the battery.

Lab zone At-Home Activity

Reviving Old Cells L1 After the batteries warm in the sunlight, they will light the bulb brightly, though the bulb may quickly dim again. Chemical reactions occur faster at higher temperatures, and so the warm D-cells produce more current, quickly depleting the energy of the cells as the chemical reactions occur.

 **Teaching Resources**

- Transparency N20

Monitor Progress L2

Answer

 A battery is a combination of two or more electrochemical cells in a series.

Assess

Reviewing Key Concepts

1. a. Volta's battery consisted of three repeated layers: a piece of zinc, a piece of paper soaked in saltwater, and a piece of silver. A wire connected the top and bottom metal layers. **b.** There was a current. **c.** Chemical reactions caused some metal layers to become negatively charged and other metal layers to become positively charged. **d.** Volta showed how chemical energy could be transformed into electrical energy.

2. a. An electrochemical cell consists of two different metals called electrodes, which are immersed in a substance called an electrolyte, and two terminals. **b.** One electrode reacts with the electrolyte and becomes negatively charged. The other electrode reacts with the electrolyte and becomes positively charged. A voltage between the electrodes causes charges to flow. If the terminals are connected by a wire, charges will flow from one terminal to the other. **c.** No. If both had the same charge, no voltage would exist between the two terminals. If no voltage exists, no current is produced.

Reteach L1

Use Figure 14 to reteach concepts related to batteries, including how an electrochemical cell transforms chemical energy into electrical energy.

Performance Assessment L2

Writing Have students write a paragraph that lists the parts of an electrochemical cell and describes the function of each part.

All in One Teaching Resources

- Section Summary: *Batteries*
- Review and Reinforce: *Batteries*
- Enrich: *Batteries*

Lab zone Consumer Lab

Build a Flashlight L2

Prepare for Inquiry

Key Concept

In order for bulbs to light, they must be part of a complete circuit. The bulb must be connected so that the current travels through the filament.

Skills Objectives

After this lab, students will be able to:

- make model flashlights that include a complete electric circuit
- predict the arrangement of circuit components that will function as the best flashlight circuit
- design a better switch

Prep Time 15 minutes
Class Time 40 minutes

Advance Planning

Have students collect and bring in cardboard tubes from paper towels and/or bathroom tissue. Have several different types of commercial flashlights available for students to examine.

Alternative Materials

Provide aluminum foil baking cups instead of having students make their own reflectors.

Safety

Remind students to be careful when using scissors. Make sure they wear safety goggles throughout the lab. Caution students to handle the glass light bulbs gently, as broken bulbs can produce serious cuts. Review the safety guidelines in Appendix A.

All in One Teaching Resources

- Lab Worksheet: *Build a Flashlight*

Guide Inquiry

Introduce the Procedure

Have students examine the photo of the students working on the flashlight. Make sure students can identify all the components needed to construct a complete circuit.

Lab zone Consumer Lab

Build a Flashlight

Problem

How can you use a battery to build a working flashlight?

Skills Focus

making models, observing, inferring

Materials

- one cardboard tube
- one D-cell
- flashlight bulb
- aluminum foil
- paper cup
- duct tape
- scissors
- 2 lengths of wire, about 10 cm each, with the insulation stripped off about 2 cm at each end
- 1 length of wire, 15–20 cm, with the insulation stripped off each end

Procedure   

1. Check that the D-cell fits inside the cardboard tube. Make two holes in the side of the tube about 2–3 cm apart. The holes should be near the middle of the tube.
2. Use duct tape to connect a 10-cm wire to each terminal of the battery. Touch the other ends of the wires to a flashlight bulb in order to find where to connect them. (*Hint*: Most bulbs have a bottom contact and a side contact. If there is no obvious side contact, try touching the metal on the side of the base.)
3. Line a paper cup with aluminum foil. Use a pencil to poke a hole in the bottom of the paper cup. The hole should be slightly smaller than the bulb, but large enough to allow the base of the bulb through.
4. Insert the base of the light bulb through the hole. Be sure the bulb fits securely.
5. Pass the long wire through one of the holes in the tube. Tape it to the inside of the tube, leaving about 2 cm outside the tube. The other end should reach the end of the tube.
6. Place the battery in the tube. Pass the wire attached to the bottom of the battery through the other hole in the tube. (Make sure the two wires outside the tube can touch.)
7. Make a sling from duct tape to hold the battery inside the tube.
8. Attach the wires from the end of the tube to the contact points on the bulb.
9. Tape the cup on top of the tube, keeping all connections tight.
10. Touch the two free ends of the wires together to see if the bulb lights. If it doesn't, check to be sure all connections are taped together securely.

58 ◆ N

Troubleshooting the Experiment

- If the bulb does not light, check to see that connections are making firm contact. Test the bulb to be certain it is not burned out. Test the battery to make sure it can light the bulb.
- Students may find it easier to construct the flashlight if they cut the tube open lengthwise on the side opposite the two wire holes. This will help them see the relative positioning of the various components. This may also help in fitting the battery in the tube.

Expected Outcome

Students should make a flashlight that includes a complete electric circuit.

Analyze and Conclude

1. **Inferring** What is the purpose of lining the cup with aluminum foil?
2. **Drawing Conclusions** Does it matter which way the battery is placed in the tube? Explain.
3. **Making Models** Why does the bulb have to be connected at two points in order for it to light?
4. **Drawing Conclusions** How could you make your flashlight brighter? How could you make it more rugged?
5. **Observing** Compare your flashlight to a manufactured one. Explain the differences.
6. **Communicating** Write an advertisement for your flashlight. In your ad, list the features of your flashlight and explain why a consumer should buy it.

Design an Experiment

People use different types of flashlights for different purposes. Some are narrow and flexible while others are wide and sturdy. Compare several different flashlights. Describe the flashlights. Note the type and number of batteries required, the type of switch used, and any other features that you observe. Suggest useful applications for each flashlight. Then design a new flashlight based on a need that you observe.

Analyze and Conclude

1. The aluminum foil is the reflector for this flashlight. It reflects some of the light forward for better illumination.
2. No. The orientation of the battery affects only the direction of the current. The bulb will light if current is flowing in either direction.
3. The circuit must include the bulb filament, so the bulb must be connected at both contact points.
4. To make a brighter bulb, add more batteries or use a different type of bulb. To make the flashlight stronger, use a plastic or metal case, or wrap something around the cardboard for more strength.
5. In the commercial flashlight, there is a permanent switch that is easy to operate; the case is plastic or metal; the bulb can be easily removed and replaced. Commercial flashlights must be durable and reliable, and operate in a variety of situations.
6. Students' advertisements will vary. The advertisements should include a description of how the flashlight works, and special features of the flashlight.

Extend Inquiry

Design an Experiment Ask students to describe situations in which people rely on flashlights *(Sample: Camping trips, power outages, emergencies)* Show them a variety of flashlights (disposable, common hand-held, camping lantern). Ask students to compare and contrast the flashlights by observing them closely and carefully. Encourage students to determine which flashlights would be best for each situation. Students should use what they learn in this discussion to design a flashlight for a specific purpose.

Objectives

After this lesson, students will be able to

N.2.4.1 Explain what Ohm's law is.

N.2.4.2 Describe the basic features of an electric circuit.

N.2.4.3 Identify how many paths currents can take in series and parallel circuits.

Target Reading Skill

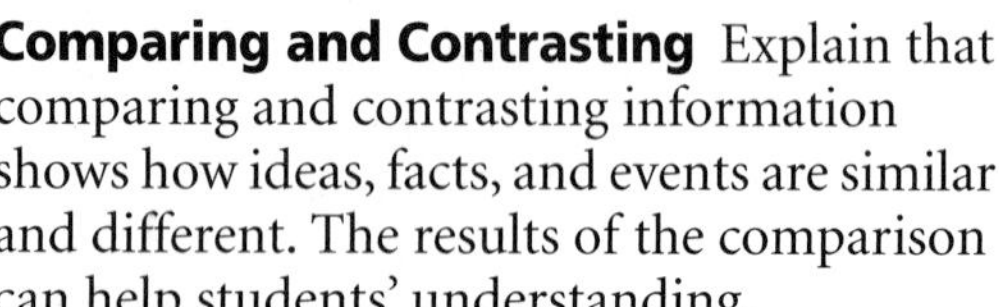

Comparing and Contrasting Explain that comparing and contrasting information shows how ideas, facts, and events are similar and different. The results of the comparison can help students' understanding.

Answers

Sample answers:

Series Circuit: Only one path for current to take

Overlap: Unbroken path that has a current

Parallel Circuit: There are several paths for current to take

All in One Teaching Resources

- Transparency N21

Preteach

Build Background Knowledge

L2

Experience With Circuits

Help students recall their experiences with electric circuits. Ask: **What happens if the wire is cut between the wall switch and a ceiling light at home?** *(The light cannot be turned on.)* **If that wire were cut between the switch and the light, would all the other lights in your home go out as well?** *(No. They could still be turned on.)*

Section 4 Electric Circuits

Reading Preview

Key Concepts

- What is Ohm's law?
- What are the basic features of an electric circuit?
- How many paths can currents take in series and parallel circuits?

Key Terms

- Ohm's law
- series circuit
- ammeter
- parallel circuit
- voltmeter

Target Reading Skill

Comparing and Contrasting

As you read, compare and contrast series circuits and parallel circuits in a Venn diagram like the one below. Write the similarities in the space where the circles overlap and the differences on the left and right sides.

Series Circuit | Parallel Circuit

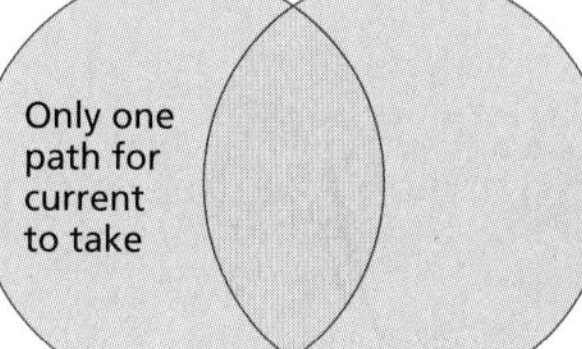

Lab zone Discover Activity

Do the Lights Keep Shining?

1. Construct both of the circuits shown using a battery, several insulated wires, and two light bulbs for each circuit.
2. Connect all wires and observe the light bulbs.
3. Now unscrew one bulb in each circuit. Observe the remaining bulbs.

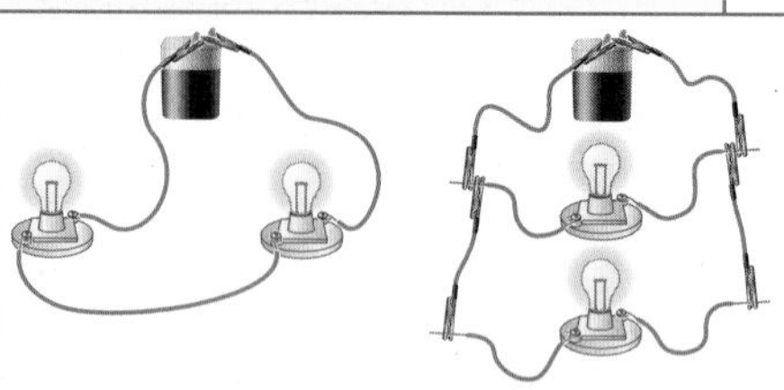

Think It Over

Observing What happened to the remaining light bulbs when you unscrewed one bulb? How can you account for your observations?

It's a cool, clear night as you stroll along the river with your family. The city is brightly lit, and the river water sparkles with reflected light. In addition to the lights at the top of the lampposts, a string of lights borders the river path. They make a striking view.

As you walk, you notice that a few of the lights in the string are burned out. The rest of the lights, however, burn brightly. If one bulb is burned out, how can the rest of the lights continue to shine? The answer depends on how the electric circuit is designed.

Although most lights are shining, some lights are burned out. ▶

Lab zone Discover Activity

Skills Focus Observing

L2

Materials 4 light bulbs with sockets, 2 dry cells with holders, several lengths of insulated wire, alligator clips

Time 15 minutes

Tips Remove insulation from ends of wire. You may want to have students include a switch in their circuits.

Think It Over Sample answer: In one circuit, the remaining bulb went out. Current stopped because the circuit contained only one path. In the other circuit, the remaining bulb stayed lit. That circuit contained a second path for the current.

Ohm's Law

To understand electric circuits, you need to understand how current, voltage, and resistance are related to one another. In the 1800s, Georg Ohm performed experiments that demonstrated how those three factors are related. Ohm experimented with many substances while studying electrical resistance. He analyzed different types of wire in order to determine the characteristics that affect a wire's resistance.

Ohm's Results Ohm set up a circuit with a voltage between two points on a conductor. He measured the resistance of the conductor and the current between those points. Then he varied the voltage and took new measurements.

Ohm found that if the factors that affect resistance are held constant, the resistance of most conductors does not depend on the voltage across them. Changing the voltage in a circuit changes the current, but will not change the resistance. Ohm concluded that conductors and most other devices have a constant resistance regardless of the applied voltage.

Calculating With Ohm's Law The relationship between resistance, voltage, and current is summed up in **Ohm's law. Ohm's law says that the resistance is equal to the voltage divided by the current.**

This relationship can be represented by the equation below:

$$\text{Resistance} = \frac{\text{Voltage}}{\text{Current}}$$

The units are ohms (Ω) = volts (V) ÷ amps (A). You can rearrange Ohm's law as follows:

$$\text{Voltage} = \text{Current} \times \text{Resistance}$$

You can use the formula to see how changes in resistance, voltage, and current are related. For example, what happens to current if voltage is doubled without changing the resistance? For a constant resistance, if voltage is doubled, current is doubled as well.

Decimals

When calculating voltage, you often use decimals. When you multiply two decimals, the number of decimal places in the product is the sum of the number of decimal places in each decimal you multiply.

If a circuit has a resistance of 30.5 ohms and a current of 0.05 amps, what is its voltage?

$$30.5 \text{ ohms} \times \frac{0.05 \text{ amps}}{1.525 \text{ volts}}$$

Practice Problems Use Ohm's law to calculate the voltage of a circuit with a resistance of 15.2 ohms and a current of 0.10 amps.

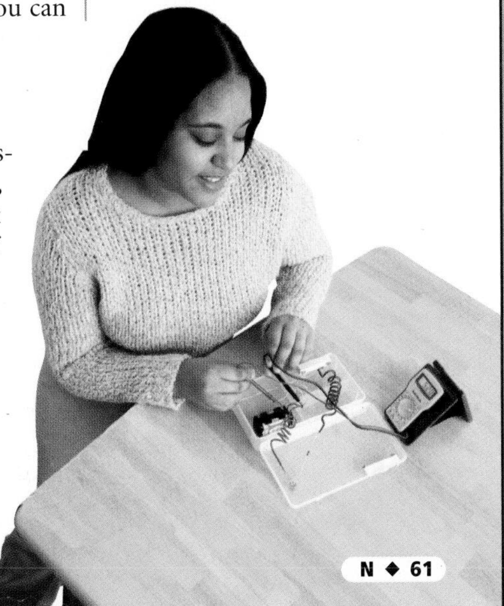

FIGURE 16
Measuring Factors in a Circuit
You can use a meter to measure voltage, current, and resistance. **Measuring** *What units are used to measure current and voltage?*

Instruct

Ohm's Law

Teach Key Concepts L2

Resistance, Voltage, and Current

Focus Explain to students that Ohm's law is about how resistance, voltage, and current are related to one another.

Teach Recall for students that the amount of charges that pass through a wire in a unit of time is the rate of electric current. Ask: **What is the unit for the rate of current?** *(Ampere, or amp)* **How does changing the voltage—the potential difference—in a circuit affect the current and the resistance in the circuit?** *(Changing the voltage changes the current, but will not change the resistance.)* **What does Ohm's law say?** *(Resistance is equal to the voltage divided by the current.)*

Apply Explain that by manipulating the values in the equation used to represent Ohm's law, any of the three values can be calculated as long as you know the other two. Ask: **What is the equation you would use to find voltage?** *(V = IR)* **What is the equation you would use to find current?** *(I = V/R)*
learning modality: logical/mathematical

Independent Practice L2

All in One Teaching Resources

- Guided Reading and Study Worksheet: *Electric Circuits*

Student Edition on Audio CD

Math Skills

Math Skill Decimals

Focus Ask students to look at the equations for Ohm's Law.

Teach Remind students that when multiplying decimals to calculate voltage the number of decimal places in the product is the sum of the number of decimal places in each number being multiplied. Refer students who need additional help to the Decimals review section of the Skills Handbook.

Answer 1.52 volts

Monitor Progress L2

Writing Ask students to write the formulas they would use to calculate each of three values in a circuit: resistance, voltage, and current.

Answer
Figure 16 Current is measured in amps, and voltage is measured in volts.

Math Sample Problem

Math Skill Formulas and equations

Focus Tell students that to calculate the resistance in a circuit, they will divide the voltage by the current. This often involves dividing a whole number by a decimal number. Review this skill by solving a division problem on the board, such as 6 divided by 0.3 *(6 ÷ 0.3 = 20).*

Teach Some students might understand the problem better if they make a drawing of a car, with a battery, a brake light, and a wire in between. Have students label the battery as 12 volts and label the wire as 0.40 amps. Ask: **What is being calculated in this problem?** *(Resistance)* **What values are given?** *(Current and voltage)* **What is the formula used to solve the problem?** *(R = V/I)* **What is the unit used for the answer?** *(Ohms)* **Why is the answer greater than either number in the fraction?** *(You are dividing the voltage by a fraction.)*

Answers

1. 8.0 Ω *(4.0 V ÷ 0.5 A)*
2. 120 V *(12 A × 10 Ω)*

All in One Teaching Resources

- Transparency N22

Features of a Circuit

Teach Key Concepts L2

Basic Features of a Circuit

Focus Tell student that there are three basic features that all electric circuits have.

Teach Ask: **What are some examples of devices that are run by electrical energy?** *(Sample answer: Radio, CD player, light bulb)* **What are sources of electrical energy we use to supply energy to those devices?** *(Batteries, generators, and electric plants)* **What connects electric circuits?** *(Wires)*

Apply Have students look at the circuit in Figure 17, and ask: **What is the device, or resistor, in this circuit?** *(The light bulb)* **What is the source of electrical energy?** *(The battery)* **What connects this electric circuit?** *(Wires)* **learning modality: visual**

Math Sample Problem

Calculating Resistance

The brake light on an automobile is connected to a 12-volt battery. If the resulting current is 0.40 amps, what is the resistance of the brake light?

1 Read and Understand

What information are you given?

Battery Voltage = 12 V

Current = 0.40 A

2 Plan and Solve

What quantity are you trying to calculate?

The resistance of the brake light.

What formula contains the given quantities and the unknown quantity?

$$\text{Resistance} = \frac{\text{Voltage}}{\text{Current}}$$

Perform the calculation.

$$\text{Resistance} = \frac{12\ \text{V}}{0.40\ \text{A}} = 30\ \Omega$$

3 Look Back and Check

Does the answer make sense?

The answer makes sense because you are dividing the voltage by a decimal. The answer should be greater than either number in the fraction, which it is.

Math Practice

1. In a circuit, there is a 0.5-A current in the bulb. The voltage across the bulb is 4.0 V. What is the bulb's resistance?
2. A waffle iron has a 12-A current. If the resistance of the coils is 10 Ω, what must the voltage be?

Features of a Circuit

All electric circuits have the same basic features. **First, circuits have devices that are run by electrical energy.** A radio, a computer, a light bulb, and a refrigerator are all devices that transform electrical energy into another form of energy. A light bulb, for example, transforms electrical energy into electromagnetic energy by giving off light. The light bulb also produces thermal energy by giving off heat. By making fan blades rotate, electric fans transform electrical energy to mechanical energy. Devices such as light bulbs and fans resist the flow of electric current. They are therefore represented as resistors in a circuit.

Second, a circuit has a source of electrical energy. Batteries, generators, and electric plants all supply energy to circuits. Recall that energy is the ability to do work. The source of electrical energy makes charges move around a circuit, allowing the device to do work.

Third, electric circuits are connected by conducting wires. The conducting wires complete the path of the current. They allow charges to flow from the energy source to the device that runs on electric current and back to the energy source. A switch is often included in a circuit to control the current in the circuit. Using a switch, you can turn a device on or off by closing or opening the circuit.

Notice that all the parts of a circuit are shown in Figure 17. Each part shown in the photograph is represented in the diagram by a simple symbol. Arrows indicate the direction of current. The + and – on the battery indicate the positive and negative terminals.

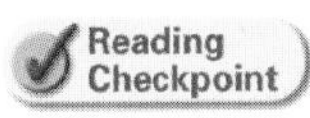
Reading Checkpoint

What is the function of conducting wires in a circuit?

Figure 17
Diagraming a Circuit
Simple symbols make it easy to diagram a circuit. The resistor represents the device that is being run by the current. Resistors include light bulbs, appliances, and huge machines.
Interpreting Diagrams *Which symbol is used to represent a battery?*

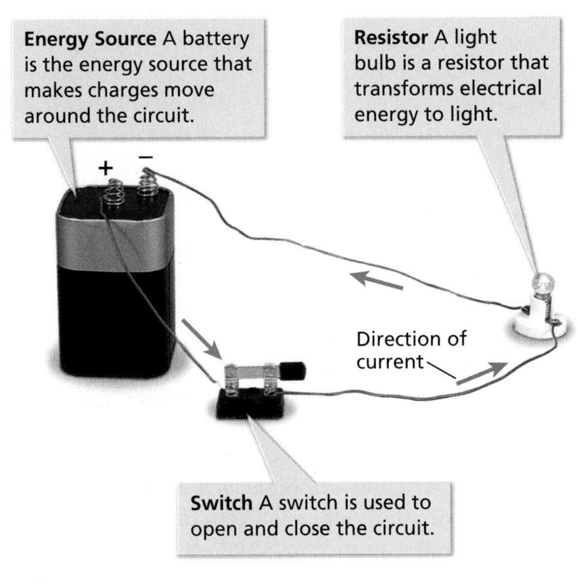
Energy Source A battery is the energy source that makes charges move around the circuit.
Resistor A light bulb is a resistor that transforms electrical energy to light.
+
–
Direction of current
Switch A switch is used to open and close the circuit.

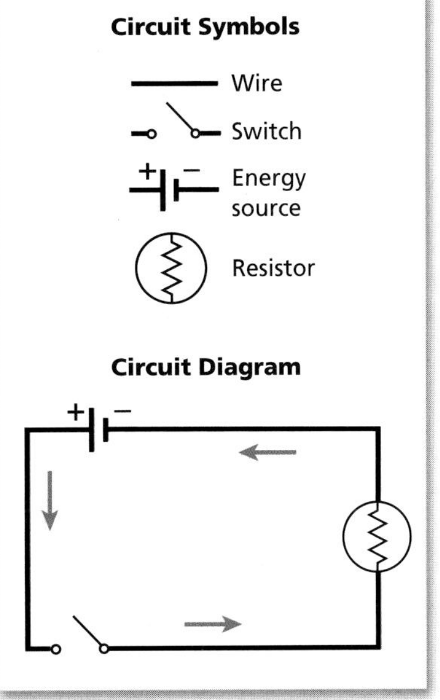
Circuit Symbols
Wire
Switch
Energy source
Resistor
Circuit Diagram

Lab zone Teacher Demo L1

A Switch in an Electric Circuit

Materials 3 wires (20 cm long with insulation stripped from the ends), contact switch, light bulb, bulb holder, D-cell (1.5 volt)

Time 5 minutes

Focus Tell students this demonstration will allow them to observe how a switch is used in an electric circuit.

Teach Make a circuit using the contact switch, bulb, battery, and wires. Ask: **How does the switch operate to light the bulb?** *(Sample answer: The switch is a conductor that, when closed, allows a current, and lights the bulb.)* **What happens when the switch is opened?** *(The switch breaks the circuit, stopping the electric current.)*

Apply Have students draw a diagram of the circuit you made that incorporates all the components, including the switch, used in the circuit. Suggest students consult the Circuit Symbols inset in Figure 17 for the symbols to use in their diagrams. **learning modality: visual**

All in One Teaching Resources

- Transparency N23

Differentiated Instruction

English Learners/Beginning L1
Comprehension: Link to Visual Guide students in using Figure 17 to learn about the features of a circuit. Explain the labels in the figure, and point out the relevant parts of the pictured circuit. Also, direct their attention to the list of circuit symbols used. **learning modality: visual**

English Learners/Intermediate L2
Comprehension: Ask Questions After students have read the information on features of an electric circuit, ask them to explain in their own words why circuits have devices, need a source of electrical energy, and are connected by conducting wires. If students make any errors, direct them to reread the relevant labels in Figure 17. **learning modality: verbal**

Monitor Progress L2

Writing Ask students to write a description of an electric circuit that includes the three basic features that all electric circuits have.

Answers

Figure 17 The symbol for energy source represents a battery.

Reading Checkpoint

The conducting wires complete the path of the current.

Series Circuits

Teach Key Concepts

L2

A Circuit With One Path

Focus Tell students that there are two main types of electric circuits, the series circuit and the parallel circuit.

Teach Ask: **In a series circuit, how many paths can the current take?** *(One)* Explain that a disadvantage of a series circuit is that the more resistors there are in the circuit, the less the current, given the same voltage. Ask: **What device is used to measure current?** *(An ammeter)*

Apply Have students use their fingers to trace the path current can take in the series circuit diagram in Figure 18. Ask: **How many resistors are there in this circuit?** *(Three)* **What happens if one of the resistors stops working, such as when a bulb burns out?** *(The circuit would be broken, and the other resistors would stop working.)*

Extend The ***Active Art*** will show students that a series circuit provides only one path for the flow of electrons. **learning modality: visual**

For: Series and Parallel Circuits activity
Visit: PHSchool.com
Web Code: cgp-4023

Students can interact with the art of series and parallel circuits online.

All in One Teaching Resources

- Transparency N24

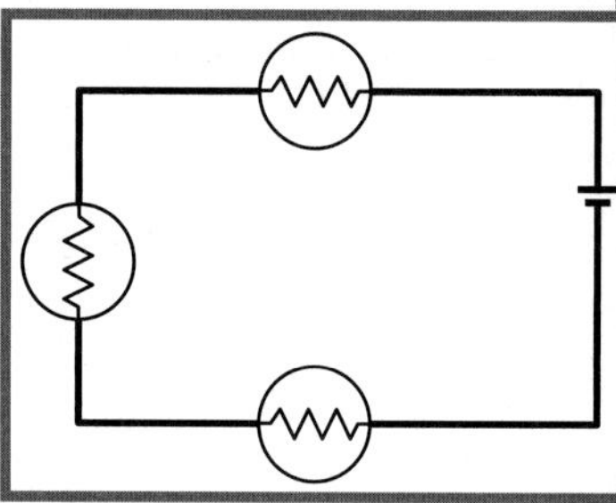

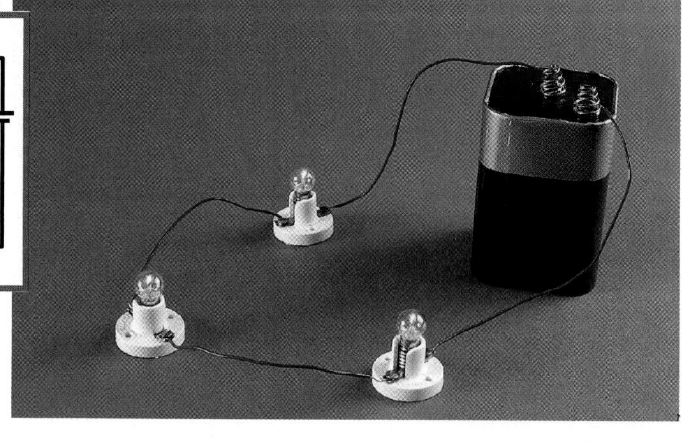

FIGURE 18
A Series Circuit
A series circuit provides only one path for the flow of electrons. **Predicting** *What will happen in a series circuit if one bulb burns out?*

For: Series and Parallel Circuits Activity
Visit: PHSchool.com
Web Code: cgp-4023

Series Circuits

If all the parts of an electric circuit are connected one after another along one path, the circuit is called a **series circuit.** Figure 18 illustrates a series circuit. **In a series circuit, there is only one path for the current to take.** For example, a switch and two light bulbs connected by a single wire are in series with each other.

One Path A series circuit is very simple to design and build, but it has some disadvantages. What happens if a light bulb in a series circuit burns out? A burned-out bulb is a break in the circuit, and there is no other path for the current to take. So if one light goes out, the other lights go out as well.

Resistors in a Series Circuit Another disadvantage of a series circuit is that the light bulbs in the circuit become dimmer as more bulbs are added. Why does that happen? A light bulb is a type of resistor. Think about what happens to the overall resistance of a series circuit as you add more bulbs. The resistance increases. Remember that for a constant voltage, if resistance increases, current decreases. So as light bulbs are added to a series circuit, the current decreases. The result is that the bulbs burn less brightly.

Measuring Current An **ammeter** is a device used to measure current. If you want to measure the current through some device in a circuit, the ammeter should be connected in series with that device.

How does resistance change as you add bulbs to a series circuit?

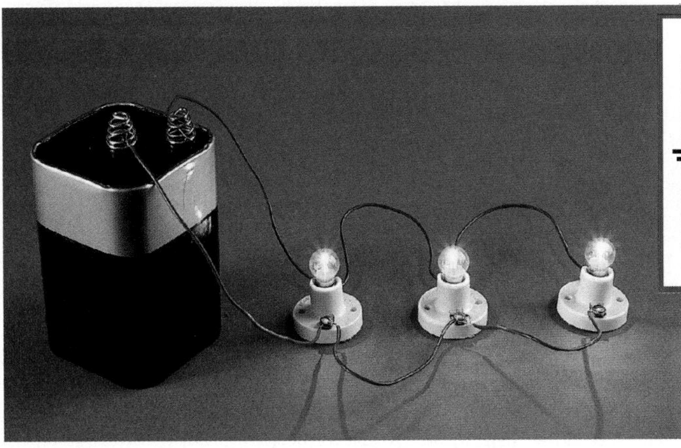

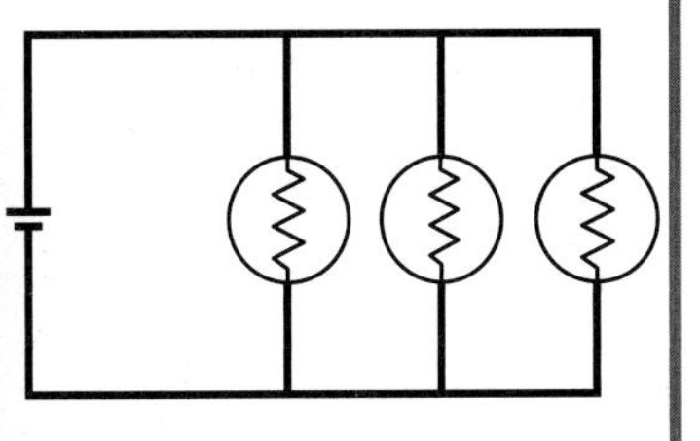

FIGURE 19
A Parallel Circuit
A parallel circuit provides several paths for the flow of electrons. **Predicting** *What will happen in a parallel circuit if one bulb burns out?*

Parallel Circuits

As you gaze at a string of lights, you observe that some bulbs burn brightly, but others are burned out. Your observation tells you that these bulbs are connected in a parallel circuit. In a **parallel circuit,** the different parts of the circuit are on separate branches. Figure 19 shows a parallel circuit. **In a parallel circuit, there are several paths for current to take.** Each bulb is connected by a separate path from the battery and back to the battery.

Several Paths What happens if a light burns out in a parallel circuit? If there is a break in one branch, charges can still move through the other branches. So if one bulb goes out, the others remain lit. Switches can be added to each branch to turn lights on and off without affecting the other branches.

Resistors in a Parallel Circuit What happens to the resistance of a parallel circuit when you add a branch? The overall resistance actually decreases. To understand why this happens, consider blowing through a single straw. The straw resists the flow of air so that only a certain amount of air comes out. However, if you use two straws, twice as much air can flow. The more straws you have, the more paths the air has to follow. The air encounters less resistance. As new branches are added to a parallel circuit, the electric current has more paths to follow, so the overall resistance decreases.

Remember that for a given voltage, if resistance decreases, current increases. The additional current travels along each new branch without affecting the original branches. So as you add branches to a parallel circuit, the brightness of the light bulbs does not change.

Lab zone Skills Activity

Predicting

1. Look at the circuit diagram below. Predict whether all three light bulbs will shine with the same brightness.

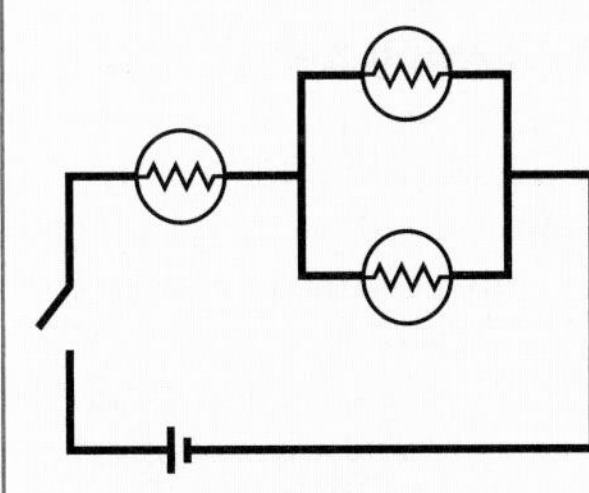

2. Construct the circuit using a battery and three identical light bulbs. Observe the brightness of the bulbs.

Does this circuit behave like a parallel circuit or a series circuit? Explain.

Parallel Circuits

Teach Key Concepts L2

A Circuit With Several Paths

Focus Tell students that in a parallel circuit, different branches allow a current in any of several paths.

Teach Ask: **How is a parallel circuit different from a series circuit?** *(In a series circuit, there is only one path for the current. In a parallel circuit, there are several paths.)* **If you add another branch to a parallel circuit, why does the resistance decrease?** *(An added branch decreases the resistance because the electric current has one more path to follow.)*

Apply Have students use their fingers to trace the paths current can take in the parallel circuit diagram in Figure 19. Ask: **How many resistors are there in this circuit?** *(Three)* **What happens if one of the resistors stops working, such as when a bulb burns out?** *(The circuit would not be broken because there is more than one path for the current. The other resistors would still keep working.)* **learning modality: visual**

Lab zone Skills Activity

Skills Focus Predicting L2

Materials dry cell, 3 light bulbs, insulated wire, switch

Time 15 minutes

Tips Help students recognize that this circuit contains one bulb in series and two bulbs in parallel.

Expected Outcome Sample answer: The circuit behaves like both types because it contains one bulb in series and two bulbs in parallel. The series bulb is brighter than the two parallel bulbs because the series bulb carries the same amount of current that the two parallel bulbs share.

Extend Have students predict what would happen if another bulb were added to the parallel circuit. **learning modality: logical/mathematical**

Monitor Progress 

Oral Presentation Call on students to name one advantage and one disadvantage each for a series circuit and a parallel circuit.

Answers

Figure 18 The other lights will go out as well.

Figure 19 The other bulbs will remain lit.

 The total resistance increases as you add bulbs to a series circuit.

Monitor Progress L2

Answer

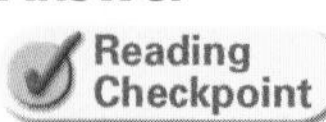

A parallel circuit

Assess

Reviewing Key Concepts

1. a. Ohm investigated resistance, voltage, and current. **b.** Resistance is equal to voltage divided by current. **c.** The current will be multiplied four times, too.
2. a. An electric circuit has one or more devices run by electrical energy, a source of electrical energy, and conducting wires.
b. Students should represent each feature of the circuit using the appropriate symbol.
c. Students' circuit diagrams should be much like the one shown in Figure 18, except that the resistor will be located between the switch and the positive terminal of the energy source.
3. a. A series circuit is one in which there is only one path for the current. A parallel circuit is one in which there are several paths for the current. **b.** The lights are in a series circuit. The current stops because part of its path has been removed.

Reteach L1

Draw circuit diagrams on four different cards—two series circuits and two parallel circuits. Make sure that the components of each diagram are only in series or only in parallel. Hold up one card at a time, and ask students to identify the type of circuit shown.

Performance Assessment L2

Drawing Have students draw two circuit diagrams—one that shows three bulbs in a series circuit and one that shows three bulbs in a parallel circuit.

Students can save their circuit diagrams in their portfolios. Portfolio

All in One Teaching Resources

- Section Summary: *Electric Circuits*
- Review and Reinforce: *Electric Circuits*
- Enrich: *Electric Circuits*

FIGURE 20
Household Circuits
Homes and businesses are wired with parallel circuits. That means that other appliances will stay on if the bulb in one light burns out.

Measuring Voltage A **voltmeter** is a device used to measure voltage, or electrical potential energy difference. When you measure the voltage of a device, the voltmeter and the device should be wired as a parallel circuit.

Household Circuits Would you want the circuits in your home to be series circuits? Of course not. With a series circuit, all the electrical devices in your home would stop working every time a switch was turned off or a light bulb burned out. Instead, the circuits in your home are parallel circuits.

Electrical energy enters a home through heavy-duty wires. These heavy-duty wires have very low resistance. Parallel branches extend out from the heavy-duty wires to wall sockets, and then to appliances and lights in each room. Switches are installed to control one branch of the circuit at a time. The voltage in most household circuits is 120 volts.

Reading Checkpoint **The wiring in your house forms what kind of circuit?**

Section 4 Assessment

Target Reading Skill Comparing and Contrasting Use the information in your Venn diagram about series and parallel circuits to help you answer Question 3.

Reviewing Key Concepts

1. a. **Reviewing** What three related electrical factors did Georg Ohm investigate?
   b. **Explaining** What did Ohm discover about the relationship between these three factors?
   c. **Predicting** In a circuit with a constant resistance, what will happen to the current if the voltage is multiplied four times?
2. a. **Listing** List three basic features of an electric circuit.
   b. **Interpreting Diagrams** Use Figure 17 to show how each feature is represented in a circuit diagram.
   c. **Applying Concepts** Draw a diagram of a circuit that includes one resistor. The resistor is located between the switch and the positive terminal of the energy source.
3. a. **Comparing and Contrasting** Compare and contrast series and parallel circuits.
   b. **Relating Cause and Effect** If you remove one bulb from a string of lights, all the remaining lights will go out. Are the lights in a series circuit or parallel circuit? Explain.

Math Practice

4. **Calculating Resistance** The current through a resistor of unknown value is 0.025 A when it is connected to a 10.0-V source. What is the value of the resistor?
5. **Calculating Resistance** Suppose that the voltage remains the same as in Question 4, and the current changes to 0.031 A. What is the new value of the resistor?

Math Practice

Answers
4. 400 Ω *(10.0 V ÷ 0.025 A)*
5. 322.58 Ω *(10.0 V ÷ 0.031 A)*

Lab zone Chapter Project

Keep Students on Track Check to see that students have begun to test their alarm circuits. If students are having a hard time getting their switches to work properly, help them by providing hints on how to get the two ends of the wires to make electrical contact. Most completed circuits will be in a primitive form on a desktop. Encourage students to improve these designs.

Section 5

Electric Power

Reading Preview

Key Concepts

- How do you calculate electric power?
- What factors are used to determine how people pay for electrical energy?

Key Term

- power

Target Reading Skill

Asking Questions Before you read, preview the red headings. In a graphic organizer like the one below, ask a *what* or *how* question for each heading. As you read, write the answer to your questions.

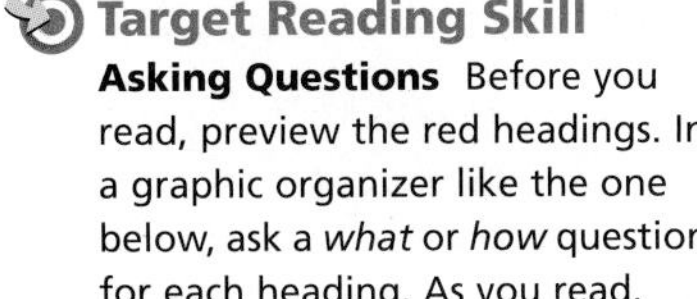

Electric Power

Question	Answer
What is electric power?	Electric power is . . .

Lab zone Discover Activity

How Can You Make a Bulb Burn More Brightly?

1. Attach a light bulb in its socket to a hand generator as shown.
2. Slowly crank the generator. Observe the brightness of the bulb.
3. Crank the generator a little faster and again observe the bulb.
4. Crank the generator quickly and observe the bulb once more.

Think It Over

Posing Questions How does the speed at which you crank the generator affect the brightness of the bulb? What questions do you need to ask to explain how the rate of generating electrical energy is related to the brightness of the bulb?

Your band is auditioning for the school dance. The drummer pounds away on his snares and cymbals. The lead guitar lays down some rockin' riffs. Deep-toned plucks from your electric bass guitar maintain the beat. The judges enjoy what they hear but say they couldn't hear your bass guitar very well. "Turn up the power of your amplfier," one of them suggests. You know that means increase the volume, but what does that have to do with power?

◀ Powering up a performance

Lab zone Discover Activity

Skills Focus Posing questions L1

Materials light bulb in socket, hand generator, 1 m insulated copper wire

Time 15 minutes

Tips Test the bulb in advance to determine how rapidly students can crank the generator without burning out the bulb. Caution students not to exceed that amount. Prepare the wire by removing the insulation from the ends. This activity can be set up in stations that students visit in turn.

Think It Over Sample answer: The faster the generator was cranked, the brighter the bulb became. Sample question: Is there a speed below which no light is produced?

Section 5

Electric Power

Objectives

After this lesson, students will be able to

N.2.5.1 Explain how to calculate electric power.

N.2.5.2 Identify the factors used to determine how people pay for electrical energy.

Target Reading Skill

Asking Questions Explain that changing a heading into a question helps students anticipate the ideas, facts, and events they are about to read.

Answer

What is electric power? *(Electric power is the rate at which electrical energy is transformed into another form of energy.)*

All in One Teaching Resources

- Transparency N25

Preteach

Build Background Knowledge L2

Paying for Electrical Energy

Ask: **What are ways that people can save money on their electric bills?** *(Sample answer: People can turn down the thermostat during the winter. They can turn off the lights when they leave a room.)* **Why will doing these things save people money?** *(Because people have to pay for the electrical energy they use, and therefore using less electrical energy will save people money)*

Instruct

Electric Power

Teach Key Concepts L2

One Form of Energy Into Another

Focus Tell students that an electrical device transforms electrical energy into some other form of energy.

Teach Ask: **What is power?** *(The rate at which energy is transformed from one form into another)* Explain that electric power is the rate at which electrical energy is transformed into another form of energy. Ask: **What is the unit of power?** *(The watt)* **What does it mean that the power rating for a stove is 6,000 watts, and the power rating for a TV is 150 watts?** *(The stove transforms electrical energy at a much faster rate than the TV.)*

Apply Show students a 40-watt light bulb and a 100-watt light bulb. If possible, screw the bulbs into two lamps and turn them on. Ask: **Which bulb is brighter?** *(The 100-watt bulb is brighter than the 40-watt bulb.)* **Why?** *(The 100-watt bulb transforms electrical energy into light energy at a faster rate than the 40-watt bulb does.)* **learning modality: visual**

Independent Practice L2

All in One Teaching Resources

- Guided Reading and Study Worksheet: *Electric Power*

Student Edition on Audio CD

FIGURE 21
Power Ratings
Consumers can use power rating information in buying and using appliances. **Interpreting Diagrams** *Which four appliances listed here use the most power?*

Power Ratings for Appliances

Appliance	Power (Watts)
Stove	6,000
Hair dryer	1,200
Microwave	1,000
Refrigerator	500
Computer	150
TV	150
Clock radio	12

Electric Power

An electrical appliance transforms electrical energy into another form. This energy transformation enables the appliance to perform its function. Hair dryers transform electrical energy to thermal energy to dry your hair. An amplifier that a guitar player uses transforms electrical energy into sound. A washing machine transforms electrical energy to mechanical energy to wash your clothes. The rate at which energy is transformed from one form to another is known as **power.** The unit of power is the watt (W).

Power Ratings You are already familiar with different amounts of electric power. The power rating of a bright light bulb, for example, might be 100 W. The power rating of a dimmer bulb might be 60 W. The bright bulb transforms (or uses) electrical energy at a faster rate than the dimmer bulb.

The appliances in your home vary greatly in their power ratings. New appliances are sold with labels that show the power rating for each product. Look at the table in Figure 21 to see some typical power ratings. Do any of these ratings surprise you?

Lab zone Skills Activity

Observing

Study the back or bottom of some electrical appliances around your home. Make a chart of their power ratings. Do you see any relationship between the power rating and whether or not the appliance produces heat?

Lab zone Skills Activity

Skills Focus Observing L2

Materials household appliances such as toaster, microwave oven, mixer, blender

Time 10 minutes

Tips Review the meaning of W (watts of power), A (amps of current), and V (volts). Some appliances will indicate 110–120 V because household voltage varies. The notation 60 Hz indicates that 120 V reverses 60 times per second. Devices that list voltage lower than 120 V may have a step-down transformer. Some appliances adapt current from alternating current to direct current; these may list input as 120 V AC and output as 12 V DC. Use the input voltage for your calculations.

Expected Outcome Appliances with high power ratings produce heat. **learning modality: kinesthetic**

Calculating Power The power of a light bulb or appliance depends on two factors: voltage and current. **You can calculate power by multiplying voltage by current.**

$$\text{Power} = \text{Voltage} \times \text{Current}$$

The units are watts (W) = volts (V) × amperes (A). Using the symbols P for power, V for voltage, and I for current, this equation can be rewritten

$$P = VI$$

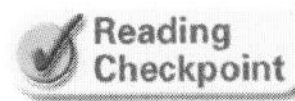

Reading Checkpoint How can you calculate power if you know the voltage and current?

Go Online SCI LINKS NSTA

For: Links on electric power
Visit: www.SciLinks.org
Web Code: scn-1425

Math Sample Problem

Calculating Power

A household light bulb has about 0.5 amps of current in it. Since the standard household voltage is 120 volts, what is the power rating for this bulb?

1 Read and Understand

What information are you given?

Current = 0.5 A

Voltage = 120 V

2 Plan and Solve

What quantity are you trying to calculate?

The power of the light bulb = ?

What formula contains the given quantities and the unknown quantity?

Power = Voltage × Current

Perform the calculation.

Power = 120 V × 0.5 A

Power = 60 W

3 Look Back and Check

Does your answer make sense?

The answer is reasonable, because 60 W is a common rating for household light bulbs.

Math Practice

1. A flashlight bulb uses two 1.5-V batteries in series to create a current of 0.5 A. What is the power rating of the bulb?
2. A hair dryer has a power rating of 1,200 W and uses a standard voltage of 120 V. What is the current through the hair dryer?

Math Sample Problem

Math Skill Formulas and equations

Focus Tell students that to calculate for power, they will need to multiply one number by another.

Teach Ask: **What is the equation you use to calculate power?** *(Power = Voltage × Current, or P = VI)* **What values are you given in this problem?** *(The current is 0.5 A, and the voltage is 120 V.)* **How do you know that the answer of 60 W is reasonable?** *(Light bulbs are commonly 60 W.)* Tell students that instead of calculating power, they could manipulate the equation to calculate voltage, if given the power and the current. Ask: **What equation would you use to calculate voltage?** *(V = I/P)* Have students calculate the voltage given that the power is 60 W and the current is 0.5 A. *(60 W ÷ 0.5 A = 120 V)*

Paying for Electrical Energy

Teach Key Concepts L2

Energy and Power

Focus Help students understand how to calculate the amount of energy used by an appliance.

Teach Ask: **What equation do you use to calculate the amount of energy used by an appliance?** *(Energy = Power × Time)* **What units are these variables usually measured in?** *(Kilowatt-hours for energy, kilowatts for power, and hours for time)*

Apply Ask: **An electric water heater that requires 40 kW runs for 5 hours. How much energy does it use?** *(200 kWh)* **How much energy does the same water heater use if it runs for 20 hours?** *(800 kWh)*

Math Practice

Answers

1. 1.5 W *(3.0 V × 0.5 A)*
2. 10 A *(1,200 W ÷ 120 V)*

All in One Teaching Resources

- Transparency N26

For: More on electric power
Visit: www.SciLinks.org
Web Code: scn-1425

Download a worksheet that will guide students' review of Internet resources on electric power.

Monitor Progress L2

Skills Check Have students calculate the power rating for a battery-powered radio that uses six 1.5-V batteries and produces a current of 0.5 A. *(9 V × 0.5 A = 4.5 W)*

Answers

Figure 21 The stove, hair dryer, microwave, and refrigerator use the most power.

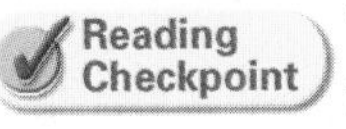

Reading Checkpoint To calculate power, multiply the voltage by the current.

Assess

Reviewing Key Concepts

1. a. Electric power is the rate at which electrical energy is transformed to another form of energy. **b.** Power = Voltage × Current ($P = VI$) **c.** No. The power rating of an electric device depends on the rate at which it transforms electrical energy to another form of energy, not on its size.
2. a. They consider energy use. The amount of energy you use depends on both power and time, and you use some electrical devices more than you use others.
b. Multiply power by time used. **c.** The stove. If you use the appliance for more time than the stove the energy cost can be more.

Reteach L1

Call on students to state the formula for power and the formula for energy use and explain the values and units involved in each.

Performance Assessment L2

Skills Check Ask each student to write a math problem related to power. Tell students the problem could call for finding power, current, or voltage, given the other two values. After students have written their problems, divide the class into groups and have members work through each member's problem.

All in One Teaching Resources

- Section Summary: *Electric Power*
- Review and Reinforce: *Electric Power*
- Enrich: *Electric Power*

FIGURE 22
Paying for Electricity
Electric bills are based on the amount of time various appliances are used. For any type of appliance, energy guides help consumers make the most efficient purchase.

Paying for Electrical Energy

The electric bill that comes to your home charges for energy use, not power. Energy use depends on both power and time. Different appliances transform electrical energy at different rates. And you use some appliances more than others. **The total amount of energy used by an appliance is equal to the power of the appliance multiplied by the amount of time the appliance is used.**

$$\text{Energy} = \text{Power} \times \text{Time}$$

Electric power is usually measured in thousands of watts, or kilowatts (kW), and time is measured in hours. The unit of electrical energy is the kilowatt-hour (kWh).

$$\text{Kilowatt-hours} = \text{Kilowatts} \times \text{Hours}$$

Ten 100-watt light bulbs turned on for one hour use 1,000 watt-hours, or 1 kilowatt-hour, of energy.

The amount of electrical energy used in your home is measured by a meter. As more lights and appliances are turned on, you can observe a dial on the meter turning more rapidly. The electric company uses the meter to keep track of the number of kilowatt-hours used. You pay a few cents for each kilowatt-hour.

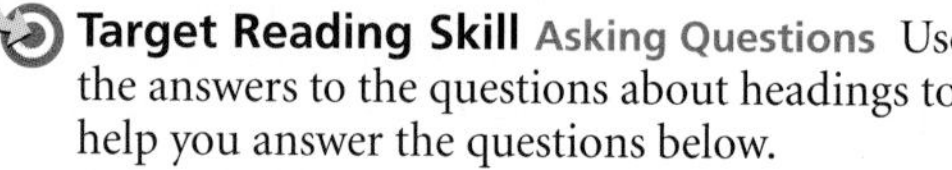

Section 5 Assessment

Target Reading Skill Asking Questions Use the answers to the questions about headings to help you answer the questions below.

Reviewing Key Concepts

1. a. Defining What is electric power?
   b. Calculating What formula can you use to calculate power?
   c. Making Generalizations Is it correct to say the bigger the electrical device, the more power it uses? Use Figure 21 to explain your answer.
2. a. Reviewing When utility companies calculate a consumer's electric bill, do they consider power or energy use? Explain.
   b. Explaining If the power rating of an appliance is known, how can you find the amount of energy it uses?
   c. Interpreting Tables Which appliance in Figure 21 has the greatest power rating? How can some appliances with lower power ratings cost more to use over a month?

Math Practice

3. Calculating Power An electric water heater that uses 40 kW runs for 5.0 hours. What is its power?
4. Calculating Power What is the power of the same water heater if it was run for 20 hours?

Math Practice

Answers
3. 200 kWh *(40 kW × 5.0 h)*
4. 800 kWh *(40 kW × 20 h)*

Lab zone Chapter Project

Keep Students on Track Make sure students have completed testing the alarm circuits they have made. Encourage students to redesign their circuits to make the circuits work as planned. Also, advise students to begin planning for their presentations. They will need to demonstrate the circuit, describe how it works, present a circuit diagram, and turn in a description.

Section 6

Integrating Health

Electrical Safety

Reading Preview

Key Concepts

- What measures help protect people from electrical shocks and short circuits?

Key Terms

- short circuit
- grounded
- third prong
- fuse
- circuit breaker

Target Reading Skill

Using Prior Knowledge Before you read, write what you know about electrical safety in a graphic organizer like the one below. As you read, write what you learn.

What You Know
1. An electric shock can be dangerous. 2.

What You Learned
1. 2.

Lab zone Discover Activity

How Can You Blow a Fuse?

1. Begin by constructing the circuit shown using a D-cell, a light bulb, and two alligator clips.
2. Pull a steel fiber out of a piece of steel wool. Wrap the ends of the steel fiber around the alligator clips.
3. Complete the circuit and observe the steel fiber and the bulb.

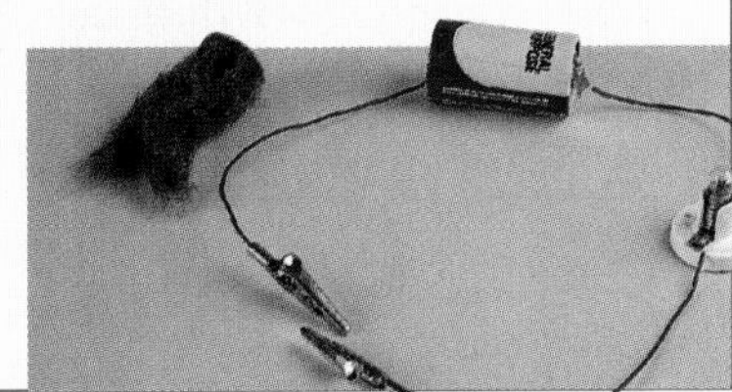

Think It Over

Developing Hypotheses Write a hypothesis to explain your observations.

The ice storm has ended, but it has left a great deal of destruction in its wake. Trees have been stripped of their branches, and a thick coating of ice covers the countryside. Perhaps the greatest danger is from the downed high-voltage electric wires. Residents are being warned to stay far away from them. What makes these high-voltage wires so dangerous?

Personal Safety

You may have noticed high-voltage wires hanging from poles beside the highway. These wires form a circuit to and from the electric plant. The wires carry electric current from the electric plant to the customer. If these wires are damaged, they can cause serious injury. Potential dangers include short circuits, electric shocks, and ungrounded wires.

Short Circuits If someone touches a downed electric wire, the person's body can form a short circuit between the wire and the ground. A short circuit can also occur in your home if you touch frayed wires. A **short circuit** is a connection that allows current to take the path of least resistance. For example, the electric charge can flow through the person rather than through the wire to the power plant. The unintended path usually has less resistance than the intended path. Therefore, the current can be very high. The shock that the person receives may be fatal.

Lab zone Discover Activity

Skills Focus Developing hypotheses L2

Materials dry cell, light bulb, 2 alligator clips, very fine steel wool (00 or 000 grade)

Time 15 minutes

Tips Use unrusted, unsoaped steel wool. If students cannot make a good contact between the steel wool fiber and the alligator clips, suggest they wrap a small piece of aluminum foil around the end of the fiber, crimp it, then clamp the alligator jaws on it.

Expected Outcome The steel wire will flash and burn. The bulb will go out.

Think It Over Sample hypothesis: If the steel wool becomes so hot that it melts and burns, then the circuit will be broken.

Section 6

Electrical Safety

Objectives

After this lesson, students will be able to

N.2.6.1 Describe measures that help protect people from electrical shocks and short circuits.

Target Reading Skill

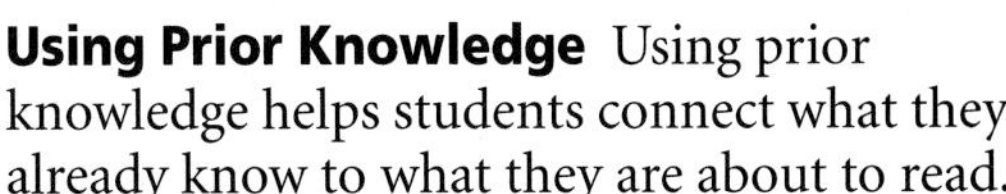

Using Prior Knowledge Using prior knowledge helps students connect what they already know to what they are about to read.

Sample Answers

What You Know

1. An electric shock can be dangerous.

What You Learned

1. An electric shock through a person can have a high current and can be fatal.

All in One Teaching Resources

- Transparency N27

Preteach

Build Background Knowledge L2

Keeping Safe When Using Appliances

Ask: **What are two ways to avoid getting shocked when using electrical devices?** *(Sample answer: Keep appliances away from water; do not overload outlets.)*

Instruct

Personal Safety

Teach Key Concepts L2

Staying Safe

Focus The severity of an electric shock depends on the current and voltage.

Teach Ask: **What is a short circuit?** *(A connection that allows current to take a path of least resistance)*

Apply Ask: **In a short circuit through a body, why would the current be high?** *(Rearranging the equation for Ohm's law, $I = V/R$, when resistance is low, the number that divides the voltage is also low. That results in a high current.)* **learning modality: logical/mathematical**

Math Analyzing Data

Math Skill Making and interpreting graphs

Focus A circle graph is used because it clearly shows the percentages of the categories that make up the whole.

Teach Explain that the graph shows four different kinds of electrical devices. Ask: **What does the size of each section on the circle graph tell you?** *(The sizes of the sections are in proportion to the percentages of fires from each different type of equipment.)*

Answers

1. The percentage of fires caused by a certain type of electrical equipment
2. 15%
3. Cooking equipment is responsible for the most fires. Heating and cooling equipment is responsible for the fewest fires.

For: Links on electric safety
Visit: www.SciLinks.org
Web Code: scn-1426

Download a worksheet that will guide students' review of Internet sources on electrical safety.

Independent Practice L2

All in One Teaching Resources

- Guided Reading and Study Worksheet: *Electrical Safety*

Student Edition on Audio CD

Math Analyzing Data

Electrical Equipment and Fires

If electrical equipment is not properly used and maintained, it can cause fires. The circle graph shows the percentage of fires caused by different types of electrical equipment.

1. **Reading Graphs** What determines the size of each wedge in the graph?
2. **Reading Graphs** What percentage of fires are caused by appliances?
3. **Interpreting Data** Which category of equipment is responsible for most fires? Which category is responsible for the fewest fires?

Fires From Electrical Equipment

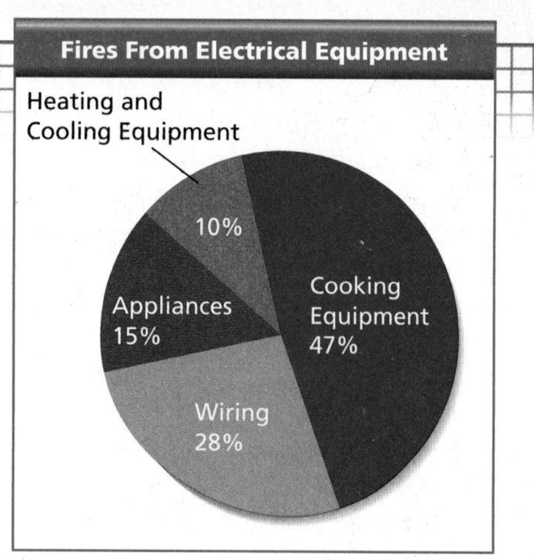

For: Links on electrical safety
Visit: www.SciLinks.org
Web Code: scn-1426

Electric Shocks Electrical signals in the human body control breathing, heartbeat, and muscle movement. If your body receives an electric current from an outside source, it can result in a shock that interferes with your body's electrical signals.

The shock you feel from static discharge after walking across a carpet is very different from the shock that could come from touching a fallen high-voltage wire. The severity of an electric shock depends on the current. A current of less than 0.01 A is almost unnoticeable. But a current greater than 0.2 A can be dangerous, causing burns or even stopping your heart.

Grounding Earth plays an important role in electrical safety. **One way to protect people from electric shock and other electrical danger is to provide an alternate path for electric current.** Most buildings have a wire that connects all the electric circuits to the ground, or Earth. A circuit is electrically **grounded** when charges are able to flow directly from the circuit into Earth in the event of a short circuit.

One method of grounding is to use a third prong on a plug. Two flat prongs of a plug connect an appliance to the household circuit. The **third prong,** which is round, connects any metal pieces of the appliance to the ground wire of the building. If a short circuit occurs in the appliance, the electric charge will flow directly into Earth. Any person who touches the device will be protected.

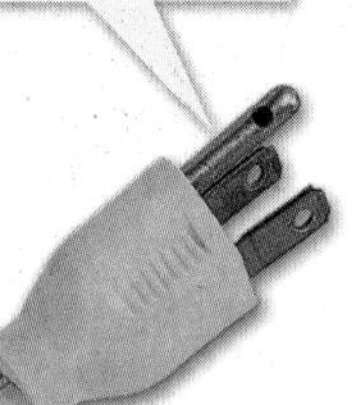

The ground prong connects the metal shell of an appliance to the ground wire of a building.

FIGURE 23
Grounding
A third prong protects against a short circuit by directing current into Earth.

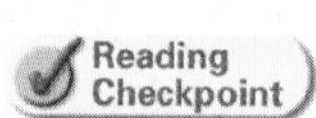

Reading Checkpoint **What is the function of a third prong?**

Differentiated Instruction

Special Needs L1

Observing Fuses and Breakers Provide a variety of fuses for students to handle and observe. Point out that each fuse has a metal strip that melts if the current becomes too high, breaking the circuit. Then, ask a member of the school's custodial staff to show the students one of the school's breaker boxes, where the circuit breakers are accessed. If possible, the staff member can switch one of the breakers off for a section of a room or the basement. Explain that when the current in a circuit becomes too high, the circuit breakers switch off on their own. **learning modality: visual**

Breaking a Circuit

If you use too many appliances at once, a circuit's current can become dangerously high and heat the wires that carry it. Overloading a circuit can result in a fire. **In order to prevent circuits from overheating, devices called fuses and circuit breakers are added to circuits.**

A **fuse** is a device that contains a thin strip of metal that will melt if there is too much current through it. When the strip of metal "blows," or melts, it breaks the circuit. The breaking of the circuit stops the current. Fuses are commonly found in cars and older buildings. Figure 24 shows how a fuse works.

A disadvantage of using a fuse is that once it burns out, it must be replaced. To avoid the task of replacing fuses, circuits in new buildings are protected by devices called circuit breakers. A **circuit breaker** is a reusable safety switch that breaks the circuit when the current gets too high. In some circuit breakers, a high current causes a small metal band to heat up. As the band heats up it bends away from wires in the circuit, disrupting the current.

It's easy to reset the circuit breaker. By pulling the switch back, you reconnect the metal band to the wires. However, the appliances that are causing the high current in the circuit need to be turned off first.

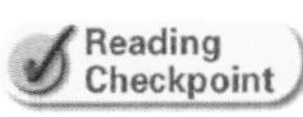
What is the difference between a fuse and a circuit breaker?

FIGURE 24
A Fuse
When a circuit becomes overloaded, a fuse stops the current. Interpreting Diagrams *How does a fuse work?*

A low current travels through the thin strip of metal to complete a circuit.

If too much current is in the thin strip of metal, it will melt and break the circuit.

Section 6 Assessment

Target Reading Skill Using Prior Knowledge Review your graphic organizer about electrical safety and revise it based on what you have just learned in the section.

Reviewing Key Concepts

1. a. Defining What are grounded electric circuits? What are fuses and circuit breakers?
   b. Explaining Explain how grounding, fuses, and circuit breakers protect people from electrical shocks and short circuits.
   c. Predicting Without a fuse or circuit breaker, what might happen in a house with an overloaded electric circuit? Explain your answer.

Lab zone At-Home Activity

Checking Circuits Along with members of your family, find out whether the circuits in your home are protected by fuses or circuit breakers. **CAUTION:** *Be careful not to touch the wiring during your inspection.* How many circuits are there in your home? Make a diagram showing the outlets and appliances on each circuit. Explain the role of fuses and circuit breakers. Ask your family members if they are aware of these devices in other circuits, such as in a car.

Lab zone At-Home Activity

Checking Circuits L2 Caution students not to approach a fuse box or circuit breaker without an adult present. Students who live in apartment buildings may need to look outside their units for circuit breakers. Encourage students to share their diagrams with family members.

Monitor Progress L2

Answers

Figure 24 A fuse contains a thin strip of metal that will melt if there is too much current through it. When the strip melts, it breaks the circuit.

Reading Checkpoint The third prong protects people from electric shock by connecting the metal shell of an appliance to Earth through a grounding wire.

Reading Checkpoint A fuse contains a thin strip of metal that will melt if there is too much current through it. A circuit breaker is a reusable safety switch that breaks the circuit when the current gets too high.

Assess

Reviewing Key Concepts

1. a. A grounded electrical circuit is one in which electric charges can flow directly from the circuit into Earth if a short circuit occurs. Fuses and circuit breakers are devices that prevent circuits from overloading. **b.** Grounding protects people from electrical shock by providing an alternate path for electric current. Fuses and circuit breakers stop the current in the event of too much current or a short circuit. When there is too much current through a fuse, a strip of metal melts and stops the current. In some circuit breakers, contact is broken when a small metal band heats up and bends away from wires. **c.** Without a fuse or circuit breaker, excessive current in wires in an overloaded electric circuit may cause the wires to overheat and start a fire.

Reteach L1

Call on students to define the key terms *short circuit, grounded, third prong, fuse,* and *circuit breaker.*

Performance Assessment L2

Writing Have students describe how voltage, current, and resistance can contribute to electric shock in the human body.

All in One Teaching Resources

- Section Summary: *Electrical Safety*
- Review and Reinforce: *Electrical Safety*
- Enrich: *Electrical Safety*

Study Guide

- Complete student edition
- Section and chapter self-assessments
- Assessment reports for teachers

Help Students Read

Building Vocabulary

Word Origin Have students look up the origin of the word *static.* They will discover that *static* comes from a Greek word meaning "stand or placed." Ask students how this meaning relates to the characteristics of static electricity. *(In static electricity, charges build up on an object, but they do not flow continuously.)*

Words in Context Help students learn the meaning of new words or phrases by examining context. Tell students to look for familiar words or phrases that surround a new term—these are clues to the new word's meaning. Have students reread the paragraphs in which the term *conduction* is defined. Ask: **What word appears in the same paragraph as *conduction* that helps you to remember its meaning?** *(Touches)*

Connect Concepts

Concept Maps Help students develop one way to show how the information in this chapter is related. Have students brainstorm to identify the key concepts, key terms, details, and examples about electricity. Write each suggestion on a self-sticking note and attach it at random on chart paper or on the board.

Tell students that this concept will be organized in hierarchical order and to begin at the top with key concepts. Ask students these questions to guide them to categorize the information on the self-sticking notes: **What is an electric field? How is an electric current produced? What is a battery? What are three basic features of an electric circuit? What is electric power? How can circuits be prevented from overheating?**

Prompt students by using connecting words or phrases, such as "includes" and "is caused by" to indicate the basis for the organization of the map. The phrases should form a sentence between or among a set of concepts.

Answer

Accept logical presentations by students.

All in One Teaching Resources

- Key Terms Review: *Electricity*
- Connecting Concepts: *Electricity*

Chapter 2 Study Guide

1 Electric Charge and Static Electricity

Key Ideas

- Charges that are the same repel each other. Charges that are different attract each other.
- An electric field is a region around a charged object where the object's electric force interacts with other charged objects.
- Static electricity charge builds up on an object but does not flow continuously.
- Static electricity is transferred through charging by friction, by conduction, and by induction.
- When negatively and positively charged objects are brought together, electrons transfer until both objects have the same charge.

Key Terms

• electric force • electric field
• static electricity • conservation of charge
• friction • conduction • induction
• static discharge

2 Electric Current

Key Ideas

- To produce electric current, charges must flow continuously from one place to another.
- A conductor transfers electric charge well. An insulator does not transfer electric charge well.
- Voltage causes a current in an electric circuit.
- The greater the resistance, the less current there is for a given voltage.

Key Terms

• electric current • electric circuit • conductor
• insulator • voltage • voltage source
• resistance

3 Batteries

Key Ideas

- Volta built the first battery by layering zinc, paper soaked in salt water, and silver.
- Chemical reactions in an electrochemical cell cause one electrode to become negatively charged and the other electrode to become positively charged.

Key Terms

• chemical energy • chemical reaction
• electrochemical cell • electrode • electrolyte
• terminal • battery • wet cell • dry cell

4 Electric Circuits

Key Ideas

- Ohm's law says that the resistance is equal to the voltage divided by the current.

$$\text{Resistance} = \text{Voltage} \div \text{Current}$$

- Circuits have a source of electrical energy and devices that are run by electrical energy. Circuits are connected by conducting wires.
- In a series circuit, there is only one path for the current to take. In a parallel circuit, there are several paths for the current to taket.

Key Terms

• Ohm's law • series circuit • ammeter
• parallel circuit • voltmeter

5 Electric Power

Key Ideas

- You can calculate power by multiplying voltage by current.

$$\text{Energy} = \text{Power} \times \text{Time}$$

- The total amount of energy used by an appliance is equal to its power multiplied by the amount of time it is used.

Key Term

• power

6 Electrical Safety

Key Ideas

- One way to protect people from electric shock and other electrical danger is to provide an alternate path for electric current.
- In order to prevent circuits from overheating, devices called fuses and circuit breakers are added to circuits.

Key Terms

• short circuit • grounded • third prong
• fuse • circuit breaker

Review and Assessment

Go Online PHSchool.com
For: Self-Assessment
Visit: PHSchool.com
Web Code: cga-4020

Organizing Information

Concept Mapping Copy the concept map about devices that prevent circuits from overheating. Then complete the concept map. (For more information on concept maps, see the Skills Handbook.)

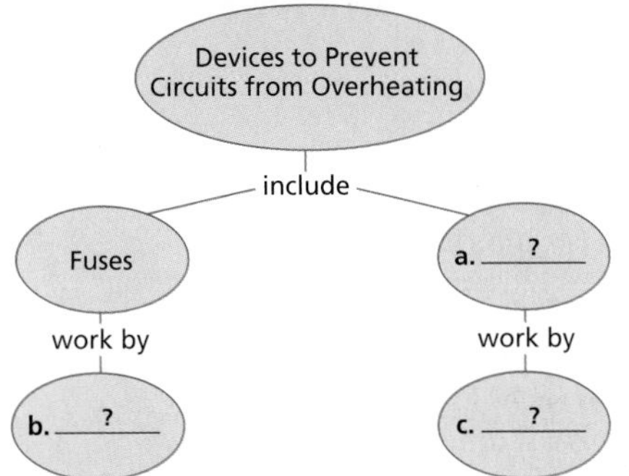

Reviewing Key Terms

Choose the letter of the best answer.

1. The attraction or repulsion between electric charges is called a(n)
   a. electric field.
   b. electric force.
   c. electron.
   d. static electricity.
2. The potential difference that causes charges to move in a circuit is called
   a. current.
   b. electric discharge.
   c. resistance.
   d. voltage.
3. A combination of two or more electrical cells in a series is called a(n)
   a. wet cell.
   b. dry cell.
   c. battery.
   d. electrode.
4. A device that measures electric current is a(n)
   a. ammeter.
   b. battery.
   c. resistor.
   d. voltmeter.
5. Connecting a circuit to Earth as a safety precaution is called
   a. a short circuit. b. an insulator.
   c. grounding. d. static discharge.

If the statement is true, write *true*. If it is false, change the underlined word or words to make the statement true.

6. Conduction is the process of charging an object without touching it.
7. Electrical resistance is low in a good conductor.
8. An electrolyte is an attachment point used to connect a cell or battery to a circuit.
9. In a series circuit, all parts of the circuit are connected in a single path.
10. Power is the rate at which energy is transformed from one form to another.

Writing in Science

Descriptive Paragraph Describe the journey of an electron in a lightning bolt. Begin at the thundercloud and follow the path of the electron until the lightning bolt strikes the ground.

Electricity
Video Preview
Video Field Trip
▶ Video Assessment

Review and Assessment

Concept Mapping

a. Circuit breakers
b. Melting
c. Bending away from wires

Reviewing Key Terms

1. b 2. d 3. c 4. a 5. c
6. Induction
7. true
8. terminal
9. true
10. true

Writing in Science

Writing Mode Description

Scoring Rubric

4 Exceeds criteria; includes a well-written and informative explanation of static discharge, how charges form in thunderclouds, and why lightning occurs
3 Meets criteria
2 Meets some criteria; fails to explain static discharge accurately and/or fails to describe accurately how charges form in thunderclouds
1 Includes an inaccurate explanation of static discharge and/or fails to describe how charges form in thunderclouds

Electricity

Show the Video Assessment to review chapter content and as a prompt for the writing assignment. Discussion question: **Explain why we hear thunder after a lightning strike.** *(The air around a lightning bolt is superheated to about 30,000 degrees Celsius. This sudden heating causes the air to expand faster than the speed of sound. The expanding air quickly cools and then contracts. Quick expansion and contraction of air around lightning starts molecules in the air vibrating back and forth, making sound waves.)*

Go Online PHSchool.com
For: Self-Assessment
Visit: PHSchool.com
Web Code: cga-4020

Students can take a practice test online that is automatically scored.

All in One Teaching Resources

- Transparency N28
- Chapter Test
- Performance Assessment Teacher Notes
- Performance Assessment Student Worksheet
- Performance Assessment Scoring Rubric

***ExamView®* Computer Test Bank CD-ROM**

Checking Concepts

11. An object can become charged by friction, by conduction, or by induction. Friction: Electrons are rubbed off one object onto another object. Conduction: One charged object touches another and transfers charges. Induction: An electric field around a charged object attracts or repels electrons in another object.

12. Voltage—the volt; current—the ampere (amp); resistance—the ohm

13. An electrochemical cell consists of two different metals called electrodes immersed in a substance called an electrolyte. A voltage is produced when one electrode reacts with the electrolyte and becomes negatively charged and the other electrode reacts with the electrolyte and becomes positively charged.

14. Resistance is equal to the voltage divided by the current.

15. If one electric appliance or device in the building failed, all the others would stop working, too. The single path for current in a series circuit would be broken.

16. The 100-W bulb glows more brightly because electrical energy is transformed to electromagnetic energy (light) at a higher rate than in the 75-W bulb.

17. A short circuit is a connection that allows an electric current to take the path of least resistance—usually an unintended path.

Thinking Critically

18. a. both **b.** series **c.** parallel **d.** series **e.** series

19. The electroscope is charged. The evidence is that the leaves are shown repelling each other, which means that the charge of both leaves is the same.

20. The third prong is a method of grounding. If the third prong of the plug is removed, a person touching the device could receive a shock.

21. Both types of cells transform chemical energy into electrical energy. In a wet cell, the electrolyte is a liquid. In a dry cell, the electrolyte is a paste.

Math Practice

22. $R = V/I$: $R = (120\text{ V})/(0.25\text{A}) = 480\Omega$

23. $P = VI$: $P = 12\text{ V} \times 40.0\text{ A} = 480\text{ W}$

Review and Assessment

Checking Concepts

11. Describe the three ways in which an object can become charged.

12. What units are used to measure voltage, current, and resistance?

13. Explain how the components of an electrochemical cell produce voltage.

14. What is Ohm's law?

15. What would happen if the circuits in your school building were series circuits? Explain.

16. Which glows more brightly—a 100-W bulb or a 75-W bulb? Explain your answer.

17. What is a short circuit?

Thinking Critically

18. Classifying Identify each of the following statements as characteristic of series circuits, parallel circuits, or both:

a. Current = Voltage ÷ Resistance

b. Total resistance increases as more light bulbs are added.

c. Total resistance decreases as more branches are added.

d. Current in each part of the circuit is the same.

e. A break in any part of the circuit will cause current to stop.

19. Interpreting Diagrams Is the electroscope shown below charged or uncharged? Explain.

20. Applying Concepts Explain why the third prong of a plug should not be removed.

21. Comparing and Contrasting Compare and contrast wet cells and dry cells.

Math Practice

22. Calculating Resistance A toaster is plugged into a 120-volt socket. If it has a current of 0.25 amps in its coils, what is the resistance of the toaster? Show your work.

23. Calculating Power The voltage of a car battery is 12 volts. When the car is started, the battery produces a 40-amp current. How much power does it take to start the car?

Applying Skills

Use the diagram below for Questions 24–27.

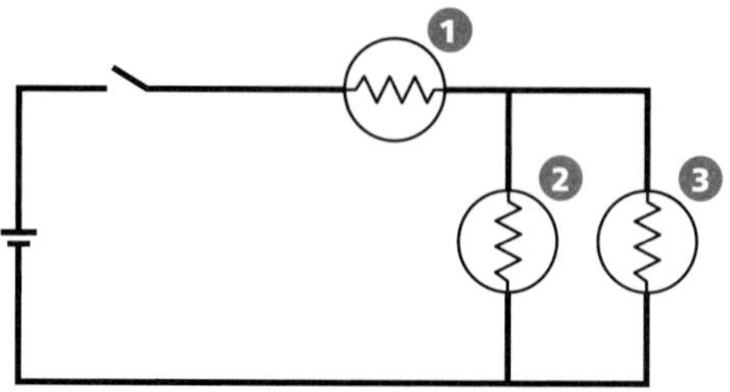

24. Classifying Is the circuit in the illustration a series or parallel circuit? Explain.

25. Controlling Variables Would the other bulbs continue to shine if you removed bulb 1? Would they shine if you removed bulb 2 instead? Explain your reasoning.

26. Predicting Will any of the bulbs be lit if you open the switch? Explain.

27. Making Models Redraw the circuit diagram to include a switch that controls only Bulb 3.

Lab zone Chapter Project

Performance Assessment Prepare a description and circuit diagram for your display. If any parts of your alarm circuit are not visible, draw a second diagram showing how all the parts are assembled. Then present your alarm to your class and explain how it could be used. Include a description of the reliability of your switch.

Lab zone Chapter Project L3

Performance Assessment Talk with each student before the presentation, and make suggestions about how to present the circuit. Many students will have to make final connections and adjustments when they set up their projects.

Have four students at a time set up their projects at separate stations. Then the class can move from station to station to see a demonstration of each project. Have each presenter ask other students if they can explain how the device works. Then the presenter can fill in the missing pieces of the explanation with remarks and diagrams. Following the presentations, have students turn in their one-page descriptions of the alarm circuit.

Standardized Test Prep

Test-Taking Tip

Using Formulas

Some test questions require you to use a formula. Find out what you are being asked to determine. Then recall formulas and other information necessary to answer the question. To solve for a specific quantity in the formula, substitute the known values for the variables.

Sample Question

Your alarm clock has a voltage of 120 V and a resistance of 1200 Ω. What is the current??

A 0.10 A
B 10.0 A
C 12.0 A
D 100 A

Answer

The answer is **A.** To find the current, you use the formula for Ohm's law, which is Resistance = Voltage ÷ Current. The rearranged formula is Current = Voltage ÷ Resistance. Divide the voltage (120 V) by the resistance (1200 Ω).

Choose the letter of the best answer.

1. Which of the following is a reusable device that protects a circuit from becoming overheated?
A a circuit breaker
B a third prong
C a fuse
D an electroscope

2. You want to build a device that can conduct current but that will be safe if touched by a person. Which of the following pairs of materials could you use?
F glass for the conductor and rubber for the insulator
G copper for the insulator and silver for the conductor
H sand for the conductor and plastic for the insulator
J plastic for the insulator and silver for the conductor

3. The graph shows the cost of using three household appliances. Which of the following is a valid interpretation of the graph?

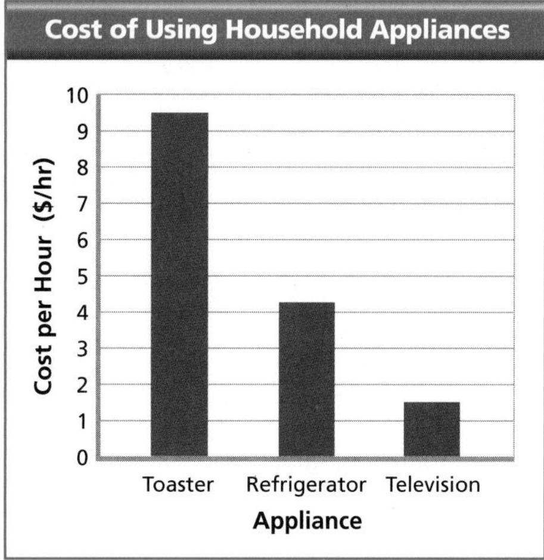

A A toaster has high voltage.
B It costs more per hour to run a refrigerator than a television.
C During a month, a family pays more to run a toaster than a refrigerator.
D A toaster uses more current than any other appliance.

4. An electrochemical cell has one copper nail and one zinc nail. When the nails are placed in vinegar, the light bulb lights up. What conclusion can be made?
F No chemical reaction occurred.
G Vinegar is an electrolyte.
H All electrochemical cells contain vinegar.
J The zinc nail reacted with the vinegar but the copper nail did not.

Constructed Response

5. Explain why people should never touch a high-voltage wire that has blown down in a storm. In your explanation, use the words *electric shock* and *short circuit.*

Applying Skills

24. Both. Bulbs 2 and 3 are in parallel with each other, and both are in series with Bulb 1.

25. If Bulb 1 were removed, the others would go out because the circuit would be broken. If Bulb 2 were removed, the others would remain lit because the current has another route to follow.

26. None of the bulbs would be lit if the switch were open because it would break the circuit and stop the current.

27. Students' drawings should show the switch either before or after Bulb 3 on the same branch.

Standardized Test Prep

1. A **2.** J **3.** B **4.** G

5. Sample answer: If a high-voltage wire has blown down during a storm, the insulator around the conductor may be torn, exposing the conductor. If a person touches the wire, a short circuit may occur as the current takes the path of least resistance through the person. The result may be an electric shock, an electric current in the body from an outside source. The shock that a person receives may be fatal.

Chapter at a Glance

Chapter Project *Electrical Energy Audit*

Technology

Local Standards

All in One Teaching Resources

- Chapter Project Teacher Notes, pp. 188–189
- Chapter Project Student Introduction, pp. 190–191
- Chapter Project Student Worksheets, pp. 192–193
- Chapter Project Scoring Rubric, p. 194

Discovery Channel School Video Preview

Section 1 What Is Electromagnetism?

2–3 periods
1–1 1/2 blocks

N.3.1.1 Explain how an electric current is related to a magnetic field.
N.3.1.2 Identify some characteristics of a magnetic field produced by a current.
N.3.1.3 Describe the characteristics of an electromagnet.

Section 2 Electricity, Magnetism, and Motion

3–4 periods
1 1/2–2 blocks

K.3.2.1 Explain how electrical energy can be transformed into mechanical energy.
N.3.2.2 Describe how a galvanometer works.
N.3.2.3 Describe what an electric motor does.

Section 3 Electricity From Magnetism

3–4 periods
1 1/2–2 blocks

N.3.3.1 Explain how an electric current can be produced in a conductor.
N.3.3.2 Describe how a generator works.
N.3.3.3 Describe the function of a transformer.

Video Field Trip

Review and Assessment

All in One Teaching Resources

- Key Terms Review, p. 221
- Transparency N42
- Performance Assessment Teacher Notes, p. 228
- Performance Assessment Scoring Rubric, p. 229
- Performance Assessment Student Worksheet, p. 230
- Chapter Test, pp. 231–234

Video Assessment

Test Preparation

Test Preparation Blackline Masters

Chapter Activities Planner

For more activities

Student Edition	Inquiry	Time	Materials	Skills	Resources
Chapter Project, p. 79	Open-ended	1–2 weeks	All in One **Teaching Resources** p. 188	Observing, applying concepts, calculating, graphing, communicating	**Lab zone Easy Planner** All in One **Teaching Resources** pp. 188–189
Section 1					
Discover Activity, p. 80	Guided	15 minutes	2 wires (20–30 cm long with insulation stripped from ends), light bulb, bulb holder, 3 compasses, D-cell battery (1.5 volt)	Inferring	**Lab zone Easy Planner**
Try This Activity, p. 83	Directed	15 minutes	1 m insulated copper wire, electric tape, iron nail, D-cell battery, container of paper clips	Inferring	**Lab zone Easy Planner**
Section 2					
Discover Activity, p. 85	Guided	15 minutes	1 m insulated copper wire, iron nail, books, metric ruler, circuit wire, switch, battery, horseshoe magnet	Inferring	**Lab zone Easy Planner**
Try This Activity, p. 86	Directed	15 minutes	1 m insulated wire, 6-volt battery, bar magnet	Drawing conclusions	**Lab zone Easy Planner**
Skills Lab, pp. 92–93	Directed	Prep: 20 minutes; Class: 40 minutes	D-cell battery, 2 large paper clips, permanent disk magnet, 3 balls of clay, empty film canister, pliers, sandpaper, 2 insulated wires (approximately 15 cm each), enamel-coated wire (22–24 gauge, approximately 1 m)	Classifying, inferring, drawing conclusions	**Lab zone Easy Planner** **Lab Activity Video** All in One **Teaching Resources** Skills Lab: *Building an Electric Motor*, pp. 209–212
Section 3					
Discover Activity, p. 94	Guided	10 minutes	1 m insulated copper wire, galvanometer or multimeter, horseshoe magnet, clay	Developing hypotheses	**Lab zone Easy Planner**
At-Home Activity, p. 101	Guided			Observing, communicating	**Lab zone Easy Planner**

Section 1 What Is Electromagnetism?

2–3 periods, 1–1 1/2 blocks

ABILITY LEVELS
L1 Basic to Average
L2 For All Students
L3 Average to Advanced

Objectives

N.3.1.1 Explain how an electric current is related to a magnetic field.

N.3.1.2 Identify some characteristics of a magnetic field produced by a current.

N.3.1.3 Describe the characteristics of an electromagnet.

Key Terms

• electromagnetism • solenoid • electromagnet

Local Standards

Preteach

Build Background Knowledge

Students recall what they have previously learned about magnets and magnetism.

Lab zone Discover Activity *Are Magnetic Fields Limited to Magnets?*  L2

Targeted Print and Technology Resources

All in One Teaching Resources

L2 Reading Strategy Transparency N29: Identifying Main Ideas

PresentationExpress™ CD-ROM

Instruct

Electric Current and Magnetism Use Figure 1 to introduce currents and magnetic fields.

Solenoids Ask students what would happen if you increased the number of coils in a solenoid.

Electromagnets Have students study how a doorbell works as shown in Figure 5.

Targeted Print and Technology Resources

All in One Teaching Resources

L2 Guided Reading, pp. 197–199

L2 Transparencies N30, N31, N32

www.SciLinks.org Web Code: scn-1431

Student Edition on Audio CD

Assess

Section Assessment Questions

Have students use their completed graphic organizers to answer the questions.

Reteach

Use Figure 5 to reteach how electricity and magnetism are related, what a solenoid is, and how an electromagnet works.

Targeted Print and Technology Resources

All in One Teaching Resources

• Section Summary, p. 196

L1 Review and Reinforce, p. 200

L3 Enrich, p. 201

Section 2 Electricity, Magnetism, and Motion

ABILITY LEVELS

L1 Basic to Average

L2 For All Students

L3 Average to Advanced

 *3–4 periods, 1 1/2–2 blocks*

Local Standards

Objectives

N.3.2.1 Explain how electrical energy can be transformed into mechanical energy.

N.3.2.2 Describe how a galvanometer works.

N.3.2.3 Describe what an electric motor does.

Key Terms

• energy • electrical energy • mechanical energy • galvanometer • electric motor

Preteach

Build Background Knowledge

Students relate experiences with home devices that transform energy from one form to another.

 Discover Activity *How Does a Magnet Move a Wire?* L2

Targeted Print and Technology Resources

 **Teaching Resources**

L2 Reading Strategy Transparency N33: Outlining

 **PresentationExpress™ CD-ROM**

Instruct

Electrical Energy and Motion Ask students to analyze the motion of a wire with a current, as shown in Figure 7.

Galvanometers Have students examine the galvanometer shown in Figure 9.

Electric Motors Ask students what would happen if the current didn't reverse but stayed in the same direction.

 Skills Lab *Building an Electric Motor* L3

Targeted Print and Technology Resources

 **Teaching Resources**

L2 Guided Reading, pp. 204–206

L2 Transparencies N34, N35, N36

L3 Skills Lab: *Building an Electric Motor,* pp. 209–212

Lab Activity Video/DVD
Skills Lab: *Building an Electric Motor*

www.SciLinks.org Web Code: scn-1432

Student Edition on Audio CD

Assess

Section Assessment Questions

Have students use their completed outlines to answer the questions.

Reteach

Call on volunteers to define the section's key terms.

Targeted Print and Technology Resources

All in One Teaching Resources

• Section Summary, p. 203

L1 Review and Reinforce, p. 207

L3 Enrich, p. 208

Section 3 Electricity From Magnetism

 *3–4 periods, 1 1/2–2 blocks*

ABILITY LEVELS
L1 Basic to Average
L2 For All Students
L3 Average to Advanced

Objectives

N.3.3.1 Explain how an electric current can be produced in a conductor.
N.3.3.2 Describe how a generator works.
N.3.3.3 Describe the function of a transformer.

Local Standards

Key Terms

- electromagnetic induction • direct current • alternating current
- electric generator • transformer • step-up transformer
- step-down transformer

Preteach

Build Background Knowledge

Students relate their understanding of where and how local electricity is produced.

 *Can You Produce Current Without a Battery?* L1

Targeted Print and Technology Resources

All in One Teaching Resources

L2 Reading Strategy Transparency N37:Previewing Visuals

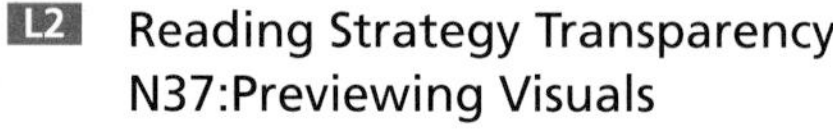
PresentationExpress™ CD-ROM

Instruct

Induction of Electric Current Ask leading questions about induction shown in Figure 12.

Generators Explain the function of a generator as students examine Figure 13.

Transformers Use Figure 15 to reinforce understanding of transformers.

Targeted Print and Technology Resources

All in One Teaching Resources

L2 Guided Reading, pp. 215–218
L2 Transparencies N38, N39, N40, N41

PHSchool.com Web Code: cgp-4033

Student Edition on Audio CD

Assess

Section Assessment Questions

 Have students use their completed questions and answers about Figure 13 to answer the questions.

Reteach

Call on volunteers to explain two ways in which an electric current can be induced.

Targeted Print and Technology Resources

All in One Teaching Resources

- Section Summary, p. 214

L1 Review and Reinforce, p. 219
L3 Enrich, p. 220

Chapter 3 Content Refresher

Go Online
NSTA-PDLINKS
For: Professional Development Support
Visit: www.SciLinks.org/PDLinks
Web Code: scf-1430

Professional Development

Section 1 What Is Electromagnetism?

Solenoids and Electromagnets A loop of wire of even one turn is considered a solenoid. But a useful solenoid usually has a coil length greater than its width. The strength of a solenoid's magnetic field increases with both the number of loops of wire and the strength of the current. In addition, how close the loops of wire are wound makes a difference in the strength of the magnetic field. If the current is the same, 10 loops of wire distributed over 10 cm produce a stronger magnetic field than 10 loops of wire distributed over 20 cm.

The addition of a ferromagnetic core to a solenoid makes an electromagnet. The first electromagnet was created in about 1825 by the English physicist William Sturgeon. Sturgeon's electromagnet was not particularly strong, though. The problem was that when the wires were wrapped around an iron core too tightly, they would touch, creating a short circuit. The American physicist Joseph Henry heard about Sturgeon's device and set about making a better electromagnet. To insulate the wire, he tore up one of his wife's petticoats and wrapped the silk around the wire. With the insulated wire, he was able to pack the loops of wire close together around a soft iron core, increasing the strength of the magnetic field. With a relatively small electromagnet, Henry was able to lift more than a ton of iron, a phenomenal feat for the time.

Section 2 Electricity, Magnetism, and Motion

Electric Motors In large electric motors, the brushes used to feed current through the commutator to the armature are spring-loaded carbon blocks. At each half revolution of the commutator, the split-ring commutator switches which brush it touches, reversing the current in the armature. The result is continuous rotation of the armature and the commutator. The stationary brushes wear down through use and must be replaced periodically in an often-used electric motor. Most commercial motors contain several coils on the armature. Use of several coils produces a smoother rotation of the armature.

Commutators are used in electric motors that operate with direct current. An automobile starter motor, which receives direct current from the car battery, is an example of a common DC motor. In the commonest AC electric motors, such as the motor in a hair dryer, there are no commutators—in fact, there is no conducting path to the armature. The current in the armature is caused by magnetic induction. These induction motors tend to last longer and cost less.

Section 3 Electricity From Magnetism

Generating Electricity The English physicist Michael Faraday invented the first electric generator in 1831. His was a simple device in which a copper disc was turned between poles of a permanent magnet, inducing an electric current. Today, the electrical energy from electric plants is produced through the use of huge generators. In most cases, steam is used to turn the armature of the generator. The steam is produced from water boiled by the burning of coal or by the heat produced in nuclear fission at a nuclear power plant. Hydroelectric dams in some areas use moving water to turn the armature that generates electric current.

Address Misconceptions

Some students may think that a step-up transformer creates energy in the secondary coil. However, energy cannot be created or destroyed. For a strategy for overcoming this misconception, see **Address Misconceptions** in the section *Electricity From Magnetism.*

Help Students Read

Asking Questions

Looking for Answers

Strategy Help students learn to apply the strategy of Asking Questions. This strategy helps students to anticipate what they will be reading and helps them look for answers in the passage as they read. With practice, students should be able to generate questions that do not simply rephrase the section headings. The headings themselves will give students hints to formulate questions about what they expect to see in the text.

Example

1. Choose a subsection within this chapter. A good example is *Induction of Electric Current* in the *Electricity From Magnetism* section.
2. Draw a two-column chart on the board. Make the heading of the first column Questions and the second heading Answers.
3. Have students scan the subsection. As they encounter the heading and subheadings, have students suggest ways to recast them as questions. For example, *Induction of Electric Current* might become the question "How is electric current induced?"
4. After students have recast the heading and subheadings as questions, ask them to read the section and supply answers to the questions. You may ask a volunteer to read aloud or have students read silently.

Interactive Textbook
- Complete student edition
- Video and audio
- Simulations and activities
- Section and chapter activities

Chapter 3 Using Electricity and Magnetism

Chapter Preview

To deliver the mail, this letter carrier rides a machine that uses electromagnetism.

78 ◆ N

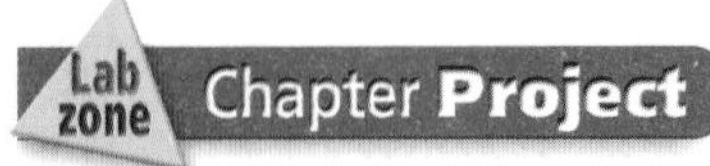

L3

Objectives

Students will analyze how electricity is used at home and determine how much electrical energy their families use. After completing this Chapter Project, students will be able to
- observe the power ratings of each appliance in the home that uses electrical energy and how long each is used during the average week
- calculate how much electrical energy is used by each appliance
- graph the data gathered about the appliances and the energy they use
- communicate results to the class

Skills Focus

Observing, applying concepts, calculating, graphing, communicating

Project Time Line 1–2 weeks

All in One Teaching Resources
- Chapter Project Teacher Notes
- Chapter Project Overview
- Chapter Project Worksheet 1
- Chapter Project Worksheet 2
- Chapter Project Scoring Rubric

Developing a Plan

Students will begin by brainstorming a list of appliances in their homes and making data tables in which they can record the use of these appliances. After recording the amount of time each appliance was used in a week, students will calculate energy in kilowatt-hours for each appliance using the equation: Energy = Power × Time. Next, students will interpret their data and create graphs that show the energy used by appliances. Students will then present the results of the energy audit to the class.

Possible Materials

Students will not need many materials other than paper and pencil to complete the Chapter Project. To help them make their calculations, students may use a calculator. Students may use poster board, colored markers, or other materials to prepare visual aids for their presentations.

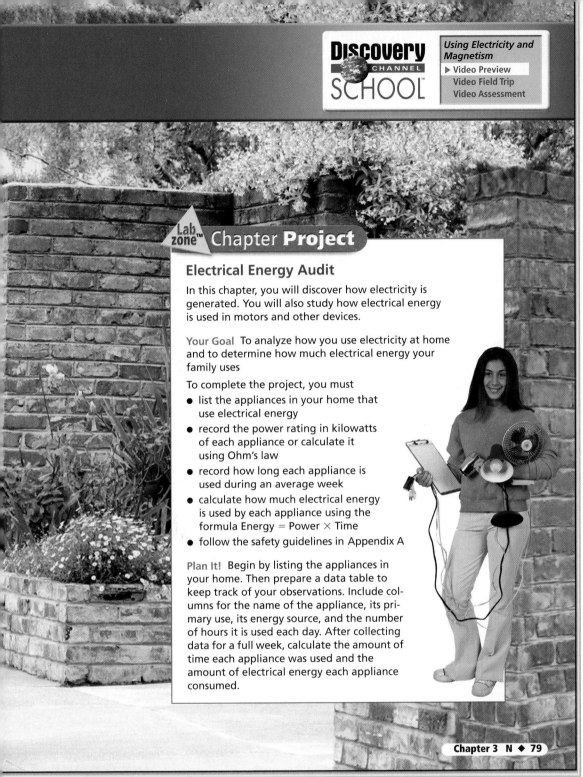

Lab zone™ Chapter Project

Electrical Energy Audit

In this chapter, you will discover how electricity is generated. You will also study how electrical energy is used in motors and other devices.

Your Goal To analyze how you use electricity at home and to determine how much electrical energy your family uses

To complete the project, you must

- list the appliances in your home that use electrical energy
- record the power rating in kilowatts of each appliance or calculate it using Ohm's law
- record how long each appliance is used during an average week
- calculate how much electrical energy is used by each appliance using the formula Energy = Power × Time
- follow the safety guidelines in Appendix A

Plan It! Begin by listing the appliances in your home. Then prepare a data table to keep track of your observations. Include columns for the name of the appliance, its primary use, its energy source, and the number of hours it is used each day. After collecting data for a full week, calculate the amount of time each appliance was used and the amount of electrical energy each appliance consumed.

Chapter 3 N ◆ 79

Using Electricity and Magnetism

Show the Video Preview to introduce the Chapter Project and provide an overview of the chapter content. Discussion question: **Why is repairing electrical transmission lines dangerous?** *(The transmission lines have a voltage of half a million volts. Linemen usually have to make their repairs without turning off the current.)*

Possible Shortcuts

- You can make this project shorter by having students analyze and record appliance use for only two or three days instead of one week.
- For a class project, each student can record appliance use for one day. Students can bring their data to class, and the results can be averaged.

Launching the Project

To introduce the project, lead a class discussion in which students consider the use of appliances in their homes. Ask: **Which appliances do you think require the most power to operate?** *(Sample answer: The hot-water heater, the dryer, and the dishwasher)*

Performance Assessment

The Chapter Project Scoring Rubric will help you evaluate how well students complete the Chapter Project. You may want to share the scoring rubric with your students so they are clear about what will be expected of them. Students will be assessed on

- how well they collect and record the data about energy use in their homes
- how accurately they calculate energy use
- how effectively they analyze and graph their data
- how well they present their results to the class

Students can keep their data tables and graphs in their portfolios. Portfolio

Section 1 What Is Electromagnetism?

Objectives

After this lesson, students will be able to
N.3.1.1 Explain how an electric current is related to a magnetic field.
N.3.1.2 Identify some characteristics of a magnetic field produced by a current.
N.3.1.3 Describe the characteristics of an electromagnet.

Target Reading Skill

Identifying Main Ideas Explain that identifying main ideas and details helps students sort the facts from the information into groups. Each group can have a main topic, subtopics, and details.

Answers

Sample answers:
Main Idea: A solenoid is useful because its magnetic field can be changed.
Detail: Its magnetic field can be turned on and off.
Detail: Its magnetic field can have its direction changed.
Detail: Its magnetic field can have its strength changed.

All in One Teaching Resources
- Transparency N29

Preteach

Build Background Knowledge L2

Recalling Magnetic Fields

Have students recall what they have learned about magnets and magnetism. Ask: **What is a magnet?** *(Any material that attracts iron and materials that contain iron)* **What is a magnetic field?** *(The area of magnetic force around a magnet)* **What particle within an atom produces a magnetic field?** *(An electron)*

For: Links on electromagnetism
Visit: www.SciLinks.org
Web Code: scn-1431

Download a worksheet that will guide students' review of Internet sources on electromagnetism.

Section 1 What Is Electromagnetism?

Reading Preview

Key Concepts

- How is an electric current related to a magnetic field?
- What are some characteristics of a magnetic field produced by a current?
- What are the characteristics of an electromagnet?

Key Terms

- electromagnetism
- solenoid
- electromagnet

Target Reading Skill

Identifying Main Ideas As you read the Solenoid section, write the main idea—the biggest or most important idea—in a graphic organizer like the one below. Then write three supporting details. The supporting details further explain the main idea.

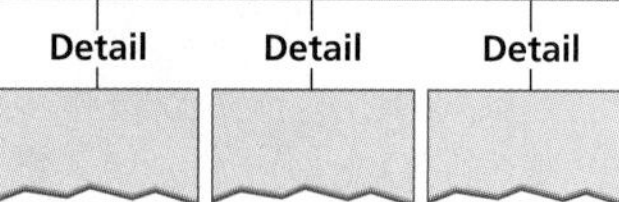
Main Idea
A solenoid is useful because its magnetic field can be changed.
Detail
Detail
Detail

For: Links on electromagnetism
Visit: www.SciLinks.org
Web Code: scn-1431

Lab zone Discover Activity

Are Magnetic Fields Limited to Magnets?

1. Obtain two wires with the insulation removed from both ends. Each wire should be 20 to 30 cm long.
2. Connect one end of each wire to a socket containing a small light bulb.
3. Connect the other end of one of those wires to a D-cell battery.
4. Place three compasses near the wire at different positions. Before you continue, note the direction in which each of the compasses is pointing.
5. Center the wire over the compasses. Make sure the compass needles are free to turn.
6. Touch the free end of the remaining wire to the battery. Observe the compasses as charges flow through the wire. Move the wire away from the battery, and then touch it to the battery again. Watch the compasses.

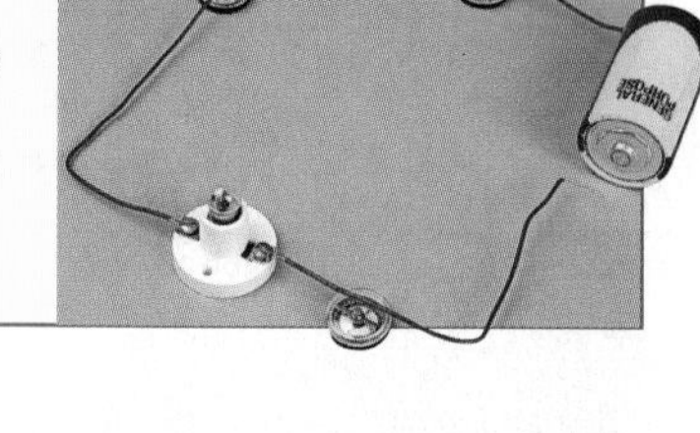

Think It Over
Inferring What happened to the compasses when charges flowed through the wire? What can you infer about electricity and magnetism?

In 1820, the Danish scientist Hans Christian Oersted (UR sted) was teaching a class at the University of Copenhagen. During his lecture he produced a current in a wire, just like the current in the wires of your appliances at home. When he brought a compass near the wire, he observed that the compass needle changed direction.

Oersted was surprised. He could have assumed that something was wrong with his equipment and ignored what he saw. Instead, he investigated further. He set up several compasses around a wire. Oersted discovered that whenever he produced a current in the wire, the compass needles lined up around the wire in the shape of a circle.

Oersted's discovery showed that magnetism and electricity are related. But just how are they related?

Lab zone Discover Activity

Skills Focus Inferring L2

Materials 2 wires (20–30 cm long), light bulb, bulb holder, 3 compasses, D-cell battery (1.5 volt)

Time 15 minutes

Tips Tell students that they'll construct an electric circuit that electricity will flow through when it is closed.

Expected Outcome The light bulb lights and some of the compass needles move when students close the circuit.

Think It Over Sample answer: The compass needles move when the free end of the wire touches the battery, completing the circuit. Current in the wire creates a magnetic field that affects the compass.

FIGURE 1
Currents and Magnetic Fields
Current in a wire affects nearby compasses.

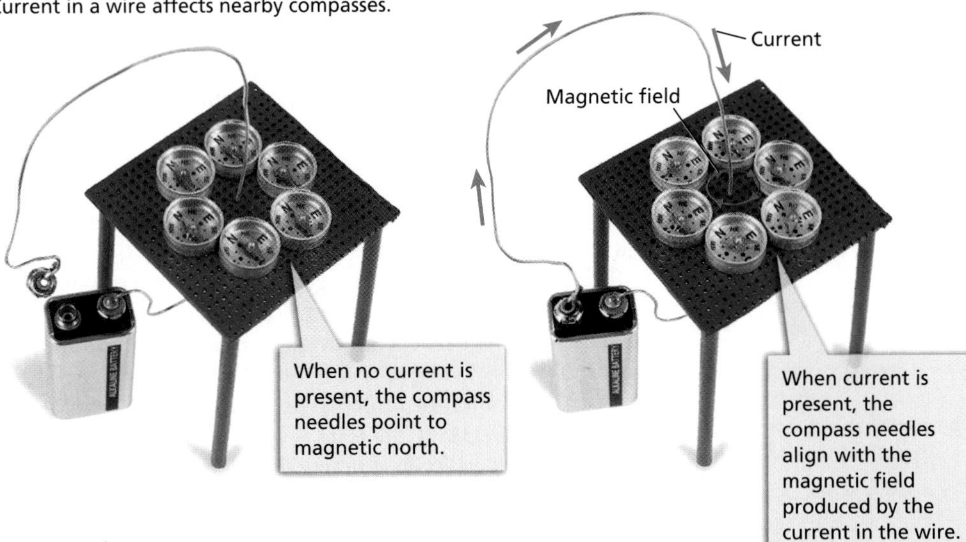

Current
Magnetic field
When no current is present, the compass needles point to magnetic north.
When current is present, the compass needles align with the magnetic field produced by the current in the wire.

Electric Current and Magnetism

Wherever there is electricity, there is magnetism. **An electric current produces a magnetic field.** This relationship between electricity and magnetism is called **electromagnetism.**

You can't see electromagnetism, but you can use a compass and an electric current to observe its effect on objects. A compass needle normally points north because it aligns itself with Earth's magnetic field. It will point in a different direction only if another magnetic field is present. For example, look at the compasses shown in the photo on the left in Figure 1. They surround a straight wire that has no current. Because there is no current, the wire has no magnetic field. Therefore, the compasses align with Earth's magnetic field and point north.

In the photo on the right in Figure 1, the wire has a current. Notice that in this case the compasses no longer point north. The needles of the compasses change direction because a magnetic field is produced around a wire that has a current. The needles of the compasses align with the magnetic field that the current produces.

In Figure 2, iron filings surround a wire that has a current. You can see that the filings form a pattern. They map out the magnetic field produced by the current in the wire.

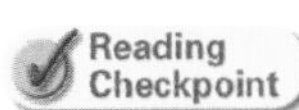 **What can produce a magnetic field?**

FIGURE 2
A Magnetic Field Map
Iron filings show the magnetic field lines around a wire with a current. Observing *What is the shape of the field lines?*

Instruct

Electric Current and Magnetism

Teach Key Concepts L2

A Relationship

Focus Tell students that just as a magnet produces a magnetic field, so too does an electric current.

Teach Ask: **What is electromagnetism?** *(The relationship between electricity and magnetism)* **Can a magnetic field produced by an electric current be seen?** *(No. A magnetic field is invisible.)*

Apply Have students study the two situations displayed in Figure 1. Then have students look at the photo on the left. Ask: **How can you tell there is no current in the wire?** *(All the compass needles are aligned with Earth's magnetic field and point north.)* **How are the compasses different in the second photo?** *(The compass needles are all pointing in different directions.)* **What caused the compass needles to point in different directions?** *(There is current in the wire, and the compass needles align with the magnetic field produced by that electric current.)* **learning modality: visual**

Independent Practice L2

All in One Teaching Resources

- Guided Reading and Study Worksheet: *What Is Electromagnetism?*

Student Edition on Audio CD

Differentiated Instruction

Special Needs L1

The Right-Hand Rule Use the "right-hand rule" to teach visually impaired students about the direction of a magnetic field or any student having difficulty understanding that reversing the direction of the current reverses the direction of the magnetic field, as shown in Figure 3. Explain that if you point the thumb of your right hand in the direction of the current, your fingers curve in the direction of the magnetic field. Tell students there is a current in one direction through a wire. Ask a student to point the thumb of the right hand in the direction of the current. Then have the student wrap his or her fingers around the wire. That is the direction of the magnetic field. **learning modality: kinesthetic**

Monitor Progress L2

Oral Presentation Call on students to explain in their own words the relationship between electricity and magnetism.

Answers

Figure 2 The magnetic field lines are circular around the wire.

 Magnets and electric currents can produce a magnetic field.

Solenoids

Teach Key Concepts

L2

Poles Change With the Current

Focus Tell students that an electric current through a coil of wire has a magnetic field.

Teach Ask: **What are the three characteristics of a magnetic field produced by an electric current?** *(The field can be turned on or off, have its direction reversed, or have its strength changed.)* **How could you turn off a current's magnetic field?** *(By turning off the current)* **How could you change the direction of a current's magnetic field?** *(By changing the direction of the current)* **What does the strength of a current's magnetic field depend on?** *(The number of loops, or coils, in the wire)*

Apply Ask: **What would happen if you increased the number of coils in a solenoid?** *(The magnetic field of the solenoid would be strengthened.)* **learning modality: logical/ mathematical**

All in One Teaching Resources

- Transparencies N30, N31

L2

Modeling a Solenoid's Magnetic Field

Materials long thin rope, coiled spring toy

Time 10 minutes

Focus Tell students they can use a rope and a spring toy to model the magnetic field of a solenoid.

Teach Have students place the rope inside the spring toy so the spring makes a cylinder around the rope. Then have students tie the ends of the rope to the outermost links of the spring. Students can bend the rope into a loop and observe what happens to the spring. Students will observe that the coils of the spring bunch up inside the loop of the rope, just as the magnetic field lines become bunched up inside a loop of wire.

Apply Ask: **What do the rope and the spring represent in this model of a solenoid?** *(The rope represents the loop of wire, and the spring represents the magnetic field around the loop.)* **learning modality: visual**

FIGURE 3
Controlling a Magnetic Field
Both the direction and strength of a magnetic field produced by a current can be controlled.

A Reversing the direction of the current reverses the direction of the magnetic field.

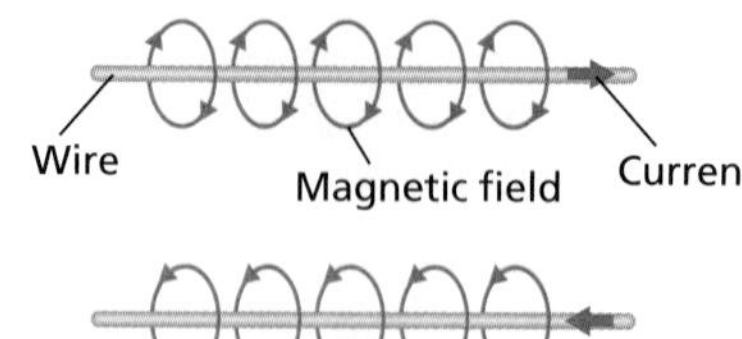

B Looping the wire increases the strength of the magnetic field.

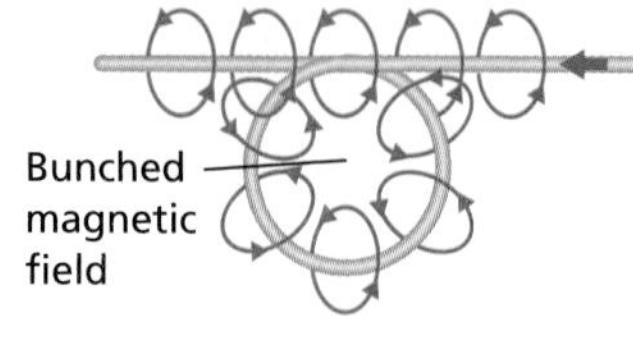

Solenoids

The magnetic field produced by a current has three distinct characteristics. The field can be turned on or off, have its direction reversed, or have its strength changed. Unlike Earth's magnetic field, you can turn a magnetic field produced by a current on or off. To do so you simply turn the current on or off. In addition, you can change the direction of the magnetic field by reversing the direction of the current. When the current reverses, the magnetic field reverses also, as shown in Figure 3A.

You can also change the strength of a magnetic field produced by a current. The magnetic field around a wire with a current forms a cylinder around the wire. If the wire is twisted into a loop, the magnetic field lines become bunched up inside the loop, as shown in Figure 3B. If the wire is bent into a second loop, the concentration of magnetic field lines within the loops is twice as great. So, the strength of the magnetic field increases as the number of loops, or coils, increases.

By winding a wire with a current into many loops you strengthen the magnetic field in the center of the coil. A coil of wire with a current is called a **solenoid.** The two ends of a solenoid act like magnetic poles. In Figure 4 you can see that the iron filings around a solenoid line up much as they would around a bar magnet. However, in a solenoid, the north and south poles change with the direction of the current.

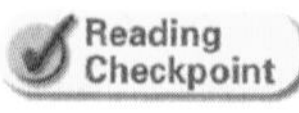

What happens to the magnetic field lines in a twisted loop of wire?

FIGURE 4
Magnetic Field Around a Solenoid
The magnetic field around a solenoid resembles that of a bar magnet.
Comparing and Contrasting *How is a solenoid different from a bar magnet?*

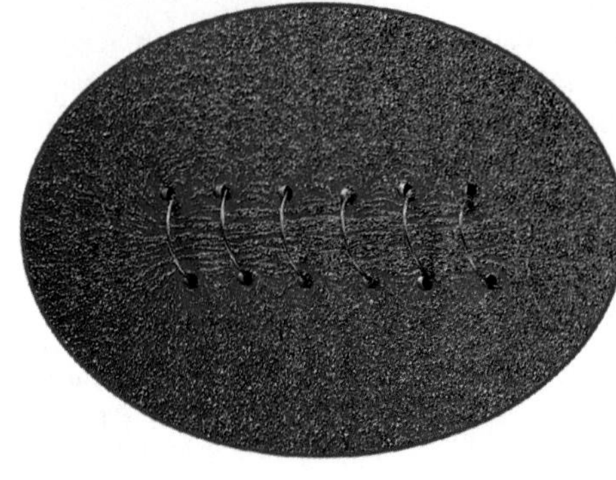

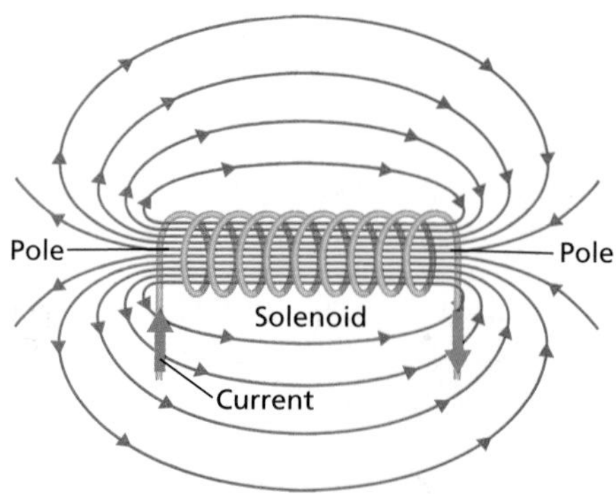

FIGURE 5
How a Doorbell Works
A doorbell rings as the magnetic field of an electromagnet changes.

Closed Circuit
Pressing the button closes the circuit of the doorbell. Closing the circuit turns on the electromagnet in the doorbell.

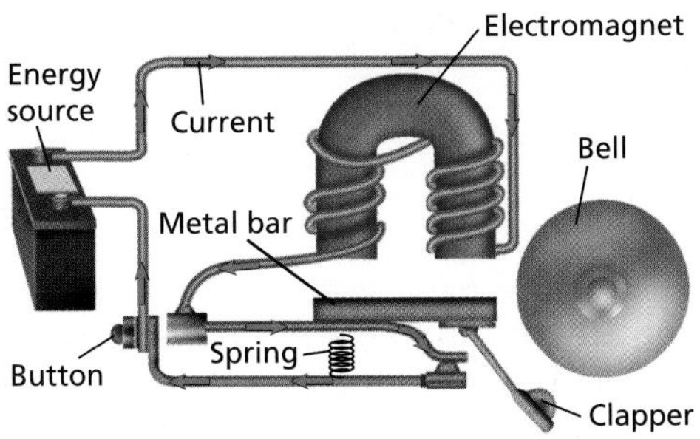

Electromagnet
Energy source
Current
Bell
Metal bar
Spring
Button
Clapper

Open Circuit
The electromagnet attracts a metal bar, and the clapper strikes the bell. At the same time, the circuit opens, turning off the electromagnet. The spring returns the metal bar to its resting position.

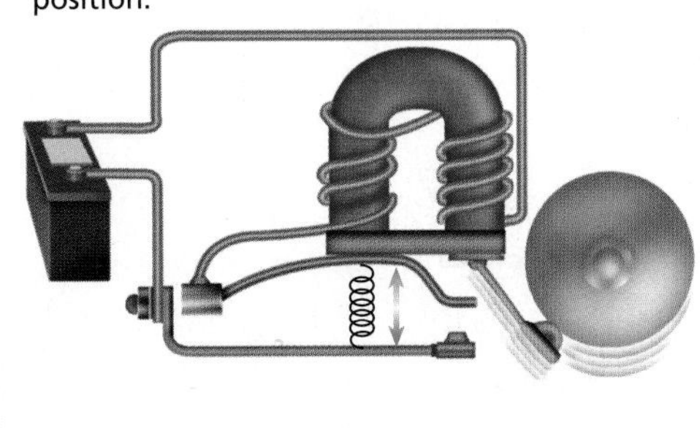

Electromagnets

If you place a ferromagnetic material such as iron inside a solenoid, the strength of the magnetic field increases. The increase in strength occurs because the ferromagnetic material becomes a magnet.

What Is an Electromagnet? A solenoid with a ferromagnetic core is called an **electromagnet.** The magnetic field of an electromagnet is produced by both the current in the wire and the magnetized core. The overall magnetic field of an electromagnet can be hundreds or thousands of times stronger than the magnetic field produced by the current alone. **An electromagnet is a strong magnet that can be turned on and off.**

You can increase the strength of an electromagnet in a number of ways. First, you can increase the current in the solenoid; second, you can add more loops of wire to the solenoid. Third, you can wind the coils of the solenoid closer together. Finally, you can increase the strength of an electromagnet by using a stronger ferromagnetic material for the core.

Common Electromagnets Electromagnets are very common. You probably use many every day. Electromagnets are used to record information onto audiotapes, videotapes, computer hard drives, and credit cards. In addition, many devices, such as the doorbell shown in Figure 5, use electromagnets.

Lab zone Try This Activity

On/Off

1. Your teacher will give you a piece of insulated copper wire. Tightly wrap it around a nail 10–12 times.
2. Tape one end of the wire to a battery terminal.
3. Touch the other end of the wire to the other battery terminal and dip the nail into a container of paper clips. Slowly lift the nail above the container.
4. Pull the wire away from the battery terminal and observe what happens.

Inferring Why did the paper clips drop when you pulled the wire away from the battery terminal?

Lab zone Try This Activity

Skills Focus Inferring L1

Materials 1 m insulated copper wire, electric tape, iron nail, D-cell battery, container of paper clips

Time 15 minutes

Tips Use wire with very thin insulation so that a large number of turns fit easily in a compact space. Caution students not to close the circuit for too long, because the nail may become magnetized and attract paper clips when the current is off.

Expected Outcome When the device is "on," or connected, it attracts paper clips because of the magnetic field produced. When the device is "off," or disconnected, it drops the paper clips because there is no magnetic field. **learning modality: kinesthetic**

Electromagnets

Teach Key Concepts L2

A Useful Solenoid

Focus Tell students that a solenoid becomes an electromagnet with the addition of a ferromagnetic core.

Teach Ask: **Why is the strength of an electromagnet so much greater than the strength of a solenoid's magnetic field?** *(The ferromagnetic core becomes magnetized by the coil's field, and the core and the coil together produce a much stronger magnetic field.)* **What are four ways to increase an electromagnet's magnetic field?** *(By increasing the current in the solenoid, by adding more loops of wire to the solenoid, by winding the coils of the solenoid closer together, and by using a stronger ferromagnetic material for the core)*

Apply Have students study how a doorbell works as shown in Figure 5. Ask: **How does pressing the doorbell's button affect the electromagnet?** *(Pressing the button closes the circuit and thus turns on the electromagnet.)* **What does the electromagnet attract?** *(The metal bar)* **Why does the clapper strike the bell?** *(The clapper is attached to the metal bar, which is attracted to the electromagnet.)* **What turns off the electromagnet?** *(The electromagnet turns off because when it attracts the metal bar, the rising metal bar breaks the circuit.)* **learning modality: visual**

All in One Teaching Resources

- Transparency N32

Monitor Progress L2

Drawing Have each student draw a labeled diagram of an electromagnet and explain how it works.

Have students keep their drawings in their portfolios.

Answers

Figure 4 In a solenoid, the north and south poles change with the direction of the current and the magnetic field can be turned on and off.

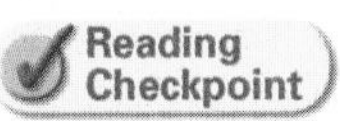

The magnetic field lines become bunched up inside the loop.

Assess

Reviewing Key Concepts

1. a. Hans Christian Oersted **b.** An electric current produces a magnetic field. **c.** A magnetic field is produced around a wire that has a current.
2. a. A solenoid is a coil of wire with a current. **b.** The magnetic field can be turned on and off, have its direction reversed, or have its strength changed. **c.** By increasing the number of loops, or coils, in the wire of a solenoid
3. a. An electromagnet has ferromagnetic material inside a solenoid, and the ferromagnetic material becomes a magnet. The magnetized core and the solenoid together produce a much stronger magnetic field. **b.** Increase the current in the solenoid, add more loops of wire to the solenoid, wind the coils of the solenoid closer together, and use a stronger ferromagnetic material for the core

Reteach L1

Use Figure 5 to reteach how electricity and magnetism are related, what a solenoid is, and how an electromagnet works.

Performance Assessment L2

Writing Ask students to design an electromagnet for a specific purpose. Students should describe how the electromagnet works and name one way it can be strengthened.

All in One Teaching Resources

- Section Summary: *What Is Electromagnetism?*
- Review and Reinforce: *What Is Electromagnetism?*
- Enrich: *What Is Electromagnetism?*

FIGURE 6
Electromagnets at Work
These heavy loads can be lifted easily because of powerful electromagnets.

Using Electromagnets Electromagnets are used to lift heavy objects. For example, at a junk-yard, old cars and other heavy metal objects can be moved by a strong electromagnet on a crane. To lift the object a switch is turned on in the crane so that a current is produced in the electromagnet. The current forms a strong magnetic field that attracts metal objects. When the object needs to be dropped, the switch is turned off and the object falls from the magnet.

Section 1 Assessment

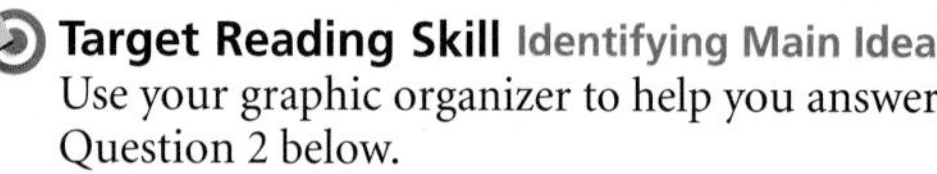

Target Reading Skill Identifying Main Ideas Use your graphic organizer to help you answer Question 2 below.

Reviewing Key Concepts

1. a. Identifying Who discovered that electricity and magnetism are related?
   b. Explaining What is the relationship between an electric current and a magnetic field?
   c. Relating Cause and Effect How can a magnetic field be produced around a wire?
2. a. Defining What is a solenoid?
   b. Explaining What are the three characteristics of a magnetic field produced by a current?
   c. Applying Concepts How could you increase the strength of a solenoid?
3. a. Reviewing What makes an electromagnet stronger than a solenoid?
   b. Describing What are four ways to make an electromagnet stronger?

Writing in Science

Product Description Suppose you are an inventor who just built a device that will lift heavy objects using an electromagnet. Write a description for your product brochure that explains how the magnet can move heavy objects.

84 ◆ N

Lab zone Chapter Project

Keep Students on Track Make sure students are listing the appliances in their homes that use electrical energy. Mention to students appliances they may not have thought about, such as an electric water heater or a furnace fan. Help students approximate electrical energy use for appliances that run discontinuously throughout the day, such as a refrigerator (about 2 kWh/day).

Writing in Science

Writing Mode Description

Scoring Rubric
4 Exceeds criteria; includes an imaginative and accurate description of an electromagnet
3 Meets criteria
2 Meets some criteria; includes a somewhat accurate description
1 Includes an inaccurate and/or incomplete description of how an electromagnet works

Section 2

Electricity, Magnetism, and Motion

Reading Preview

Key Concepts

- How can electrical energy be transformed into mechanical energy?
- How does a galvanometer work?
- What does an electric motor do?

Key Terms

- energy
- electrical energy
- mechanical energy
- galvanometer
- electric motor

Target Reading Skill

Outlining As you read, make an outline about the section that you can use for review. Use the red headings for the main ideas and the blue headings for the supporting ideas.

Electricity, Magnetism, and Motion

I. Electrical Energy and Motion
   A. Types of Energy
   B.
II. Galvanometers
III. Electric Motors
   A.

Lab zone Discover Activity

How Does a Magnet Move a Wire?

1. Make an electromagnet by winding insulated copper wire around a steel nail. Leave 30–40 cm of wire at each end of the electromagnet.
2. Pile up some books. Place a ruler between the top two books.
3. Hang the electromagnet over the ruler so that it hangs free.
4. Complete the circuit by connecting the electromagnet to a switch and a battery.
5. Place a horseshoe magnet near the electromagnet. Then close the switch briefly and observe what happens to the electromagnet.
6. Reverse the wires connected to the battery and repeat Step 5.

Think It Over

Inferring What happened to the electromagnet when you closed the switch? Was anything different when you reversed the wires? How can you use electricity to produce motion?

What do you think about when you hear the word *electricity?* You may think about the bright lights of a big city, the lightning during a thunderstorm, or the music from your stereo in the morning. You might think about how useful electricity is. For example, if you are familiar with electric motors like the one in a blender, then you already know about an important use of electricity. Electricity can produce motion.

Electricity makes the blades spin. ▶

Section 2

Electricity, Magnetism, and Motion

Objectives

After this lesson, students will be able to

N.3.2.1 Explain how electrical energy can be transformed into mechanical energy.

N.3.2.2 Describe how a galvanometer works.

N.3.2.3 Describe what an electric motor does.

Target Reading Skill

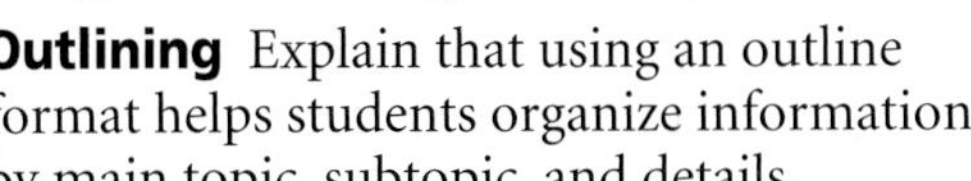

Outlining Explain that using an outline format helps students organize information by main topic, subtopic, and details.

Answer

I. Electrical Energy and Motion
   A. Types of Energy
   B. Energy Transformation
II. Galvanometers
III. Electric Motors
   A. How a Motor Works
   B. Parts of a Motor

All in One Teaching Resources

- Transparency N33

Preteach

Build Background Knowledge L2

Energy Transformations

Ask: **What are some devices in your home that are run by electric motors?** *(Sample answer: Hair dryer, vacuum cleaner, electric can opener, electric drill, fan, sewing machine, leaf blower, electric razor)* **What type of energy is put into the electric motor to make it operate?** *(Electrical energy)* **What types of energy do these devices produce?** *(Sample answer: Mechanical energy of moving parts, sound, heat, light)* Explain to students that in this section they will learn how electrical energy is transformed into other types of energy.

Lab zone Discover Activity

Skills Focus Inferring L2

Materials 1 m insulated copper wire, iron nail, books, metric ruler, circuit wire, switch, battery, horseshoe magnet

Time 15 minutes

Tips The nail should be parallel to the horseshoe magnet. Test the device in advance to be sure the magnet is strong enough to attract the electromagnet.

Expected Outcome The electromagnet swings when the switch is closed and swings in the opposite direction when connections are reversed.

Think It Over Sample answer: Electric current in a wire creates a magnetic field that interacts with a magnet's magnetic field, and the interaction causes the wire to move.

Instruct

Electrical Energy and Motion

Teach Key Concepts L2

Magnetic Force Can Produce Motion

Focus Tell students that when magnetic fields interact, motion is the result.

Teach Ask: **What is the difference between electrical energy and mechanical energy?** *(Electrical energy is the energy associated with electric currents, while mechanical energy is the energy an object has due to its movement or position.)* **When can electrical energy be transformed into mechanical energy?** *(When a wire with a current is placed in a magnetic field)*

Apply Have students examine Figure 7. Ask: **Why does the wire move when current is present?** *(The wire moves because the magnetic field produced by the current interacts with the magnetic field from the permanent magnet.)* **Why does the wire move up in the second case shown instead of down as in the first case shown?** *(The wire moves up in the second case because the current through the wire has been reversed. The direction in which the wire moves depends on the direction of the current.)* **learning modality: visual**

All in One Teaching Resources

- Transparency N34

Independent Practice L2

All in One Teaching Resources

- Guided Reading and Study Worksheet: *Electricity, Magnetism, and Motion*

Student Edition on Audio CD

FIGURE 7
Producing Motion
The magnetic field of a permanent magnet interacts with the magnetic field produced by a current.
Relating Cause and Effect
How does the direction of the current affect the motion of the wire?

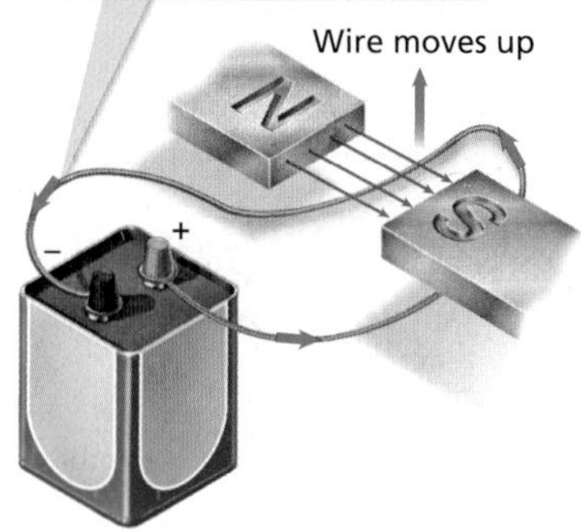
The wire moves when current is present.
Wire moves down
When the current is reversed, the wire moves in the opposite direction.
Wire moves up

Lab zone Try This Activity

Making Motion

1. Attach one end of the wire your teacher gives you to a terminal of a 6-volt battery. Let the wire hang over the edge of a table.
2. Slowly move the north pole of a bar magnet toward the wire and observe what happens. Switch poles and repeat.
3. Attach the other end of the wire to the other terminal. Let the loop of wire hang over the edge of the table.
4. Repeat Step 2. Then immediately disconnect the wire.

Drawing Conclusions What happened each time you moved the magnet near the wire? What can you conclude from your observations?

Electrical Energy and Motion

As you know, magnetic force can produce motion. Magnets can move together or move apart, depending on how their poles are arranged. You also know that an electric current in a wire produces a magnetic field similar to that of a permanent magnet. So a magnet can move a wire with a current, just as it would move another magnet.

In Figure 7 you can see how a wire placed in the magnetic field of two permanent magnets can move. With current in the wire, the magnetic field of the wire interacts with the magnetic field of the permanent magnets. The wire moves down. If the current is reversed, the wire moves up. The direction in which the wire moves depends on the direction of the current.

Types of Energy When electricity and magnetism interact, something can move—in this case, a wire moved. The ability to move an object over a distance is called **energy.** The energy associated with electric currents is called **electrical energy.** And the energy an object has due to its movement or position is called **mechanical energy.**

Energy Transformation Energy can be transformed from one form into another. **When a wire with a current is placed in a magnetic field, electrical energy is transformed into mechanical energy.** This happens when the magnetic field produced by the current causes the wire to move.

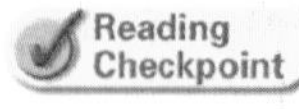

Reading Checkpoint **What is mechanical energy?**

86 ◆ N

Lab zone Try This Activity

Skills Focus Drawing conclusions L2

Materials 1 m insulated wire, 6-volt battery, bar magnet

Time 15 minutes

Tips Cut and strip wire in advance. No one should touch the wire with the magnet.

Expected Outcome Nothing happens when only one end of the wire is attached to a terminal. When both ends are attached, the loop moves because the current in the loop creates a magnetic field that interacts with the magnet's field.

Extend Have students experiment with magnets of different strengths. **learning modality: kinesthetic**

Galvanometers

The wire shown in Figure 7 that moves in the magnetic field is straight. But what happens if you place a loop with a current in a magnetic field? Look at Figure 8. The current in one side of the loop is in the opposite direction than the current in the other side of the loop. Because the direction of the current determines the direction in which the wire moves, the two sides of the loop move in opposite directions. Once each side has moved as far up or down as it can go, it will stop moving. As a result, the loop can rotate a half turn.

The rotation of a wire loop in a magnetic field is the basis of a galvanometer. A **galvanometer** is a device that measures small currents. In a galvanometer, an electromagnet is suspended between opposite poles of two permanent magnets. The electromagnet's coil is attached to a pointer, as shown in Figure 9. When a current is in the electromagnet's coil, a magnetic field is produced. This field interacts with the permanent magnet's field, causing the loops of wire and the pointer to rotate. **An electric current is used to turn the pointer of a galvanometer.** The distance the loops and the pointer rotate depends on the amount of current in the wire.

A galvanometer has a scale that is marked to show how much the pointer turns for a known current. An unknown current can then be measured using the galvanometer. So galvanometers are very useful in everyday life. For example, electricians use them in their work and drivers of cars use them to know when to stop for fuel.

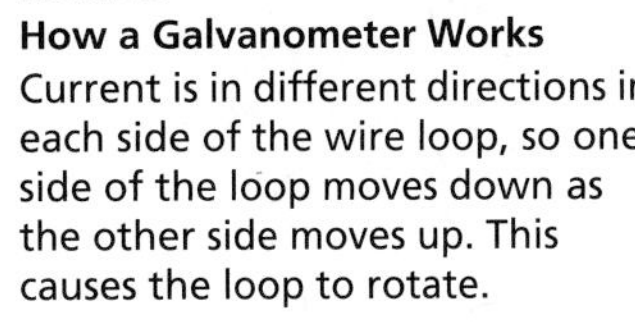

FIGURE 8
How a Galvanometer Works
Current is in different directions in each side of the wire loop, so one side of the loop moves down as the other side moves up. This causes the loop to rotate.

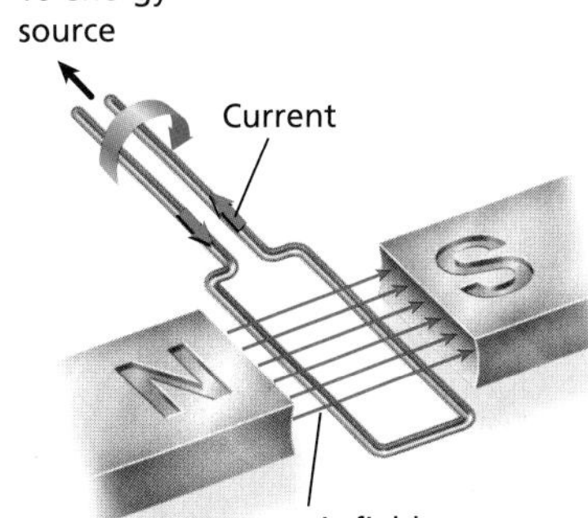

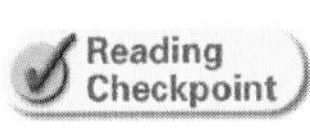
Reading Checkpoint — Where are galvanometers used?

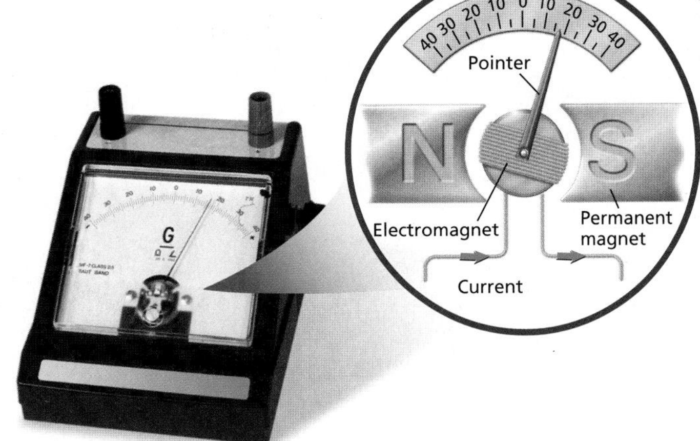

FIGURE 9
Inside a Galvanometer
An electromagnet turns the pointer to indicate the amount of current present. The amount of current can be read on the scale.

Galvanometers

Teach Key Concepts L2

Measuring Current

Focus Tell students that the rotation of a wire loop in a magnetic field can be used to measure small electric currents.

Teach Ask: **In a galvanometer, what is an electromagnet suspended between?** *(Unlike poles of two permanent magnets)* **When a current is in the galvanometer's electromagnet, what is produced?** *(A magnetic field)* **What causes the loops of wire and the pointer in a galvanometer to rotate?** *(The interaction of the magnets' magnetic field and the electromagnet's magnetic field)* **Why do the two sides of a galvanometer's wire loops move in opposite directions?** *(The current in one side of the loops is in the opposite direction of the current in the other side, and the direction of the current determines the direction in which the wire moves.)*

Apply Have students examine the galvanometer shown in Figure 9. Ask: **How do you know that the galvanometer is measuring a current?** *(The pointer is rotated to the right of 0 on the scale.)* **If the current suddenly increased, what would the pointer do? Why?** *(The pointer would rotate farther to the right, indicating a larger current. The distance the pointer rotates depends on the amount of current in the wire.)* **learning modality: visual**

All in One Teaching Resources

- Transparency N35

Differentiated Instruction

Less Proficient Readers L1

Identifying Supporting Ideas Have students listen to this section on the **Student Edition on Audio CD.** As they listen, they can identify supporting ideas and add them under the appropriate headings and subheadings in their section outlines. **learning modality: verbal**

Special Needs L1

Modeling a Galvanometer As students examine Figure 8, have them hold one hand flat, palm down, to represent the loop of wire between the poles. Ask students to move the hand to show what happens to the loop of wire when current moves through the wire. Students should rotate the hand a quarter turn. **learning modality: kinesthetic**

Monitor Progress L2

Skills Check Have students compare and contrast electrical energy and mechanical energy.

Answers

Figure 7 Changing the direction of the current in the wire changes the direction that the wire moves.

Reading Checkpoint — The energy an object has due to its movement or position

Reading Checkpoint — Electricians use them in their work and drivers of cars use them to know when to stop for fuel.

Electric Motors

Teach Key Concepts

L2

Electricity into Motion

Focus Tell students that the basis of the electric motor is an electromagnet in a magnetic field.

Teach Ask: **What energy transformation takes place in an electric motor?** *(An electric motor transforms electrical energy into mechanical energy.)* Have students examine Figure 10, and ask: **Why does the armature in an electric motor spin continuously?** *(Because the current reverses every half turn)*

Apply Point out that in a motor, the current reverses after each half turn of the armature loops. Ask: **What would happen if the current didn't reverse but kept flowing in the same direction?** *(The armature would stop spinning, because the reversing of the current causes the side that moved down on the right to move back up on the left.)* **learning modality: verbal**

All in One

Teaching Resources

- Transparency N36

Lab zone **Teacher Demo**

L1

Electric Motor

Materials parts of an electric motor, including armature, commutator, brushes

Time 10 minutes

Focus Tell students they will be able to observe the insides of an electric motor.

Teach Ask an automobile repair shop, especially one that repairs electric motors, to borrow an old, disassembled starter motor. Display the parts for students to observe. Challenge students to identify the armature, commutator, and brushes.

Apply Hold up the armature of the motor, and ask: **What are the advantages of having so many loops?** *(Having many loops increases the strength of the motor and allows the armature to rotate more quickly.)* **learning modality: visual**

Go Online
SCILINKS
NSTA

For: Links on electric motors
Visit: www.SciLinks.org
Web Code: scn-1432

Download a worksheet that will guide students' review of Internet sources on electric motors.

Go Online
SCILINKS
NSTA

For: Links on electric motors
Visit: www.SciLinks.org
Web Code: scn-1432

Electric Motors

The electromagnet in the magnetic field of a galvanometer cannot rotate more than half a turn. But suppose you could make it rotate continuously. Instead of moving a pointer, the electromagnet could turn a rod, or axle. The axle could then turn something else, such as the blades of a fan or a blender. Such a device would be what is called an electric motor. An **electric motor** is a device that uses an electric current to turn an axle. **An electric motor transforms electrical energy into mechanical energy.**

How a Motor Works How can you make a loop of wire continue to spin? Recall that the direction in which the loop moves in a magnetic field depends on the direction of the current in the loop. In a motor, current is reversed just as the loop, or armature, gets to the vertical position. This reverses the direction of the movement of both sides of the loop. The side of the loop that moved up on the left now moves down on the right. The side of the loop that moved down on the right now moves up on the left. The current reverses after each half turn so that the loop spins continuously in the same direction. You can see how a motor works in Figure 10.

FIGURE 10
An Electric Motor
A loop of wire in a motor spins continuously because the current reverses every half turn.
Observing *What part of an electric motor must be attached directly to the energy source?*

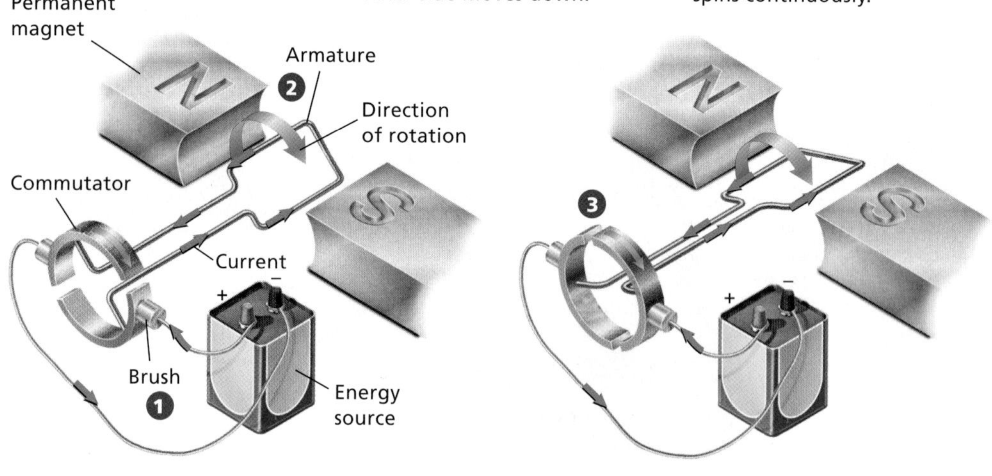

1 Brushes
The brushes that touch the commutator conduct current to the armature. The brushes do not move.
2 Armature
The current is in opposite directions on each side of the armature causing one side to move up while the other side moves down.
3 Commutator
The commutator rotates with the armature. The direction of current reverses with each half turn so the armature spins continuously.
Permanent magnet
Armature
Direction of rotation
Commutator
Current
Brush
Energy source
N
S
+
–

Parts of a Motor Notice that the armature in Figure 10 is only one loop of wire. However, practical armatures, like the one shown in Figure 11, have dozens or hundreds of wire loops wrapped around a ferromagnetic core. Using many loops increases the strength of the motor and allows it to rotate more smoothly. Large electric motors also use electromagnets instead of permanent magnets to increase the strength of the magnetic field.

A commutator repeatedly reverses the flow of current through the armature. A commutator is a ring split in half. Each half is attached to one end of the armature. When the armature rotates, the commutator rotates as well. As it moves, the commutator slides past two contact points called brushes. Each half of the commutator is connected to the current source by one of the brushes. As the armature rotates, each part of the commutator contacts one brush and then the other. Because the brushes conduct the current, changing brushes reverses the direction of the current in the armature. The reversing of the direction of the current causes the armature to spin continuously.

FIGURE 11
Inside a Motor
The armature inside this motor contains hundreds of loops of copper wire wrapped around a ferromagnetic core.
Applying Concepts *How does a motor transform energy?*

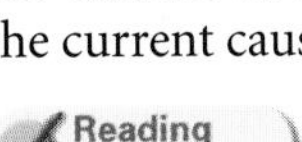

How can the strength of a motor be increased?

Section 2 Assessment

Target Reading Skill Outlining Use the information in your outline about electricity, magnetism, and motion to help you answer the questions below.

Reviewing Key Concepts

1. a. Identifying What is energy?
   b. Applying Concepts What energy transformation occurs when a wire with a current is placed in a magnetic field?
   c. Predicting If a wire with a current moved upward in a magnetic field, how would it move when the direction of the current reversed?
2. a. Reviewing What does a galvanometer measure?
   b. Describing What energy transformation occurs in a galvanometer?
   c. Relating Cause and Effect What causes the pointer to move in a galvanometer?
3. a. Defining What is an electric motor?
   b. Classifying What type of energy transformation occurs in a motor?
   c. Relating Cause and Effect What does the commutator do in an electric motor?

Writing in Science

Make a List Make a list of at least ten motor-operated devices in your community. Beside each device, describe the motion produced by the motor.

Monitor Progress L2

Answers
Figure 10 The brushes
Figure 11 An electric motor transforms electrical energy into mechanical energy.

Reading Checkpoint Using many loops of wire in the armature increases the strength of a motor. Using an electromagnet instead of a permanent magnet also increases the strength.

Assess

Reviewing Key Concepts

1. a. The ability to move an object over a distance **b.** Electrical energy is transformed into mechanical energy. **c.** The wire would move downward.
2. a. Small currents **b.** Electrical energy is transformed into mechanical energy. **c.** An electric current is used to turn the pointer of a galvanometer. The distance the pointer rotates depends on the amount of current in the wire.
3. a. A device that uses an electric current to turn an axle **b.** Electrical energy is transformed to mechanical energy. **c.** The commutator reverses the direction of the current through the armature. The reversing of the direction of the current causes the armature to spin continuously.

Reteach L1

Call on students to define in their own words the key terms *energy, electrical energy, mechanical energy, galvanometer,* and *electric motor.*

Performance Assessment L2

Drawing Have students draw a diagram of an electric motor and write captions and labels to describe the relationships among its parts.

All in One Teaching Resources

- Section Summary: *Electricity, Magnetism, and Motion*
- Review and Reinforce: *Electricity, Magnetism, and Motion*
- Enrich: *Electricity, Magnetism, and Motion*

Lab zone Chapter Project

Keep Students on Track Make sure students are making daily entries into their data tables. As they begin to total the amount of time each appliance was in use, help them convert minutes to decimal hours so they can compare results more easily. For example: 6 min = 6 min ÷ 60 min/h = 0.1 h.

Writing in Science

Writing Mode Description
Scoring Rubric
4 Exceeds criteria; accurately and creatively describes more than 10 devices
3 Meets criteria
2 Meets some criteria; includes descriptions of less than 10 devices
1 Fails to describe 10 devices or inaccurately describes their function

Technology and Society

Magnetic Resonance Imaging

Key Concept
Electromagnets are used in a technology that can safely scan the human body.

Build Background Knowledge
Electromagnets
Help students recall what they have learned about electromagnets. Ask: **What is an electromagnet?** *(An electromagnet is a solenoid with a ferromagnetic core.)* **How does the ferromagnetic core affect the strength of an electromagnet?** *(The overall magnetic field of an electromagnet can be hundreds or thousands of times stronger than the magnetic field produced by the electric current alone.)* **How can you vary the strength of an electromagnet?** *(You can vary the strength of the current in the solenoid. You can wind the coils of the solenoid closer together or farther apart. You can add more coils. And you can use a stronger or weaker ferromagnetic material for the core.)*

Introduce the Debate
Point out that MRI technology is a safe way to examine the insides of a human body. The problem for some people is that they cannot afford an MRI scan because an MRI machine is costly to build and use. This is especially a concern for people who have no health insurance. Tell students that they will debate this proposition: "The use of MRI technology should be provided for all patients in the United States, regardless of their means to pay for the scan."

Facilitate the Debate
- Have students read the feature and answer the Weigh the Impact questions individually as a homework assignment. The next day, organize the class into small groups for discussion. Have students consider these questions: Why can't everyone afford to pay for an MRI scan? Is the use of advanced technology in healthcare a right that everyone has? Do the taxpayers of the United States have an obligation to pay for MRI scans for people who cannot afford to pay on their own?
- Organize the class into two groups. Arbitrarily assign one group to argue that people should be provided MRI scans despite not being able to pay. Assign the other group to argue that U.S. taxpayers cannot afford to pay for this expensive technology for everyone. Alternately call on students from each group to state the group's position or refute an idea from someone in the other group.

Technology and Society • Tech & Design •

Magnetic Resonance Imaging

Imagine powerful magnets and electromagnetic energy scanning you from head to toe. Science fiction? No, it's magnetic resonance imaging (MRI.) MRI is a safe and painless way of looking inside the body. The technology uses large electromagnets, radio waves, and computers to make a three-dimensional model of the body.

Hydrogen, Magnets, and Radio Waves
Different types of body tissue contain different amounts of hydrogen atoms. The MRI machine uses the magnetic properties of hydrogen atoms to create images. The main electromagnet of an MRI machine creates a strong magnetic field that causes the magnetic fields of the hydrogen atoms in a body to align. Three weaker magnetic coils—the X-coil, the Y-coil, and the Z-coil—specify an area, or "slice," of the body to be imaged. Short pulses of radio waves knock the hydrogen atoms out of alignment. When the radio wave pulses are stopped, the atoms realign. As they do, they release energy in the form of radio signals. The signals are collected and sent to a computer that translates them into images.

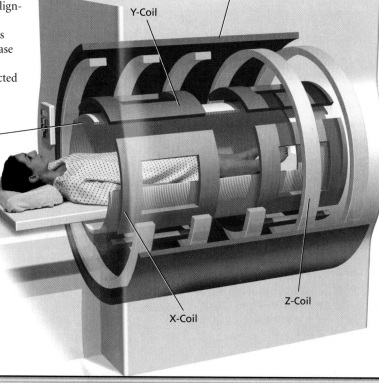

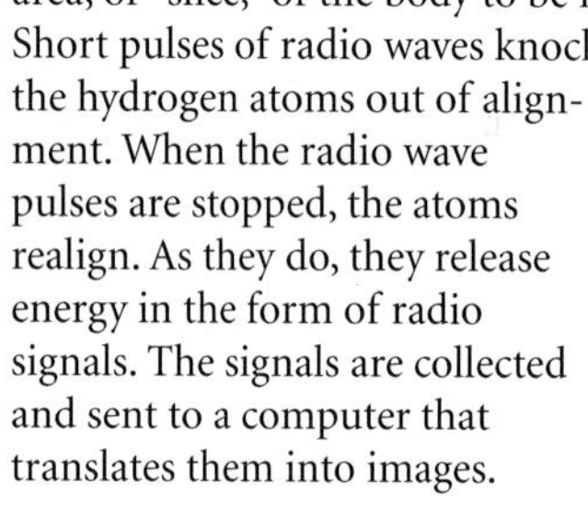

Main Electromagnet
The main electromagnet produces an even, strong magnetic field around the patient.
Y-Coil
Radio-frequency Coil
This coil applies short radio pulses to knock the hydrogen atoms in a person's body out of alignment. It also acts as an antenna, receiving radio signals from the realigning atoms.
X-Coil
Z-Coil

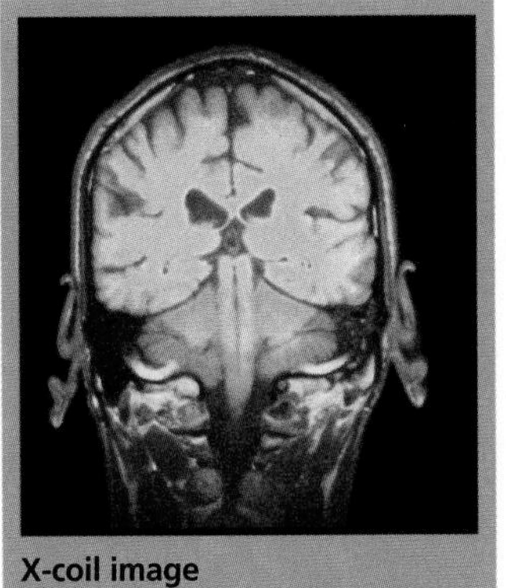
X-coil image

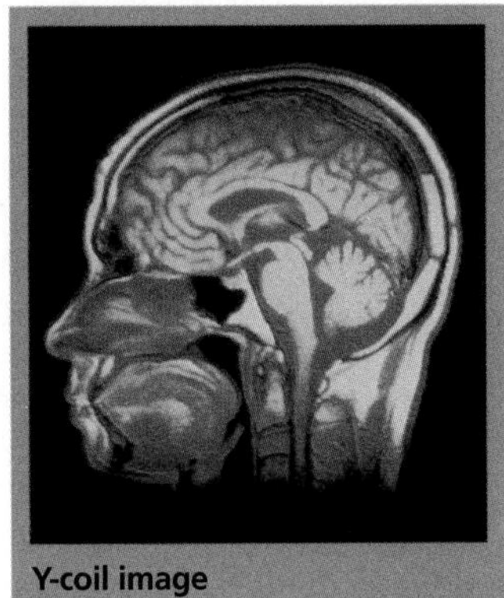
Y-coil image

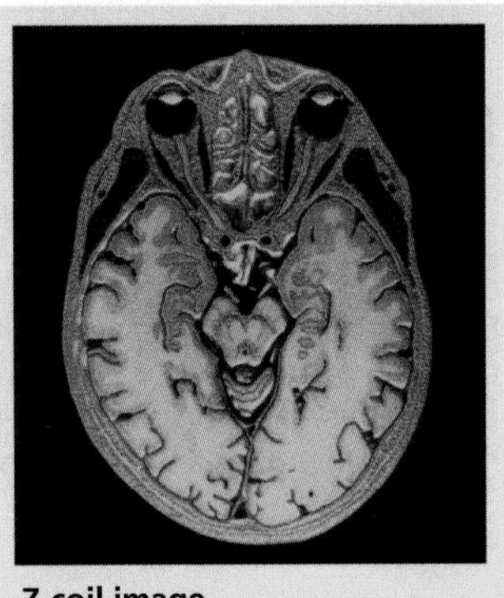
Z-coil image

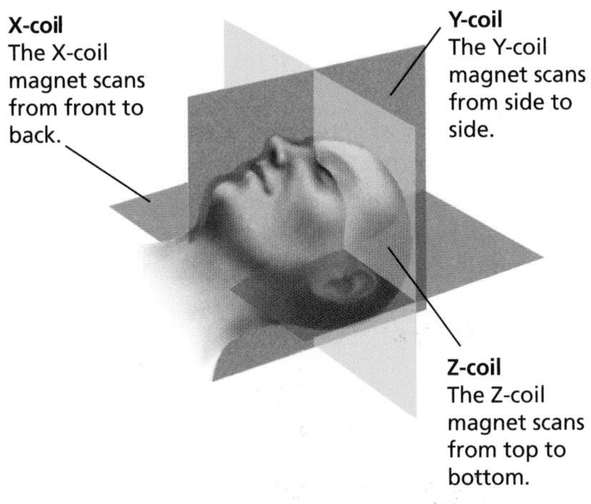
X-coil
The X-coil magnet scans from front to back.
Y-coil
The Y-coil magnet scans from side to side.
Z-coil
The Z-coil magnet scans from top to bottom.

Seeing Inside the Body

MRI has advantages over X-ray scanning. MRI is safer because it doesn't use radiation. Also, unlike an X-ray machine, MRI shows soft tissues clearly. Therefore, MRI is used to examine ligaments and parts of organs, such as the brain and circulatory system.

Why isn't MRI used more often? There are many answers. An MRI machine is costly to build and use. Very large people cannot fit inside the machine. People with a pacemaker or with some types of metallic implants in their bodies cannot have MRI. In addition, some people find this procedure uncomfortable because the machine is noisy and they must lie very still inside it for a long time.

Weigh the Impact

1. Identify the Need
MRI is not used in every medical situation. What factors might a doctor consider before ordering an MRI test?

2. Research
Explore the latest MRI technology on the Internet. Focus on how MRI technology is being improved for children.

3. Write
Use your research to create a pamphlet for children describing an MRI test. Include facts about how MRI technology is improving.

For: More on magnetic resonance imaging
Visit: PHSchool.com
Web Code: cgh-4030

Weigh the Impact

1. Sample answer: The doctor might consider the part or system of the body that needs to be examined. Other considerations include the size of the person to be scanned, whether the person has some type of metallic implant, and whether the person would be bothered by the noise and the confined space of an MRI machine.
2. Students could use an Internet search engine to find Web sites that include information about MRI technology. They might also consult with the school librarian or a reference librarian at a public library to find books and reference materials that have information about MRI technology. Ask that students take notes about what they have found and record the name of the Web sites or publications they used.
3. Students' pamphlets should include basic information about how an MRI machine functions and what it is used for, as well as a description of the experience a person would have who is scanned by the machine. Students should also include up-to-date information about the improvements being made in MRI technology.

For: More on magnetic resonance imaging
Visit: PHSchool.com
Web Code: cgh-4030

Students can research this issue online.

Extend

Encourage interested students to check with a local hospital to find out more about MRI technology in their area. A first step might be asking a family physician where a patient might go to have an MRI test. Groups of students might schedule a visit to an MRI laboratory where they could talk with a doctor or technician who carries out the MRI scans.

Background

Facts and Figures The main electromagnet used in an MRI machine is extremely powerful. Magnetic field strength is commonly measured using a unit called gauss, named after a nineteenth-century German mathematician; 10,000 gauss = 1 tesla. Earth's magnetic field is rated at 0.5 gauss. An MRI machine's main electromagnet range from 0.5 tesla to 2.0 tesla.

Improvements in MRI technology include the development of very small scanners. Instead of a person having to enter the machine, such a small scanner can simply be placed on the part of the body that needs to be scanned. This technology could prove to be very useful when the patient is an infant or small child.

L3

Building an Electric Motor

Prepare for Inquiry

Key Concept
A motor is a device that transforms electrical energy into mechanical energy.

Skills Objective
After this lab, students will be able to:
- classify which part of the setup contains a permanent magnet
- infer what the effect was of removing all the insulation from only one end of the wire coil
- draw a conclusion about how magnetism and electricity interact to cause the wire coil to rotate.

Prep Time 20 minutes
Class Time 40 minutes

Advance Planning
Construct a motor yourself to make sure the materials you have available are appropriate and functional. Test the batteries to be certain they are strong enough to operate the motor.

Alternative Materials
If film canisters are unavailable, use plastic test tubes, glue sticks, thick markers, or any cylinder that is 1.5–3 cm in diameter as a guide for wrapping the coil.

Safety
Caution students not to poke themselves with the sharp ends of the coil wire. If the coil is left on the paper clip supports for more than about 10 seconds, it may become very hot. Review the safety guidelines in Appendix A.

All in One Teaching Resources
- Lab Worksheet: *Building an Electric Motor*

Lab zone **Skills Lab**

Building an Electric Motor

Problem
Electric trolley cars, food blenders, garage door openers, and computer disk drives are only some of the everyday devices that have electric motors. How does an electric motor operate?

Skills Focus
classifying, inferring, drawing conclusions

Materials
- D-cell
- 2 large paper clips
- permanent disk magnet
- 3 balls of clay
- empty film canister
- pliers
- sandpaper
- 2 insulated wires, approximately 15 cm each
- enamel-coated wire, 22–24 gauge, approximately 1 meter

Procedure 
1. Wrap about 1 meter of enamel-coated wire around a film canister to produce a wire coil. Leave approximately 5 cm free at each end.
2. Remove the film canister and wrap the two free ends three or four times around the wire coil to keep the coil from unwinding.
3. Use sandpaper to scrape off all the enamel from about 2 or 3 centimeters of one end of the wire coil.
4. Use sandpaper to scrape off one side of the enamel from about 2 or 3 centimeters of the other end of the wire. See the illustration below.
5. Bend two paper clips as shown in the photo on the next page.

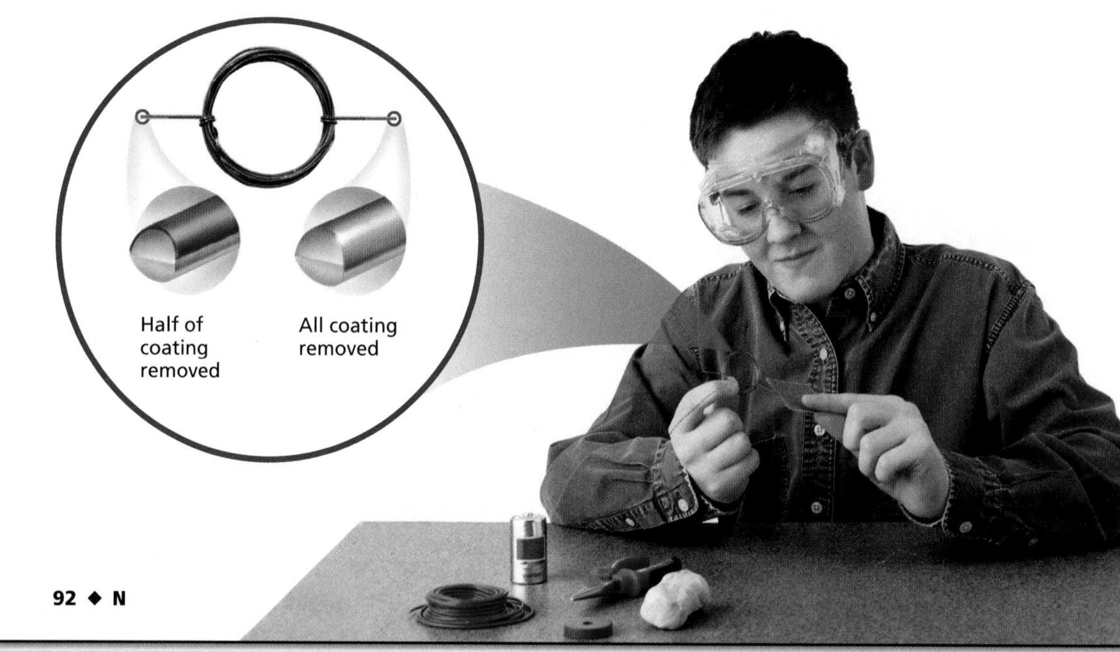

92 ◆ N

Guide Inquiry

Invitation
Ask: **What are some examples of electric motors?** *(Sample answer: Motors in vacuum cleaners, electric clocks, refrigerators, hair dryers, and remote-controlled cars)* Explain that most electric motors are very similar, even though they may perform very different functions.

Introduce the Procedure
Have students read the procedure, and answer any questions. Before students begin, demonstrate how to wrap the wire around the film canister. Also show students how to sand the ends of the wire. For best results, hold the coil edgewise while sanding off the lower half of the insulation from one end of the wire.

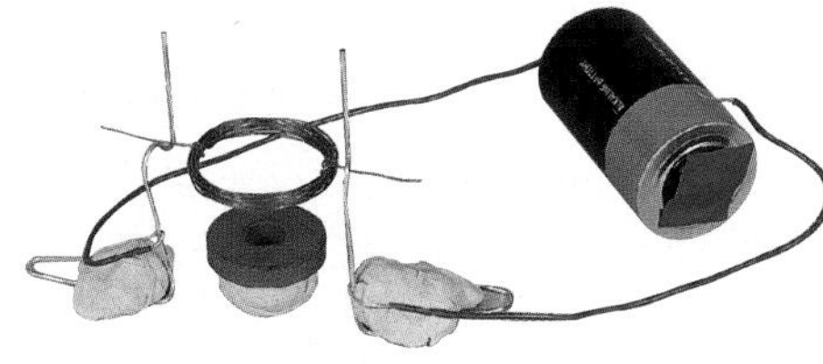

6. Place the free ends of the wire coil on the paper clips. Make sure the coil is perfectly balanced. Adjust the paper clips and wire so that the coil can rotate freely.
7. Use clay to hold a permanent magnet in place directly below the wire coil. The coil needs to be able to rotate without hitting the magnet.
8. Remove the insulation from the ends of two 15-cm insulated wires. Use these wires to connect the paper clips to a D-cell.
9. Give the coil a gentle push to start it turning. If it does not spin or stops spinning after a few seconds, check the following:
   - Are the paper clips in good contact with the D-cell?
   - Will the coil spin in the opposite direction?
   - Will the coil work on someone else's apparatus?

Analyze and Conclude

1. **Observing** Describe the movement of the wire coil when your setup was complete and working.
2. **Classifying** Which part of your setup contained a permanent magnet? Describe the location of the magnetic field produced by that magnet.
3. **Inferring** What was the effect of removing all the insulation from one end of the wire coil but only half from the other end?
4. **Inferring** Explain how a magnetic field is produced when the motor is connected to the D-cell.
5. **Drawing Conclusions** How do magnetism and electricity interact to cause the wire coil to rotate?
6. **Communicating** Your motor produced motion, but it does not yet do useful work. Think of an object your motor might cause to move. Consider how you could modify the motor to move that object. Write a procedure for changing your motor to carry out the task.

Design an Experiment

You have built a simple electric motor. List three factors that may affect the motion of the coil. Design an experiment to test one of those factors. *Obtain your teacher's permission before carrying out your investigation.*

Analyze and Conclude

1. Sample answer: The coil rotated continuously.

2. The permanent magnet was directly below the coil of wire. The magnetic field of the permanent magnet surrounded the magnet.

3. Sample answer: When both uninsulated ends are in contact with the supports, there is a current and the coil rotates. If the current did not reverse its direction, the coil would be able to turn only half way. The insulated part of the wire turns the current off, so the coil is allowed to continue turning. As it turns, the uninsulated parts again complete the circuit. This produces a current, and the coil turns completely around.

4. Sample answer: The D-cell produces an electric current in the coil, creating a magnetic field that surrounds the coil.

5. Sample answer: The magnetic field produced by an electric current in the coil causes sides of the coil to be pushed or pulled as the field interacts with the field of the permanent magnet.

6. Students' procedures should reflect their suggested modifications. Sample answer: A foam or cork cylinder could be added at one end of the coil of wire. One end of a piece of string could be attached to the other end of the cylinder. If the other end of the string were attached to a small object such as a paper clip, the string would lift the object as the motor turned.

Extend Inquiry

Design an Experiment Students' plans should identify three factors that may affect the rotation of the coil, such as the voltage applied, whether the coil is balanced, and whether the ends of the wire are insulated. Students should describe an experiment to test one of those factors. Check students' plans for safety before giving permission to carry out the investigations.

Troubleshooting the Experiment

If students have difficulty getting their motors to operate, try the following:

- Check both ends of the wire to see that one end has all the insulation sanded off and the other has only half sanded off.
- Check the balance of the coil. If it has more weight on one side, it will not spin freely.
- Make sure the paper clips make firm contact with the D-cell.
- Try the coil on another group's apparatus.
- Move the paper clips downward so the coil is closer to the permanent magnet.
- Lift the coil, reverse its connections, and then set it back on the supports.
- Substitute a stronger permanent magnet.

Expected Outcome

Students will build a working electric motor that transforms electrical energy into mechanical energy.

Section 3

Electricity From Magnetism

Objectives

After this lesson, students will be able to

N.3.3.1 Explain how an electric current can be produced in a conductor.

N.3.3.2 Describe how a generator works.

N.3.3.3 Describe the function of a transformer.

Target Reading Skill

Previewing Visuals Explain that looking at the visuals before they read helps students activate prior knowledge and predict what they are about to read.

Answers

Sample questions and answers:

What are the parts of a generator? *(Magnets, crank, slip ring, armature, and brushes are parts of a generator.)* **How is a current induced in the armature?** *(As a crank is turned, the armature rotates in a magnetic field. The rotating motion of the armature induces a current in the wire.)*

All in One Teaching Resources

- Transparency N37

Preteach

Build Background Knowledge

L2

How Is Electricity Produced?

Ask: **Where does the electric current you use at school and in your homes come from?** *(Some students might name a local electric plant.)* **How is the electric current produced at that electric plant?** *(Students might mention burning coal, oil, or natural gas; nuclear energy; hydroelectric turbines; or wind turbines.)* **What process occurs at the electric plant that results in an electric current?** *(Sample answer: The electric current is produced by a generator.)* **What is the voltage of the electric current in your homes?** *(Sample answer: 120 volts)* Remind students that there are "high-voltage" wires in their area. Ask: **How does the high voltage in those wires become 120 volts in your homes?** *(Sample answer: There are transformers in the neighborhood that reduce voltage.)*

Section 3 • Tech & Design •

Electricity From Magnetism

Reading Preview

Key Concepts

- How can an electric current be produced in a conductor?
- How does a generator work?
- What is the function of a transformer?

Key Terms

- electromagnetic induction
- direct current
- alternating current
- electric generator
- transformer
- step-up transformer
- step-down transformer

Target Reading Skill

Previewing Visuals When you preview, you look ahead at the material to be read. Preview Figure 13. Then write two questions that you have about the diagram in a graphic organizer like the one below. As you read, answer your questions.

Generators

Q. What are the parts of a generator?
A.
Q.

Lab zone Discover Activity

Can You Produce Current Without a Battery?

1. Obtain one meter of wire with the insulation removed from both ends.
2. Connect the wire to the terminals of a galvanometer or a sensitive multimeter.
3. Hold the wire between the poles of a strong horseshoe magnet. Observe the meter.
4. Move the wire up and down between the poles. Observe the meter.
5. Move the wire faster, and again observe the meter.

Think It Over

Developing Hypotheses In which steps does the meter indicate a current? Propose a hypothesis to explain why a current is present. Try using an "If . . . then . . ." statement.

An electric motor uses electrical energy to produce motion. Is the reverse true? Can motion produce electrical energy? In 1831, scientists found out that moving a wire in a magnetic field can cause an electric current. That discovery has allowed electrical energy to be supplied to homes, schools, and businesses all over the world.

Induction of Electric Current

Before you can understand how electrical energy is supplied by your electric company, you need to know how it is produced. A magnet and a conductor, such as a wire, can be used to induce a current in the conductor. The key is motion. **An electric current is induced in a conductor when the conductor moves through a magnetic field.** Generating an electric current from the motion of a conductor through a magnetic field is called **electromagnetic induction.** Current that is generated in this way is called induced current.

Lab zone Discover Activity

Skills Focus Developing hypotheses L1

Materials 1 m insulated copper wire, galvanometer or multimeter, horseshoe magnet, clay

Time 10 minutes

Tips To save time, set up the wires and galvanometer before the activity. Use wire strippers to remove the insulation from the ends of the wires.

Expected Outcome A current is produced when the wire moves. The faster the wire moves, the greater the current.

Think It Over A current is present in Steps 4 and 5. Sample hypothesis: If a wire is moved between the poles of a magnet, then electric current is produced.

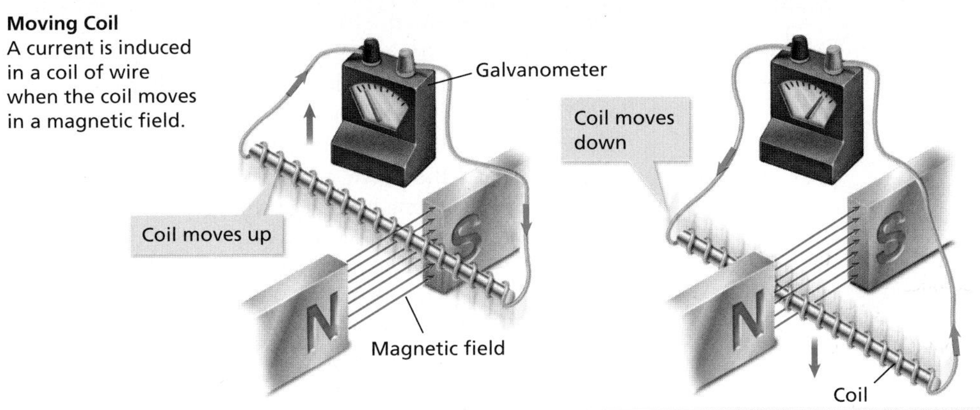

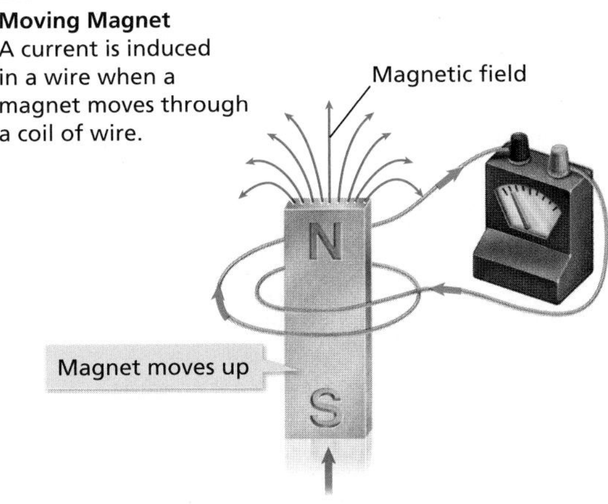

Moving Magnet
A current is induced in a wire when a magnet moves through a coil of wire.
Magnetic field
Magnet moves up

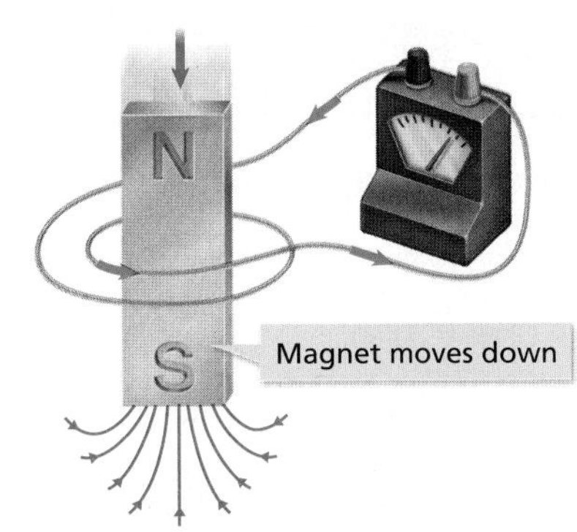

FIGURE 12
Inducing Current
When a coil of wire moves up or down in a magnetic field, a current is induced in the wire.
If a magnet moves up or down through a coil of wire, a current is induced in the wire.
Interpreting Diagrams *How does the direction in which you move the wire and magnet affect the current?*

To induce a current in a conductor, either the conductor can move through the magnetic field or the magnet itself can move. In Figure 12, you can see what happens when a wire coil moves in a magnetic field. The coil of wire is connected to a galvanometer forming a closed circuit. If the wire coil is held still, the galvanometer will not register any current. But if the coil is moved up or down, the galvanometer shows an electric current is present. A current is induced without a battery or other voltage source by moving the coil! You saw this for yourself if you did the Discover Activity. In Figure 12, you can also see what happens when a magnet placed inside a wire coil is moved instead of the wire. The result is the same as moving the coil in the magnetic field. An electric current is induced in the coil.

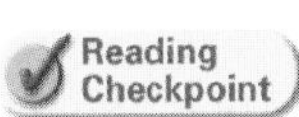 **Reading Checkpoint** **What happens when a wire coil moves in a magnetic field?**

Instruct

Induction of Electric Current

Teach Key Concepts L2

Electromagnetic Induction

Focus Tell students that movement through a magnetic field can produce an electric current.

Teach Remind students that charging by induction is the movement of electrons to one part of an object by the electric field of a second object. Ask: **In that process, do objects touch?** *(No)* Explain that in the induction of an electric current there is also no touching. Ask: **How is an electric current induced in a conductor or a wire?** *(An electric current is induced in a conductor or wire when the conductor moves through a magnetic field.)*

Apply Have students study Figure 12. Ask: **What are two ways in which an electric current can be induced by motion?** *(A coil of wire can move through a magnetic field, and a magnet can move through a coil of wire.)* Emphasize that which moves—the conductor or the magnet—makes no difference. The result of both motions is the induction of an electric current. **learning modality: verbal**

All in One Teaching Resources
- Transparencies N38, N39

Independent Practice L2

All in One Teaching Resources
- Guided Reading and Study Worksheet: *Electricity From Magnetism*

Student Edition on Audio CD

Differentiated Instruction

Gifted and Talented L3

Local Electrical Energy Generation Ask students to investigate the devices and processes involved in the generation of electrical energy in their area, with an emphasis on the generators involved. Students might set up an appointment to visit the electric plant. Have students prepare a presentation for the class. **learning modality: verbal**

Less Proficient Readers L1

Applying Concepts Pair less proficient readers with students who excel in reading, and have the pairs create diagrams showing how step-up transformers and step-down transformers are used between the generating plant and homes and businesses. **learning modality: visual**

Monitor Progress L2

Oral Presentation Ask students to list the materials needed to induce a current.

Answer

Figure 12 Reversing the direction of either the coil of wire or the magnet reverses the direction of the current.

 **Reading Checkpoint** A current is induced in the wire coil.

Science and **History**

Focus Point out that the first entry on the timeline is at the year 1820, almost two centuries ago. Explain that this time is about midway between the American Revolution and the U.S. Civil War. Ask: **What year is the last entry on the time line?** *(1893)* Therefore, this time line covers most of the nineteenth century.

Teach Call on volunteers to read the annotations for each entry on the timeline. After a student has read an annotation, have students recall what they have learned about the concept or inventions described. For example, after a student has read the annotation for 1830–1831, ask: **What is electromagnetic induction?** *(Generating an electric current from the motion of a conductor through a magnetic field)* **What is a current called that is generated in this way?** *(Induced current)*

Writing in Science

Writing Mode Description

Scoring Rubric

4 Exceeds criteria

3 Meets criteria

2 Meets some criteria; includes reasonably accurate descriptions of the procedures, equipment, and discoveries of at least one of the three scientists

1 Includes inaccurate or incomplete descriptions of the work of at least one of the three scientists

Help Students Read L1

Asking Questions Refer to the Content Refresher in this chapter, which provides the guidelines for the Asking Questions strategy.

Draw a two-column chart on the board. Make the heading for the first column *Questions,* and the heading for the second column *Answers.* Before students read the subsection *Induction of Electric Current,* have them scan the subsection. As they encounter the headings, ask: **How can you recast the headings as questions?** *(Sample answer: What is the induction of electric current? What is direct current? What is alternating current?)* After students have read the subsection, ask volunteers to supply the answers to the questions in the first column. Suggest that students make their own copies of the chart.

Direct Current In an induced current, charges may flow in one direction only, or they may alternate directions. The direction of an induced current depends on the direction in which the wire or magnet moves. You probably noticed in Figure 12 on the previous page that when the direction of the motion of the wire coil changed, the direction of the current reversed.

A current consisting of charges that flow in one direction only is called **direct current,** or DC. A direct current can be induced from a changing magnetic field or produced from an energy source such as a battery. When a battery is placed in a circuit, charges flow away from one end of the battery, around the circuit, and into the other end of the battery. Thomas Edison used direct current in his first electric generating plant.

Science and **History**

Generating Electrical Energy

Several scientists were responsible for bringing electricity from the laboratory into everyday use.

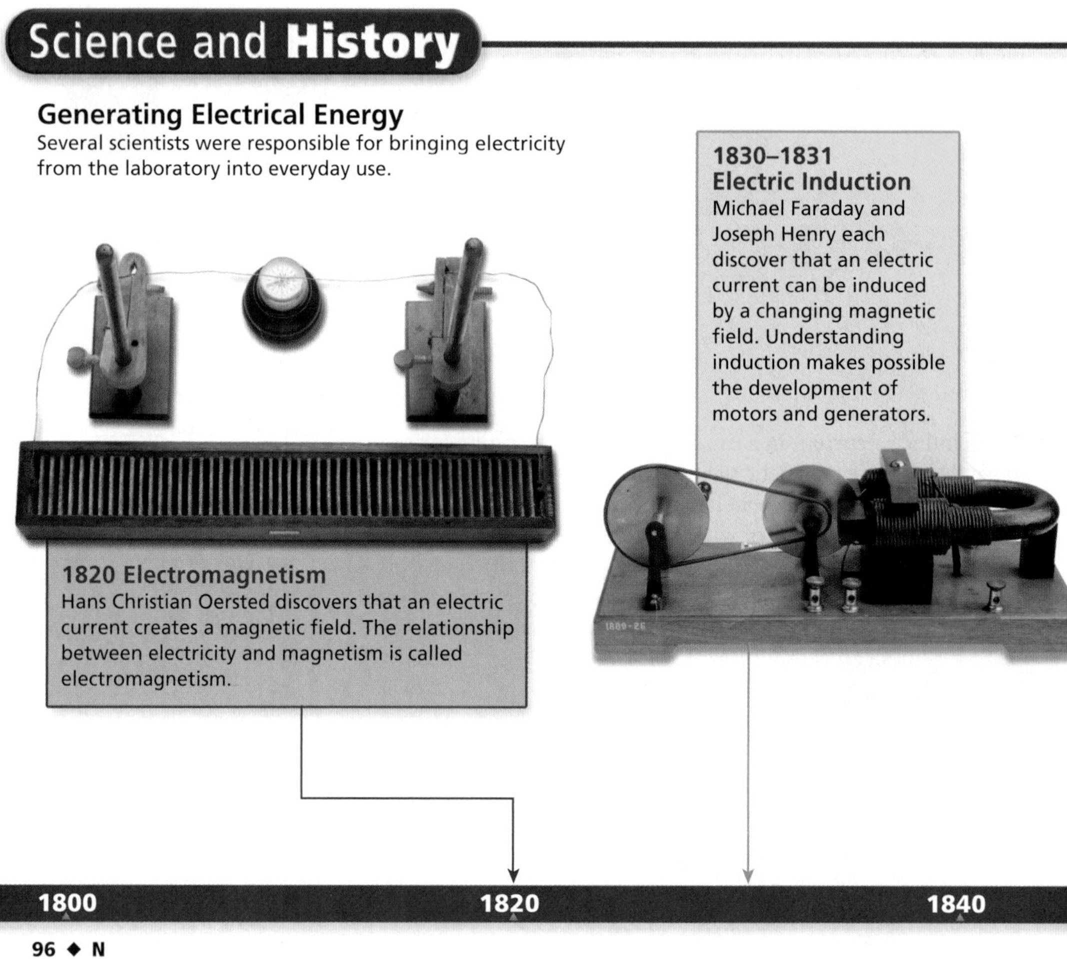

1820 Electromagnetism
Hans Christian Oersted discovers that an electric current creates a magnetic field. The relationship between electricity and magnetism is called electromagnetism.
1830–1831
Electric Induction
Michael Faraday and Joseph Henry each discover that an electric current can be induced by a changing magnetic field. Understanding induction makes possible the development of motors and generators.
1800
1820
1840

Alternating Current What would happen if a wire in a magnetic field were moved up and down repeatedly? The induced current in the wire would reverse direction repeatedly as well. This kind of current is called **alternating current,** or AC. An alternating current consists of charges that move back and forth in a circuit. The electric current in the circuits in homes, schools, and other buildings is alternating current.

Alternating current has a major advantage over direct current. An AC voltage can be easily raised or lowered to a higher or lower voltage. This means that a high voltage can be used to send electrical energy over great distances. Then the voltage can be reduced to a safer level for everyday use.

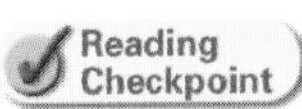
What is the advantage of using alternating current?

Writing in Science

Letter Find out more about the work of Michael Faraday, Joseph Henry, or Hans Christian Oersted. Write a letter to a friend in which you describe your work as a research assistant for the scientist you choose. Include descriptions of his experimental procedures and the equipment he uses. Tell how his work has led to surprising discoveries.

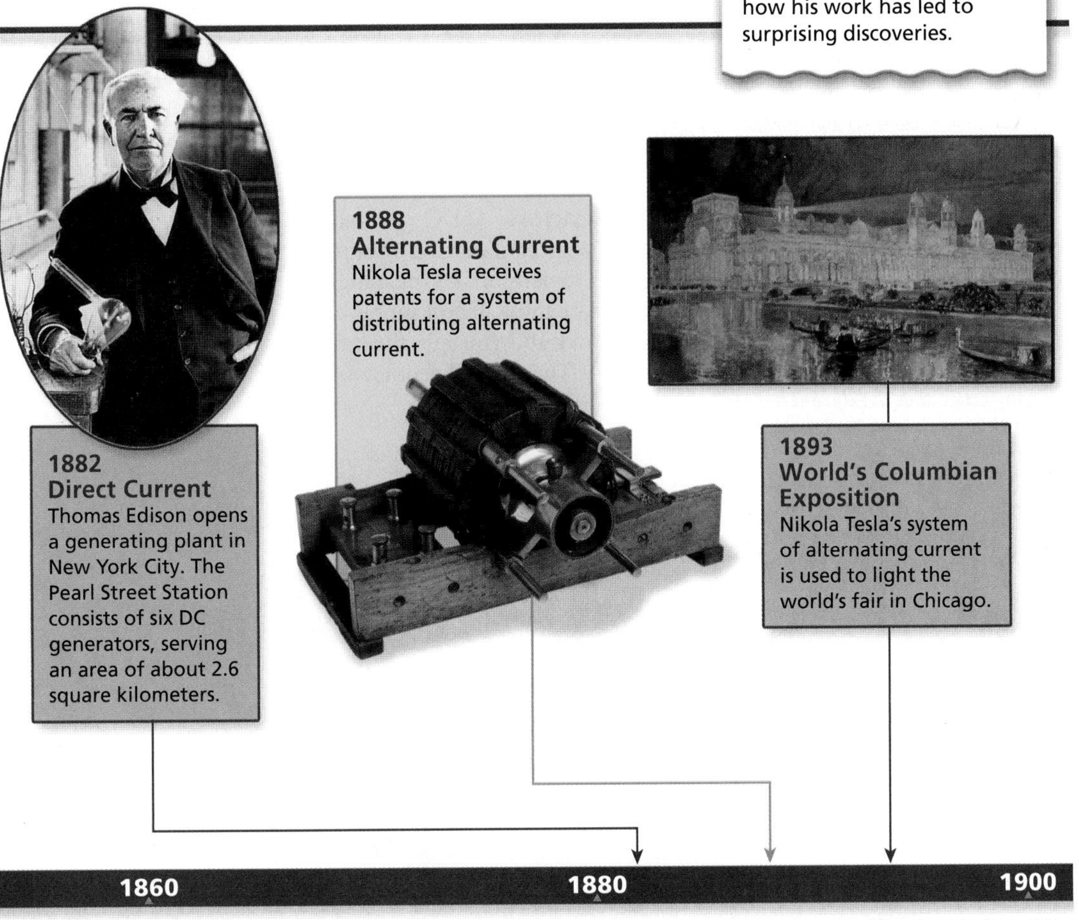

1882 Direct Current
Thomas Edison opens a generating plant in New York City. The Pearl Street Station consists of six DC generators, serving an area of about 2.6 square kilometers.

1888 Alternating Current
Nikola Tesla receives patents for a system of distributing alternating current.

1893 World's Columbian Exposition
Nikola Tesla's system of alternating current is used to light the world's fair in Chicago.

Teacher Demo L1

Generating Alternating Current

Materials hand-operated generator, insulated wire (2 strands), galvanometer

Time 15 minutes

Focus Tell students they will observe the induction of an alternating current using a device called a generator.

Teach Obtain a demonstration-type generator, found in many school labs. Connect the output terminals of the generator to the two strands of insulated wire, stripped at both ends of each strand. Connect the other ends of the wires to the terminals of a galvanometer. Turn the generator crank slowly and smoothly, and allow students to observe the changes in the galvanometer pointer. After students have observed the galvanometer changes, explain that the device inducing the current is an example of an electric generator, which students will learn about as they read. Have students examine the hand-operated generator to see how it induces a current.

Apply Ask: **How do you know that the current induced is alternating current?** *(The galvanometer pointer moves back and forth, which indicates that the direction of the current changes.)* **learning modality: visual**

Monitor Progress L2

Skills Check Have students make a compare/contrast table about direct current and alternating current.

Students can keep their tables in their portfolios.

Answer

An AC voltage can be easily raised or lowered to a higher or lower voltage.

Generators

Teach Key Concepts

L2

Mechanical Energy Into Electrical Energy

Focus Tell students that a device called an electric generator induces an electric current in a conductor.

Teach Ask: **How is an electric generator the opposite of an electric motor?** *(An electric motor uses an electric current in a magnetic field to produce motion. An electric generator uses motion in a magnetic field to produce an electric current.)* **In an electric generator, what rotates in a magnetic field that induces a current?** *(An armature)* **In an AC generator, why is an alternating current induced and not a direct current?** *(As the armature rotates, each side first moves up through the magnetic field and then moves down through the magnetic field. Since the wires of the armature change direction in the magnetic field, the direction of the current changes as well.)*

Apply Have students examine Figure 13. Ask: **In an electric generator, what makes contact with brushes?** *(The slip rings)* **What are the brushes connected to?** *(The rest of the electric circuit)* Explain that the current is induced in the armature and follows a path into the slip rings, the brushes, and then into the rest of the electric circuit.

Extend The ***active art*** will show students how a generator uses motion in a magnetic field to produce an electric current.
learning modality: visual

For: Motors and Generators activity
Visit: PHSchool.com
Web Code: cgp-4033

Students can interact with the art of motors and generators online.

All in One Teaching Resources
- Transparency N40

Generators

An **electric generator** is a device that transforms mechanical energy into electrical energy. An electric generator is the opposite of an electric motor. An electric motor uses an electric current in a magnet field to produce motion. **A generator uses motion in a magnetic field to produce an electric current.**

AC Generators In Figure 13 you can see how a simple AC generator works. As the crank is turned, the armature rotates in the magnetic field. One side of the armature moves up, and the other side moves down. The up and down motion induces a current in the wire. The current is in opposite directions on the two sides of the armature.

After the armature turns halfway, each side of it reverses direction in the magnetic field. The side that moved up moves down, and vice versa. The current in the wire changes direction as well. The result is an alternating current is induced.

As the armature turns, slip rings turn with it. Slip rings may remind you of the commutator in a motor. They are attached to the ends of the armature. As they turn, they make contact with the brushes. The brushes can be connected to the rest of the circuit. In this way, a generator becomes an energy source.

DC Generators A DC generator is like an AC generator, except that it contains a commutator instead of slip rings. In fact, a DC generator and the motor you read about in Section 2 are the same thing. If you supply electrical energy to the motor, it will spin. But if you spin the motor, you will produce electrical energy. The motor becomes a DC generator.

For: Motors and Generators activity
Visit: PHSchool.com
Web Code: cgp-4033

FIGURE 13
How a Generator Works
In an AC generator, an armature is rotated in a magnetic field. This induces an electric current in the armature. **Applying Concepts** *How many times does the current reverse direction each time the armature rotates?*

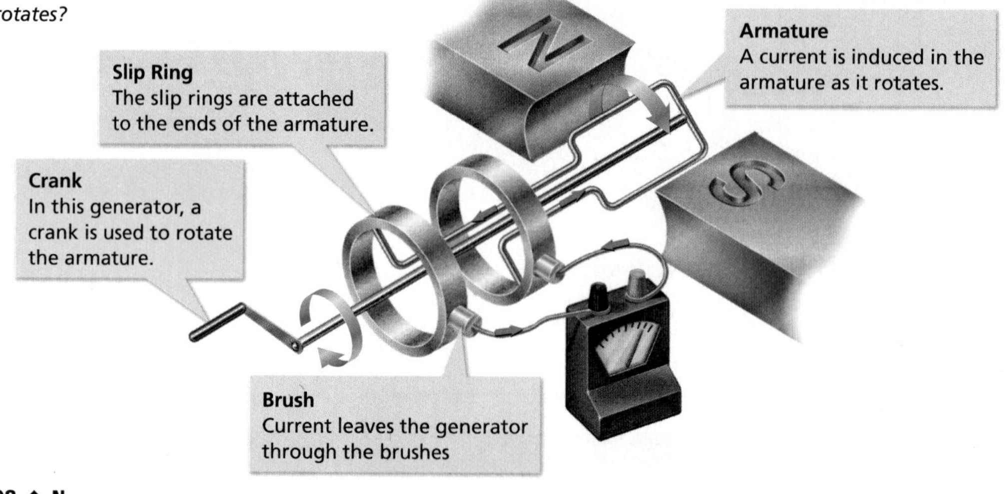
Slip Ring
The slip rings are attached to the ends of the armature.
Armature
A current is induced in the armature as it rotates.
Crank
In this generator, a crank is used to rotate the armature.
Brush
Current leaves the generator through the brushes
N
S

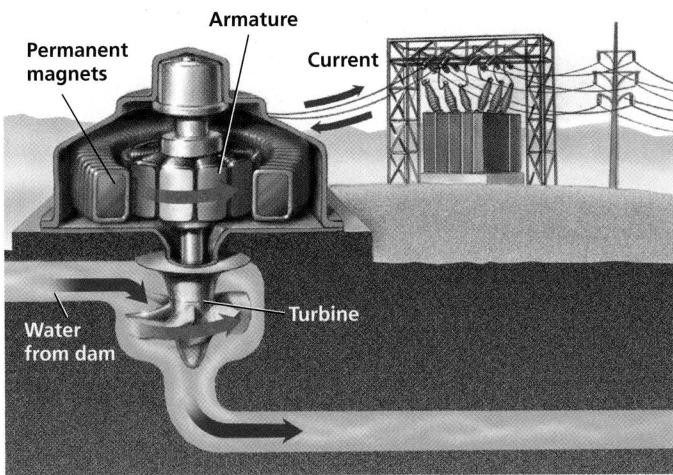

FIGURE 14
Turbines
In most generators, a source of mechanical energy turns huge turbines such as this one. The turbine is attached to the armature of a generator, which produces current.

Using Generators The electric company uses giant generators to produce most of the electrical energy you use in your home and school. But, instead of using a crank to supply the mechanical energy to turn the armature, a turbine is used. Turbines are large circular devices made up of many blades. Figure 14 shows how a turbine is attached to the armature in a generator. The turbine spins as the water flows by it. As a result, the armature spins and generates electric current.

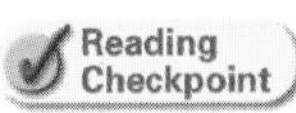

What is a turbine?

Transformers

The electrical energy generated by electric companies is transmitted over long distance at very high voltages. However in your home, electrical energy is used at much lower voltages. What changes the voltage of the electrical energy? The answer is transformers.

What is a Transformer? A transformer is a device that increases or decreases voltage. A **transformer** consists of two separate coils of insulated wire wrapped around an iron core. One coil, called the primary coil, is connected to a circuit with a voltage source and alternating current. The other coil, the secondary coil, is connected to a separate circuit that does not contain a voltage source.

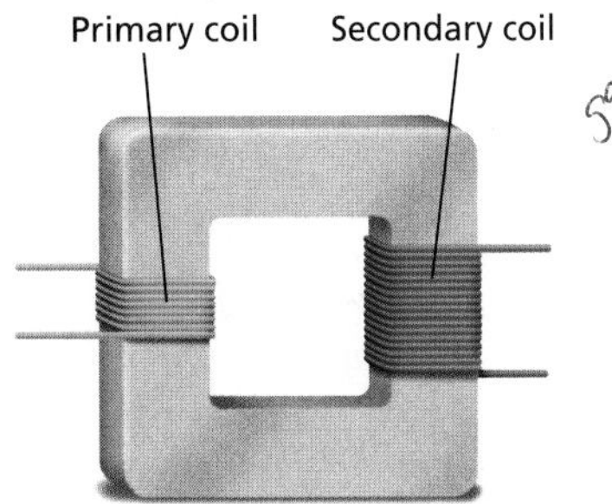

FIGURE 15
A Transformer
The primary coil of a transformer is connected to a voltage source. The secondary coil is not connected to a voltage source.

Transformers

Teach Key Concepts L2

Increasing or Decreasing Voltage

Focus Tell students that changing the voltage of a current is a simple process with a transformer.

Teach Ask: **Why does voltage have to be decreased before electrical energy enters a home?** *(Electrical energy is transmitted over long distances at very high voltages, while in homes electrical energy is used at lower voltages.)* **What is a transformer?** *(A device that increases or decreases voltage)*

Apply Have students examine Figure 15. Ask: **What is the difference between a primary coil and a secondary coil?** *(The primary coil is connected to a circuit with a voltage source and alternating current, while the secondary coil is connected to a separate circuit that doesn't have a voltage source.)* **What causes an electric current in the secondary coil?** *(The changing magnetic field produced by the alternating current in the primary coil)* Point out that the primary coil has fewer loops of wire than the secondary coil. Remind students that one way to increase the strength of an electromagnet is to add more loops to the solenoid. Ask: **Do you think the voltage in the secondary coil would be higher or lower than in the primary coil?** *(Higher)* **learning modality: visual**

Differentiated Instruction

English Learners/Beginning L1

Vocabulary: Science Glossary
Pronounce the key terms *electric generator* and *transformer.* Encourage students to repeat them after you. Define the words using section figures to communicate meaning. Suggest that students write the terms and definitions in a science glossary. **learning modality: verbal**

English Learners/Intermediate L2

Vocabulary: Science Glossary Expand on the Beginning activity by adding the rest of the key terms in this section. Also suggest that students write a sentence for each term in their glossaries. Invite students to read their sentences aloud. **learning modality: verbal**

Monitor Progress L2

Skills Check Ask students to make a flowchart of the steps involved in the production of an electric current by an AC generator.

Students can keep their flowcharts in their portfolios. Portfolio

Answers

Figure 13 For each complete rotation of the armature, the current reverses direction twice.

Reading Checkpoint A turbine is a large circular device made up of many blades. A turbine is attached to a generator's armature. The turbine is used to spin the armature, generating electric current.

Use Visuals: Figure 16 L2

Changing Voltage

Focus Tell students that changing the voltage of an electric current is essential for the efficient transmission of electrical energy.

Teach Ask: **What is a step-up transformer?** *(A transformer that increases voltage)* **What is a step-down transformer?** *(A transformer that decreases voltage)* **Why are transformers used in the transmission of electrical energy from generating plants to consumers?** *(The most efficient way to transmit electrical energy over long distances is to maintain high voltages. But the high voltage must be decreased for use by consumers.)*

Apply Ask: **In which kind of transformer does the primary coil have more loops than the secondary coil?** *(Step-down transformer)* **In which kind of transformer does the secondary coil have more loops than the primary coil?** *(Step-up transformer)*
learning modality: verbal

All in One Teaching Resources

- Transparency N41

Address Misconceptions L2

Transformers Do Not Create Energy

Focus Some students may think that a step-up transformer creates energy in the secondary coil. Tell students that according to the law of conservation of energy, energy cannot be created or destroyed, and a transformer does not violate that law.

Teach Remind students of the equation: Power = Voltage × Current. Explain that in a high-voltage line, the current is not as high as in a low-voltage line. The power of each, then, is the same.

Apply Ask: **When the voltage is decreased by a step-down transformer, is energy destroyed in the process?** *(No. Although the voltage decreases, the current increases.)*
learning modality: logical/mathematical

A Transformer at Work When a current is in the primary coil of the transformer, it produces a magnetic field. The magnetic field changes as the current alternates. This changing magnetic field is like a moving magnetic field. It induces a current in the secondary coil. A transformer works only if the current in the primary coil is changing. If the current does not change, the magnetic field does not change. No current will be induced in the secondary coil. So a transformer will not work with direct current.

Types of Transformers If the number of loops in the primary and secondary coils of a transformer is the same, the voltage of the induced current is the same as the original voltage. But if the secondary coil has more loops than the primary coil, the voltage in the secondary coil will be greater. A transformer that increases voltage is called a **step-up transformer.**

FIGURE 16
Changing Voltage
Transformers are involved in the transmission of electrical energy from an electric plant to a home. Relating Cause and Effect *How does the number of loops in the primary and secondary coils affect the voltage of the induced current?*

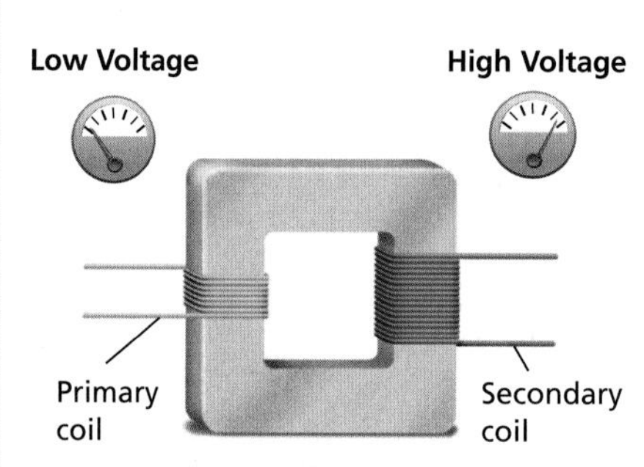

Step-down Transformer
A step-down transformer decreases voltage. The primary coil has more loops than the secondary coil.
High Voltage
Low Voltage
Primary coil
Secondary coil

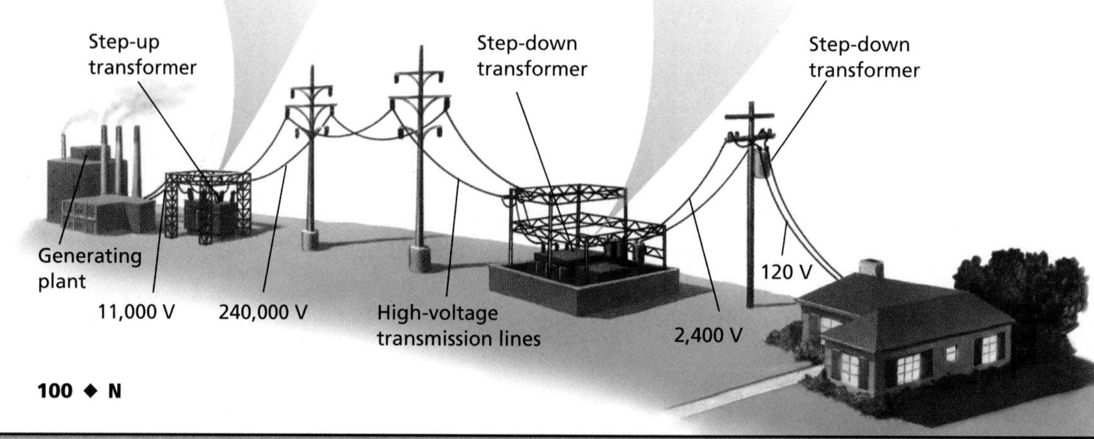

Lab zone Chapter Project

Keep Students on Track Help students who are having trouble with calculating energy use by appliances. For some appliances, finding the appliance plate that contains data may be difficult. Suggest students call local repair shops to ask about energy use for these appliances. Help students begin to prepare for their presentations by reviewing types of graphs.

Suppose there are fewer loops in the secondary coil than in the primary coil. The voltage in the secondary coil will be less than in the primary coil. A transformer that decreases voltage is called a **step-down transformer.** Figure 16 shows both types of transformers.

Uses of Transformers An important use of transformers is in the transmission of electrical energy from generating plants. The most efficient way to transmit current over long distances is to maintain high voltages—about 11,000 volts to 765,000 volts. But the high voltage must be decreased to be used safely in your home. The use of step-up and step-down transformers allows safe transmission of electrical energy from generating plants to the consumer.

Transformers are also used in some electrical devices. Fluorescent lights, televisions, and X-ray machines require higher voltages than the current in your home, which is about 120 volts. These devices contain step-up transformers. Other devices, such as doorbells, electronic games, and portable CD players, require lower voltages, about 6 to 12 volts. They contain step-down transformers.

Discovery Channel School
Using Electricity and Magnetism
Video Preview
▶Video Field Trip
Video Assessment

What is the voltage in your house?
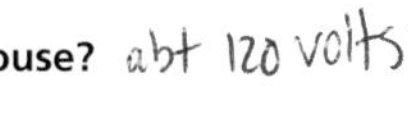

Section 3 Assessment

Target Reading Skill **Previewing Visuals** Refer to your questions and answers about Figure 13 to help you answer Question 2 below.

Reviewing Key Concepts

1. a. **Defining** What is electromagnetic induction?
   b. **Describing** What are two ways to induce an electric current?
   c. **Relating Cause and Effect** What determines whether an induced current is a direct current or an alternating current?
2. a. **Reviewing** How is energy transformed by a generator?
   b. **Summarizing** How does a generator produce an alternating current?
   c. **Comparing and Contrasting** How are an AC generator and a DC generator the same? How are they different?
3. a. **Reviewing** What does a transformer do?
   b. **Interpreting Diagrams** Look at Figure 16. What is the difference between a step-up transformer and a step-down transformer?
   c. **Applying Concepts** Why do some appliances have step-down transformers built into them?

Lab zone At-Home Activity

Step-Up and Step-Down Draw a diagram that shows how electrical energy gets to your home from the place it is generated. Include in your diagram the likely locations of step-up and step-down transformers. Explain your diagram to a family member. Then with your family member, try to locate the step-down transformer that provides your home's electricity.

Using Electricity and Magnetism

Show the Video Field Trip to let students see how electrical power can be generated. Discussion question: **How are magnetism and electricity related?** *(An electric current can generate a magnetic field, and a wire with an electric current can make a magnet rotate.)*

Monitor Progress 

Answers

Figure 16 The voltage is stepped up if the secondary coil has the greater number of loops and stepped down if the primary coil has the greater number of loops.

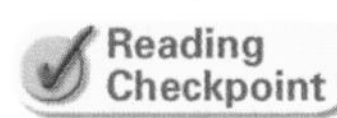

About 120 volts

Assess

Reviewing Key Concepts

1. a. Generating an electric current from the motion of a conductor through a magnetic field **b.** Either the conductor can move through a magnetic field or the magnet itself can move. **c.** A direct current is induced when the conductor or magnet moves in only one direction. An alternating current results when the conductor or magnet moves back and forth.

2. a. A generator transforms mechanical energy into electrical energy by moving an armature in a magnetic field. **b.** In an AC generator, an armature is rotated in a magnetic field, inducing an electric current in the wire. After the armature turns halfway, each side of it reverses direction. The current in the wire also changes direction; the result is alternating current. **c.** Both generate electric currents. A DC generator contains a commutator that allows the current to continue in one direction. An AC generator contains slip rings, and therefore the current direction alternates.

3. a. It increases or decreases voltage. **b.** In a step-up transformer, the secondary coil has the greater number of loops. In a step-down transformer, the primary coil has the greater number. **c.** Because they operate at voltages lower than the 120 volts in home circuits

Lab zone At-Home Activity

Step-up and Step-down L2

Students' diagrams should include a drawing of a generating plant, a step-up transformer outside of the plant, and a step-down transformer near the home. Encourage students to take their diagrams home to show to an adult. Students should be able to locate step-down transformers in their neighborhoods.

Reteach L1

Call on students to explain two ways in which an electric current can be induced.

All in One Teaching Resources

- Section Summary: *Electricity From Magnetism*
- Review and Reinforce: *Electricity From Magnetism*
- Enrich: *Electricity From Magnetism*

- Complete student edition
- Section and chapter self-assessments
- Assessment reports for teachers

Help Students Read L1

Building Vocabulary

Words in Context Help students learn the meaning of new terms by examining context. Tell students to look for familiar words or phrases that surround a new term—these are clues to the new term's meaning. Have students read the paragraph that introduces the key term *electromagnetic induction* in the section *Electricity From Magnetism.* Ask: **Which words that appear in the same paragraph as *electromagnetic induction* can help you remember its meaning?** *(Electric current, magnetic field, generated)*

Word Origin Have students look up the origins of the words *armature* and *commutator.* The will discover that *armature* comes from the Latin word *armare,* meaning "to arm" and that *commutator* comes from the Latin word *commutare,* meaning "to exchange or change." Challenge students to develop memory devices using these meanings to help them recall the terms.

Connect Concepts

Concept Maps Help students develop one way to show how the information in this chapter is related. Have students brainstorm to identify the key concepts, key terms, details, and examples. Ask students to write these suggestions down in their notebooks.

Tell students that this concept map will be organized in hierarchical order and to begin at the top with key concepts or key terms. Ask students these questions to guide them to categorize the information in their notebooks: **How is a magnetic field related to an electric current? How can electrical energy be transformed into mechanical energy? How can motion induce an electric current?**

Chapter 3 Study Guide

1 What Is Electromagnetism?

Key Concepts

- An electric current produces a magnetic field.
- The magnetic field produced by a current has three characteristics. The field can be turned on or off, have its direction reversed, or have its strength changed.
- An electromagnet is a strong magnet that can be turned on and off.

Key Terms

electromagnetism
solenoid
electromagnet

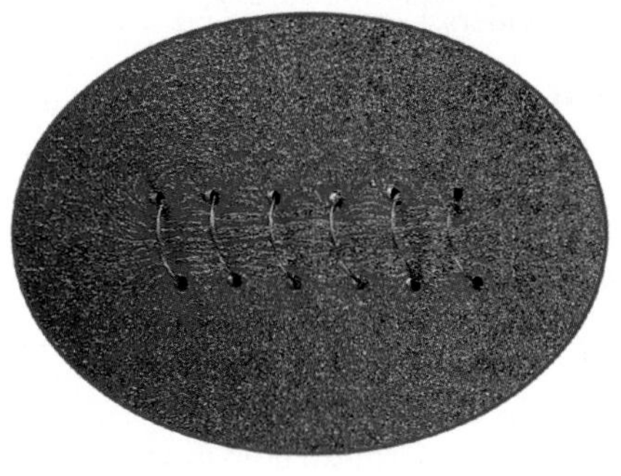

2 Electricity, Magnetism, and Motion

Key Concepts

- When a wire with a current is placed in a magnetic field, electrical energy is transformed into mechanical energy.
- Electric current is used to turn the pointer of a galvanometer.
- An electric motor transforms electrical energy into mechanical energy.

Key Terms

energy
electrical energy
mechanical energy
galvanometer
electric motor

3 Electricity From Magnetism

Key Concepts

- An electric current is induced in a conductor when the conductor moves through a magnetic field.
- A generator uses motion in a magnetic field to produce an electric current.
- A transformer is a device that increases or decreases voltage.

Key Terms

electromagnetic induction
direct current
alternating current
electric generator
transformer
step-up transformer
step-down transformer

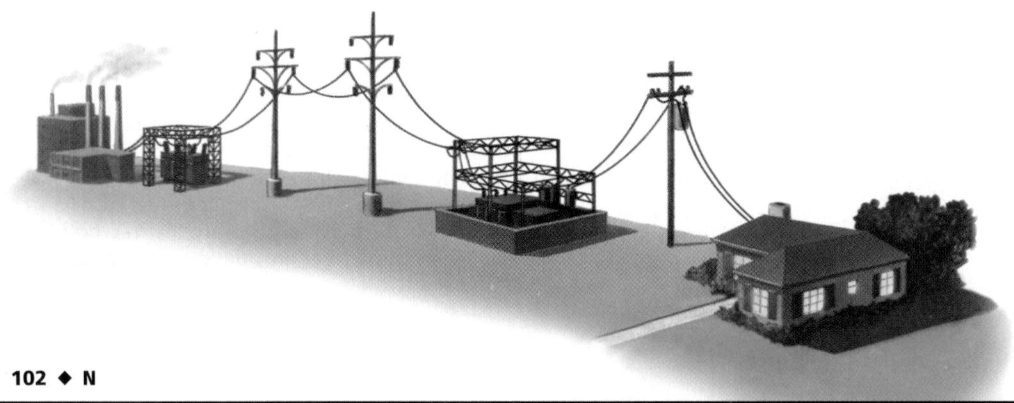

Prompt students by using connecting words or phrases, such as "includes" and "produces," to indicate the basis for the organization of the map. The phrases should form a sentence between or among a set of concepts.

Answer

Accept logical presentations by students.

All in One Teaching Resources

- Key Terms Review: *Using Electricity and Magnetism*
- Connecting Concepts: *Using Electricity and Magnetism*

Review and Assessment

Go Online PHSchool.com
For: Self-Assessment
Visit: PHSchool.com
Web Code: cga-4030

Organizing Information

Concept Mapping Copy the concept map about electromagnetism onto a separate sheet of paper. Then complete the concept map and add a title. (For more about concept maps, see the Skills Handbook.)

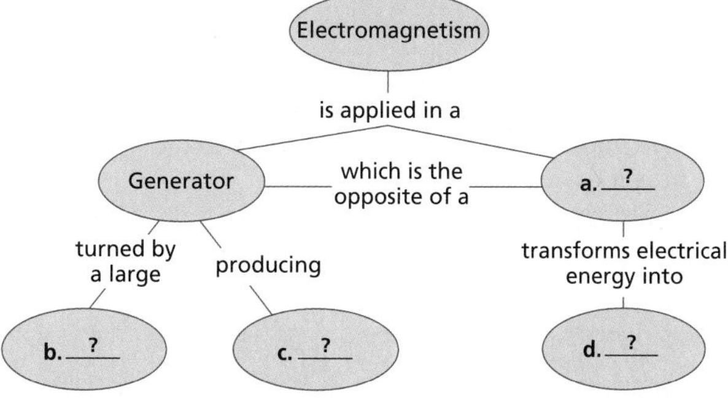

Reviewing Key Terms

Choose the letter of the best answer.

1. The relationship between electricity and magnetism is called
   a. electrical energy.
   b. an electromagnet.
   c. electromagnetism.
   d. induced current.
2. A coil of wire with a current is called a
   a. generator.
   b. motor.
   c. solenoid.
   d. transformer.
3. When a ferromagnetic material is placed within a solenoid, the resulting device is called a(n)
   a. galvanometer. **b.** electromagnet.
   c. motor. **d.** transformer.
4. Electrical energy is transformed into mechanical energy in a
   a. motor. **b.** generator.
   c. transformer. **d.** electromagnet.
5. A device that changes the voltage of alternating current is a
   a. transformer. **b.** motor.
   c. generator. **d.** galvanometer.

If the statement is true, write *true*. If it is false, change the underlined word or words to make the statement true.

6. The device that turns a needle in a galvanometer is called an <u>electromagnet</u>.
7. Several loops of wire wrapped around an iron core form the <u>armature</u> of a motor.
8. Generating a current from the motion of a conductor in a magnetic field is <u>induction</u>.
9. An <u>electric motor</u> transforms mechanical energy into electrical energy.
10. A <u>solenoid</u> increases or decreases voltage.

Writing in Science

News Report You are a television news reporter covering the opening of a new dam that generates electrical energy. Write a short news story describing how the dam transforms mechanical energy from the motion of the water into electrical energy.

Using Electricity and Magnetism
Video Preview
Video Field Trip
▶ Video Assessment

Review and Assessment

Organizing Information

a. Electric motor
b. Turbine
c. Electric current
d. Mechanical energy

Reviewing Key Terms

1. c **2.** c **3.** b **4.** a **5.** a
6. true
7. true
8. true
9. electric generator
10. transformer

Writing in Science

Writing Mode Description
Scoring Rubric
4 Exceeds criteria; includes an accurate description of how the dam transforms mechanical energy into electrical energy
3 Meets criteria
2 Meets some criteria; description lacks important details
1 Includes minimal or inaccurate details

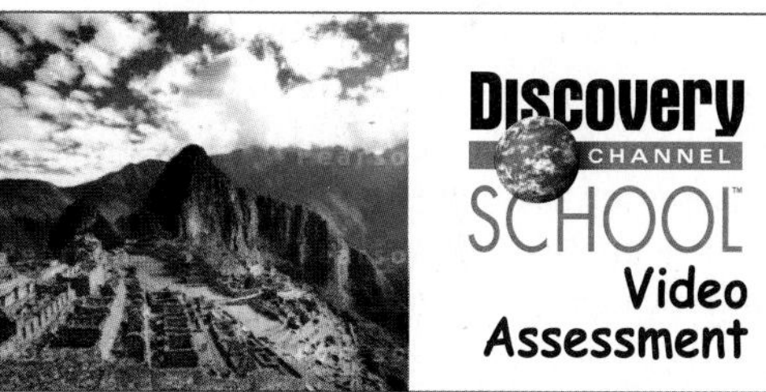

Using Electricity and Magnetism

Show the Video Assessment to review chapter content and as a prompt for the writing assignment. Discussion questions: **What are the three different forms in which geothermal energy can be harnessed?** *(Dry steam, hot water, and warm water.)* **How are these methods different from one another?** *(Dry steam can be used directly to turn generator turbine blades. To generate electrical energy from hot water reservoirs, flash steam electric plants are used, in which hot water expands into steam and turns turbine blades. Warm geothermal reservoirs work by transferring the heat from warm geothermal water to a second liquid. Vapor from the second liquid spins turbine blades.)*

For: Self-Assessment
Visit: PHSchool.com
Web Code: cga-4030

Students can take a practice test online that is automatically scored.

All in One Teaching Resources

- Transparency N42
- Chapter Test
- Performance Assessment Teacher Notes
- Performance Assessment Student Worksheet
- Performance Assessment Scoring Rubric

***ExamView®* Computer Test Bank CD-ROM**

Checking Concepts

11. You can change the magnetic field produced by a current by reversing the direction of the current, increasing or decreasing the current, or stopping the current.

12. Similar: Both transform electrical energy to mechanical energy. Different: The loop in a galvanometer can turn only half way; the loop in a motor can turn full circle. A motor uses commutators and brushes to reverse the direction of current in the loop.

13. Together, the commutator and brushes change the direction of current in a DC motor. A commutator consists of two halves of a ring, each of which rubs past two brushes. As the loop of wire in the motor rotates, the halves of the commutator switch from one brush to the other, changing the direction of current through the circuit.

14. Both consist of electric charges that flow. A current consisting of charges that flow in one direction is direct current. An alternating current consists of charges that move back and forth in a circuit.

15. In an AC generator, an armature is turned in a magnetic field by a crank. As the armature turns, a current is induced in the wire. The direction of the current changes with each half turn of the loop.

16. A turbine turns the armature in a generator.

17. The voltage is increased by a step-up transformer as it leaves the utility company and is decreased by step-down transformers before reaching a home.

Thinking Critically

18. A compass needle moves because an electric current produces a magnetic field. When there is no current, the compass aligns with Earth's magnetic field.

19. You could add more loops to the solenoid, wind the loops closer together, or convert the solenoid to an electromagnet by adding a ferromagnetic core.

20. Diagrams should show that the direction of rotation changes with the direction of current.

21. B will produce a stronger magnetic field than A because the nail in B adds a ferromagnetic core to the solenoid. B will produce a stronger magnetic field than C because B has more loops through which the current travels.

Review and Assessment

Checking Concepts

11. How can the magnetic field produced by a current be changed?

12. How is a galvanometer similar to a motor? How is it different?

13. What are the roles of the commutator and the brushes in an electric motor?

14. How are alternating current and direct current the same? How are they different?

15. Describe how an AC generator operates.

16. What role does a turbine play in generating electricity?

17. Explain how transformers are used to efficiently transmit electrical energy from the electric company where it is produced to your home where it is used.

Thinking Critically

18. Relating Cause and Effect Why does a compass needle move when placed near a wire with an electric current? What do you think happens to the compass needle when the circuit is shut off?

19. Inferring How could you modify a solenoid to produce a stonger magnetic field?

20. Applying Concepts Make a diagram of a wire loop in a magnetic field. Show how the direction of a current in the wire is related to the direction of rotation of the loop.

21. Predicting Four electromagnets are illustrated in the diagram below. Will the electromagnet labeled **A** or **B** produce a stronger magnetic field? Will the electromagnet **B** or **C** produce a stronger field? Explain your choices.

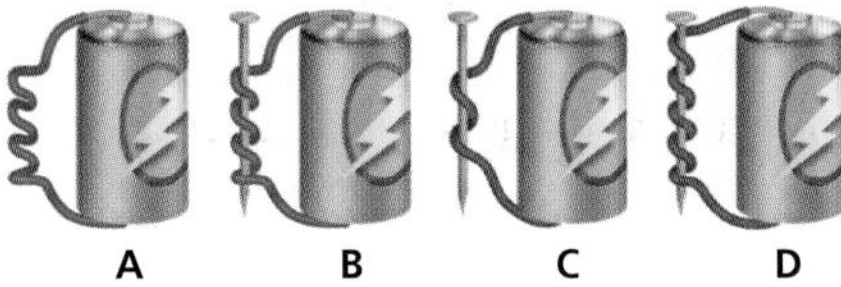

22. Comparing and Contrasting Compare a motor and a generator. Include information about the kind of energy conversion that takes place in each device.

23. Applying Concepts How are the uses of an electromagnet different from those of a permanent magnet?

Applying Skills

Use the illustration of a transformer to answer Questions 24–26.

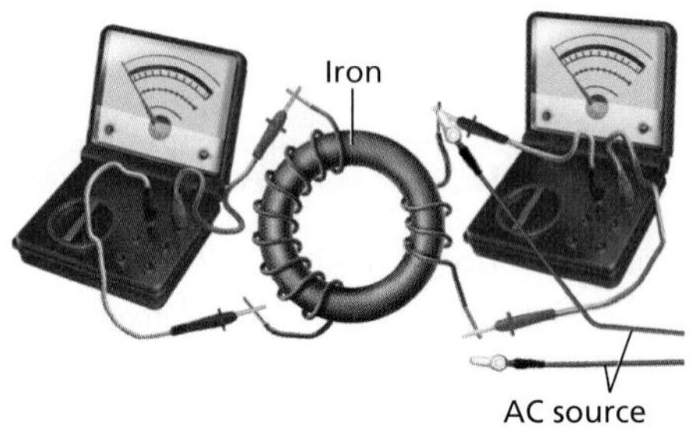

24. Classifying What type of transformer is shown in the illustration above? Explain how you know.

25. Inferring Which coil is the primary coil and which is the secondary coil?

26. Predicting What will the two voltmeters show when the circuit on the right side of the diagram is completed?

Performance Assessment Present the results of your energy audit to the class in a visual format. Make a bar, circle, or line graph showing the appliances and the energy they used. Identify the appliance that uses the most electrical energy in a week. Also discuss the way you calculated energy use. What problems did you have? What information couldn't you collect?

L3

Performance Assessment Talk with each student before the presentation. Offer encouragement, and make suggestions about how to present their data. For students who are having trouble creating their graphs, suggest they make bar graphs of weekly electrical energy use in kilowatt-hours per appliance. Students should present the graphs and conclusions of their energy audits to the class and describe the appliances in their homes that use the most electricity. Assess the presentations on the quality and accuracy of the data gathered, the quality of the graphs, and the thoroughness and organization of the presentation.

Standardized Test Prep

Test-Taking Tip

Interpreting a Graph

If you are asked to interpret a line graph, look at the labels of the horizontal and vertical axes. The labels inform you what relationship is plotted on the graph—in other words, what variables are being compared. Study the graph for Questions 4–5 and answer the sample question.

Sample Question

What variable is plotted on the *x*-axis?

A the number of solenoids
B the magnetic field strength
C the number of loops in the solenoid
D the length of solenoid

Answer

Choice **C** is correct. You can eliminate **A** and **D,** because neither axis mentions the number of solenoids or the length of the solenoid. **B** is incorrect because it is on the vertical axis, or *y*-axis.

Choose the letter of the best answer.

1. If a step-up transformer is to increase voltage, it needs
A a DC source connected to the primary coil.
B a DC source connected to the secondary coil.
C more turns in the primary coil than in the secondary coil.
D more turns in the secondary coil than in the primary coil.

2. To measure the current induced from moving a wire through a magnetic field, which piece of equipment would a scientist need?
F a galvanometer
G a flashlight bulb
H an insulated wire
J an LED

3. What happens when a magnet moves through a coil of wire?
A The magnet loses magnetism.
B A current is induced in the magnet.
C A current is induced in the wire.
D Electrical energy is transformed into mechanical energy.

A scientist measured the magnetic field strength of a solenoid after increasing the number of loops. Magnetic field strength is measured using a unit called a gauss. The graph below plots the results. Use the graph to answer Questions 4–5.

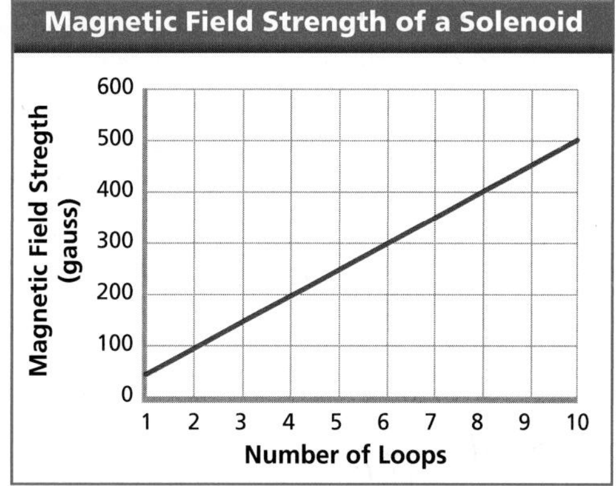

4. Which of the following statements expresses the relationship shown on the graph?
F As the number of loops decreases, the magnetic field strength increases.
G As the number of loops increases, the magnetic field strength decreases.
H As the number of loops increases, the magnetic field strength increases.
J The number of loops does not affect the magnetic field strength.

5. What would you expect the magnetic field strength of the solenoid with 12 loops to be?
A 300 gauss
B 600 gauss
C 700 gauss
D 1200 gauss

Constructed Response

6. Explain how a generator transforms mechanical energy into electrical energy.

Standardized Test Prep

1. D **2.** F **3.** C **4.** H **5.** B

6. A generator uses motion to produce an electric current. In a simple AC generator, a loop of wire called the armature is rotated by a crank. As the crank is turned, the armature rotates in a magnetic field. One side of the armature moves up, and the other side moves down. The up and down motion induces a current in the wire.

22. An electric motor transforms electrical energy into mechanical energy. A generator uses motion in a magnetic field to produce an electric current. So an electric generator transforms mechanical energy into electrical energy.

23. Electromagnets can be switched on and off and can be made to create very strong or very weak magnetic fields. Therefore, electromagnets are most useful in devices in which magnetic fields must be turned on and off during operation and in devices that must exert very strong or very weak magnetic forces. A permanent magnet is best when a continuous magnetic field of a single strength is required and when electricity is not readily available.

Applying Skills

24. The illustration shows a step-up transformer. The primary coil has fewer loops than the secondary coil.

25. The primary coil is on the right, and the secondary coil is on the left.

26. The voltmeter on the right will show a lower voltage than the voltmeter on the left.

Chapter at a Glance

PRENTICE HALL TeacherEXPRESS™ Plan • Teach • Assess

Chapter Project *Bits and Bytes*

Technology | **Local Standards**

 **Teaching Resources**

- Chapter Project Teacher Notes, pp. 242–243
- Chapter Project Student Overview, pp. 244–245
- Chapter Project Student Worksheets, pp. 246–247
- Chapter Project Scoring Rubric, p. 248

Video Preview

Electronic Signals and Semiconductors

3–4 periods
1 1/2–2 blocks

N.4.1.1 Describe two types of electronic signals.
N.4.1.2 Explain how semiconductors are used to make electronic components.

Electronic Communication

3–4 periods
1 1/2–2 blocks

N.4.2.1 Describe how sound is transmitted by telephone.
N.4.2.2 Describe two ways that sound can be reproduced.
N.4.2.3 Explain how electromagnetic waves are involved in the transmission of radio and television signals.

Video Field Trip

Computers

3–4 periods
1 1/2–2 blocks

N.4.3.1 Explain how information is stored and processed in a computer.
N.4.3.2 Describe the functions of computer hardware and software.

The Information Superhighway

1–2 periods
1/2–1 blocks

N.4.4.1 Describe the purpose of a computer network.
N.4.4.2 Explain how people can protect themselves and their property as they use computer networks.

Review and Assessment

All in One Teaching Resources

- Key Terms Review, p. 287
- Transparency N51
- Performance Assessment Teacher Notes, p. 294
- Performance Assessment Scoring Rubric, p. 295
- Performance Assessment Student Worksheet, p. 296
- Chapter Test, pp. 297–300

Discovery Channel School Video Assessment

Go Online PHSchool.com

Test Preparation

Test Preparation Blackline Masters

Lab zone Chapter Activities Planner

For more activities

Student Edition	Inquiry	Time	Materials	Skills	Resources
Chapter Project, p. 107	Open-ended	2–3 weeks	All in One **Teaching Resources** p. 242	Observing, applying concepts, designing a solution, communicating	**Lab zone Easy Planner** All in One **Teaching Resources** pp. 242–243
Section 1					
Discover Activity, p. 108	Guided	15 minutes	Flashlight	Inferring	**Lab zone Easy Planner**
Skills Activity, p. 110	Directed	15 minutes	Dictionary	Communicating	**Lab zone Easy Planner**
Technology Lab, p. 113	Guided	Prep: 15 minutes; Class: 40 minutes	2 D-cell batteries, LED, bicolor LED (optional), flashlight using 2 D-cells, flashlight bulb and socket, 2 insulated wires with alligator clips	Evaluating the design, redesigning, observing, drawing conclusions	**Lab zone Easy Planner** **Lab Activity Video** All in One **Teaching Resources** Technology Lab: *Design a Battery Sensor,* pp. 257–259
Section 2					
Discover Activity, p. 114	Guided	10 minutes	Hand lens, color television	Classifying	**Lab zone Easy Planner**
At-Home Activity, p. 122	Guided			Observing	**Lab zone Easy Planner**
Section 3					
Discover Activity, p. 123	Guided	10 minutes	Calculator	Inferring	**Lab zone Easy Planner**
Skills Activity, p. 124	Directed	10 minutes		Calculating	**Lab zone Easy Planner**
Skills Lab, pp. 130–131	Directed	Prep: 20 minutes; Class: 40 minutes	2 identical sets of 10 interlocking bricks, newspaper, pencil, and paper	Observing, classifying, making models	**Lab zone Easy Planner** **Lab Activity Video** All in One **Teaching Resources** Skills Lab: *Computer Programming,* pp. 276–279
Section 4					
Discover Activity, p. 132	Guided	15 minutes	Newspapers	Inferring	**Lab zone Easy Planner**
Try This Activity, p. 133	Directed	30 minutes	Poster board, markers, colored pencils, magazines, scissors, glue	Communicating	**Lab zone Easy Planner**
At-Home Activity, p. 135	Guided			Communicating	**Lab zone Easy Planner**

Section 1 Electronic Signals and Semiconductors

 *3–4 periods, 1 1/2–2 blocks*

ABILITY LEVELS
L1 Basic to Average
L2 For All Students
L3 Average to Advanced

Objectives

N.4.1.1 Describe two types of electronic signals.
N.4.1.2 Explain how semiconductors are used to make electronic components.

Local Standards

Key Terms

• electronics • electronic signal • analog signal • digital signal
• semiconductor • diode • transistor • integrated circuit

Preteach

Build Background Knowledge

Students identify electronic devices used at home.

 Discover Activity *Can You Send Information With a Flashlight?*  L2

Targeted Print and Technology Resources

All in One Teaching Resources
- L2 Reading Strategy Transparency N43: Asking Questions

PresentationExpress™ CD-ROM

Instruct

Analog and Digital Signals Ask students why using a line graph to represent the readings of a digital thermometer could be misleading.

Semiconductor Devices Ask students leading questions about diodes, transistors, and integrated circuits.

Lab zone Technology Lab *Design a Battery Sensor*  L2

Targeted Print and Technology Resources

All in One Teaching Resources
- L2 Guided Reading, pp. 251–254
- L2 Transparencies N44, N45
- L2 Technology Lab: *Design a Battery Sensor*, pp. 257–259

Lab Activity Video/DVD
Technology Lab: *Design a Battery Sensor*

www.SciLinks.org Web Code: scn-1441

Student Edition on Audio CD

Assess

Section Assessment Questions

Have students use their completed graphic organizers of Asking Questions to answer the questions.

Reteach

Help students make a concept map that shows how the section's key terms are related.

Targeted Print and Technology Resources

All in One Teaching Resources
- Section Summary, p. 250
- L1 Review and Reinforce, p. 255
- L3 Enrich, p. 256

Section 2 Electronic Communication

 *3–4 periods, 1 1/2–2 blocks*

ABILITY LEVELS
- L1 Basic to Average
- L2 For All Students
- L3 Average to Advanced

Objectives

N.4.2.1 Describe how sound is transmitted by telephone.

N.4.2.2 Describe two ways that sound can be reproduced.

N.4.2.3 Explain how electromagnetic waves are involved in the transmission of radio and television signals.

Local Standards

Key Terms

- electromagnetic wave • amplitude • frequency • amplitude modulation (AM)
- frequency modulation (FM)

Preteach

Build Background Knowledge

Students attempt to explain how voices are transmitted over telephone lines.

 *Are You Seeing Spots?* 

Targeted Print and Technology Resources

 **Teaching Resources**

L2 Reading Strategy: Building Vocabulary

Instruct

Telephones Ask students to explain why telephones need batteries to operate.

Sound Recordings Have students classify compact discs as either analog or digital technology.

Electromagnetic Waves Ask students to explain why a carrier wave is necessary for radio and television transmission.

Radio Have students explain why they adjust a dial to make the radio sound clearer.

Television Ask students to explain what a television's receiver does with the carrier wave it receives.

Targeted Print and Technology Resources

All in One **Teaching Resources**

L2 Guided Reading, pp. 262–265

L2 Transparencies N46, N47

PHSchool.com Web Code: cgp-4042

Student Edition on Audio CD

Assess

Section Assessment Questions

Have students use their completed lists of what they know and learned to answer the questions.

Reteach

Use Figures 11 and 12 to review concepts related to how radios and televisions work.

Targeted Print and Technology Resources

All in One **Teaching Resources**

- Section Summary, p. 261

L1 Review and Reinforce, p. 266

L3 Enrich, p. 267

Section 3 Computers

ABILITY LEVELS

L1 Basic to Average
L2 For All Students
L3 Average to Advanced

 *3–4 periods, 1 1/2–2 blocks*

Objectives

N.4.3.1 Explain how information is stored and processed in a computer.
N.4.3.2 Describe the functions of computer hardware and software.

Local Standards

Key Terms

• computer • binary system • hardware • central processing unit (CPU) • input device • output device • software • computer programmer

Preteach

Build Background Knowledge

Students relate their experiences with computers.

 *How Fast Are You?* 

Targeted Print and Technology Resources

All in One Teaching Resources

- L2 Reading Strategy Transparency N48: Outlining

 **PresentationExpress™ CD-ROM**

Instruct

What Is a Computer? Use the table in Figure 14 to introduce students to binary numbers.

Computer Hardware Have students identify common input and output devices.

Computer Software Ask students to identify the input device and the software of a computer game.

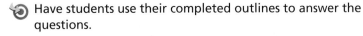

 *Computer Programming* L3

Targeted Print and Technology Resources

 **Teaching Resources**

- L2 Guided Reading, pp. 270–273
- L2 Transparency N49
- L2 Skills Lab: *Computer Programming*, pp. 276–279

 **Lab Activity Video/DVD**
Skills Lab: *Computer Programming*

www.SciLinks.org Web Code: scn-1443

 **Student Edition on Audio CD**

Assess

Section Assessment Questions

 Have students use their completed outlines to answer the questions.

Reteach

Call on students to define in their own words each of the section's key terms.

Targeted Print and Technology Resources

All in One Teaching Resources

- Section Summary, p. 269
- L1 Review and Reinforce, p. 274
- L3 Enrich, p. 275

Section 4 The Information Superhighway

1–2 periods, 1 block

ABILITY LEVELS
L1 Basic to Average
L2 For All Students
L3 Average to Advanced

Local Standards

Objectives

N.4.4.1 Describe the purpose of a computer network.

N.4.4.2 Explain how people can protect themselves and their property as they use computer networks.

Key Terms

• computer network • Internet • World Wide Web • encryption • computer virus • chat room • intellectual property

Preteach

Build Background Knowledge

Students relate what they know about the Internet.

 *How Important Are Computers?* 

Targeted Print and Technology Resources

All in One Teaching Resources

L2 Reading Strategy Transparency N50: Identifying Main Ideas

PresentationExpress™ CD-ROM

Instruct

Computer Networks Ask students to explain how they would respond to an Internet service provider's offer of service.

Using Computers Safely Have students explain what they would do if they were to meet someone online.

Targeted Print and Technology Resources

All in One Teaching Resources

L2 Guided Reading, pp. 282–284

www.SciLinks.org Web Code: scn-1444

Student Edition on Audio CD

Assess

Section Assessment Questions

Have students use their completed graphic organizers of main ideas to answer the questions.

Reteach

Call on volunteers to explain the difference between the Internet and the World Wide Web.

Targeted Print and Technology Resources

All in One Teaching Resources

• Section Summary, p. 281

L1 Review and Reinforce, p. 285

L3 Enrich, p. 286

Chapter 4 Content Refresher

Section 1 Electronic Signals and Semiconductors

Electronic Components Electronic components are often called solid-state components, a term that distinguishes them from the old-fashioned vacuum tubes that were once common in electronic devices. The most common types of electronic components, found in almost all electronic devices, include resistors, capacitors, inductors, diodes, and transistors. Diodes and transistors are discussed in this section. Resistors function mainly to reduce the voltage or to limit current to a desired value in a circuit. Some resistors are fixed resistors, which means the component has a resistance that doesn't change. Other resistors, including rheostats and potentiometers ("pots"), are variable. A rheostat is used to vary the amount of current in a circuit, such as when a circuit has a light that can be dimmed or brightened. Inductors are coils of wire used for their ability to induce voltage when current varies. Diodes are components that allow current in one direction only. The main function of diodes in electronic devices is to change alternating current to direct current. A transistor is a component that is used as a switch or used to amplify AC signals.

Integrated circuits are becoming very common in electronic devices. An integrated circuit may contain hundreds of thousands of electronic components.

Address Misconceptions

Some students may have heard the term transistor radio and believe that the radio itself is a transistor. For a strategy for overcoming this misconception, see **Address Misconceptions** in the section *Electronic Signals and Semiconductors.*

Section 2 Electronic Communication

The Cathode-Ray Tube The images displayed on many televisions and computer monitors are the product of an electronic device called a cathode-ray tube (CRT). Essentially, a cathode is a negative terminal and an anode is a positive terminal. Thomas Edison discovered that when a cathode inside a vacuum tube is heated, electrons flow across the tube to the anode. The negative electrons from the cathode are attracted to the positive anode, just as electrons are attracted to the positive terminal of a battery in an electric circuit. In a cathode-ray tube, the video signal enters the CRT, and a high-speed beam of electrons is emitted from the cathode, as shown in the figure below. The electron beam passes through a small hole in the anode and is focused onto the screen at the opposite end of the tube. Deflection plates place the electron beam at any point on the screen. The glass of the screen is coated with dots of phosphor, a fluorescent substance that glows when struck by electrons. The electron beam sweeps over the screen in less than 1/30 of a second. The dots on the screen glow red, green, or blue, and the brightness of the glow depends on the voltage of the beam. Since the beam's voltage is determined by the video signal, the continuous sweeping of the beam over the screen causes a picture to be displayed.

Cathode-Ray Tube

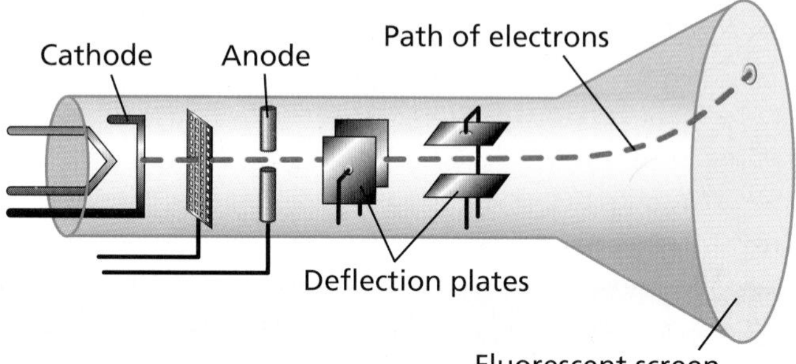

Section 3 Computers

Binary Numbers The binary system has positional values just as the decimal system does. These values can be expressed in terms of the base to a certain power. In base-10 number of 5 digits, the places represent multiples of the following powers of 10: 10^4, 10^3, 10^2, 10^1, 10^0. Thus, the number 51,624 can be expressed as 5×10^4, or 50,000, plus 1×10^3, or 1,000, and so on.

Similarly, in base 2, the first five positions are $2^4, 2^3, 2^2, 2^1, 2^0$. That translates to these values in base 10: 16, 8, 4, 2, 1. Thus, the binary number 10011 in base 10 equals 1×16, or 16, plus 0×8, or 0, plus 0×4, or 0, plus 1×2, or 2, plus 1×1, or 1. That is, $16 + 0 + 0 + 2 + 1 = 19$. Therefore, 10011 in base 2 equals 19 in base 10.

There is a simple method of converting a base-10 number into a base-2 number. The method involves successive divisions by the number 2. The remainder of each division—either 1 or 0—is the digit, or "bit," of a place in the binary number. Consider the conversion of 25 in base 10 to a binary number.

$25 \div 2 = 12$, with a remainder of 1

$12 \div 2 = 6$, with a remainder of 0

$6 \div 2 = 3$, with a remainder of 0

$3 \div 2 = 1$, with a remainder of 1

$1 \div 2 = 0$, with a remainder of 1

The binary number is the successive remainders of these divisions, with the remainder of the last division being the first digit of the binary number. Reading from bottom to top, then, the binary number that equals the base-10 number 25 is 11001.

Section 4 The Information Superhighway

The Internet and the World Wide Web In 1969, a network of computers was established called ARPANET (Advanced Research Projects Agency network). The network of computers was designed in great part to protect the exchange of military information between bases. Another reason the network was created was to connect all of the relatively few powerful research computers in the United States. The first data were exchanged between computers at Stanford University and UCLA. The first e-mail—a simple message from one person to another through the network—was sent in 1971. In 1983, ARPANET expanded to become the Internet, an international computer network. Computer scientist Vinton Cerf was instrumental in that transformation.

In 1989, British physicist Tim Berners-Lee invented the World Wide Web (WWW). At the time, he was working in Geneva, Switzerland, at the European Particle Physics Laboratory called CERN. The Internet had been in existence for several years, but exchanges of information were mainly limited to e-mails. Berners-Lee envisioned something much more extensive, a system that would provide international access to sounds and images. He developed the code in which Web sites are written, called HyperText Markup Language (HTML), as well as the addresses by which Web sites are known (URLs). The first Web site was Berners-Lee's own invention, and it was put online in 1991. It provided explanations for how to operate on the World Wide Web. In 1994, Berners-Lee founded the World Wide Web Consortium at the Massachusetts Institute of Technology (MIT).

For: Professional development support
Visit: www.SciLinks.org/PDLinks
Web Code: scf-1440

Professional Development

Help Students Read

Monitoring Your Understanding

Self-Questioning and Self-Adjusting While Reading

Strategy Help students read and understand difficult technical material. This strategy enables students to focus on their own thought processes as they actively question and apply fix-up strategies to improve comprehension. First, present the three steps in the example below, reviewing the fix-up strategies in Step 2. Then, before students begin, choose a subsection in this chapter, such as *Computer Software*.

Example

1. Self-Question Have students read and think about the paragraphs under each subheading, stopping to ask themselves questions such as Do I understand this?, Is this clear?, and Does this answer my questions?

2. Identify Trouble Spots and Apply Fix-Up Strategies

- **Reread/Adjust Reading Pace** When students do not understand a paragraph, have them reread it slowly, making sure they understand each sentence before they continue.
- **Clarify** When students encounter a difficult paragraph, suggest that they state what they do understand, talk through confusing points or steps in a process, or relate new information to concepts and examples that are already familiar to them.
- **Read Ahead/Use Visuals and Captions** Show students how to use visuals and captions to help clarify a process or a concept. Suggest that they can also read ahead to see whether a process or concept is discussed further as part of another concept.
- **Use Outside Resources** Point out, too, that students should seek assistance from friends, teachers, or other resources. Hearing additional examples or more than one person's explanation often aids comprehension.

3. Self-Check After students read, have them check their understanding by summarizing or retelling the main idea of a paragraph or subsection.

Interactive Textbook
- Complete student edition
- Video and audio
- Simulations and activities
- Section and chapter activities

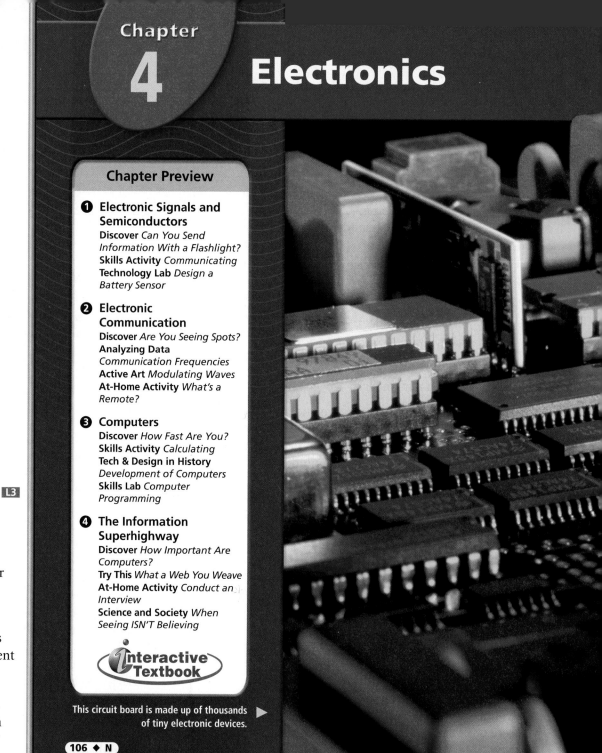

Chapter 4 Electronics

Chapter Preview

1. **Electronic Signals and Semiconductors**
   Discover *Can You Send Information With a Flashlight?*
   Skills Activity *Communicating*
   Technology Lab *Design a Battery Sensor*
2. **Electronic Communication**
   Discover *Are You Seeing Spots?*
   Analyzing Data *Communication Frequencies*
   Active Art *Modulating Waves*
   At-Home Activity *What's a Remote?*
3. **Computers**
   Discover *How Fast Are You?*
   Skills Activity *Calculating*
   Tech & Design in History *Development of Computers*
   Skills Lab *Computer Programming*
4. **The Information Superhighway**
   Discover *How Important Are Computers?*
   Try This *What a Web You Weave*
   At-Home Activity *Conduct an Interview*
   Science and Society *When Seeing ISN'T Believing*

Interactive Textbook

This circuit board is made up of thousands of tiny electronic devices. ▶

L3

Objectives

Students will research and describe an existing computer application and then develop a new computer application. After completing this Chapter Project, students will be able to
- observe what an existing computer application does and explain its benefits
- apply chapter concepts in the development of a new computer application
- design a solution to the problem of developing a new computer application
- communicate their understanding of an existing computer application and their design of a new application to the class

Skills Focus

Observing, applying concepts, designing a solution, communicating

Project Time Line 2–3 weeks

All in One Teaching Resources
- Chapter Project Teacher Notes
- Chapter Project Overview
- Chapter Project Worksheet 1
- Chapter Project Worksheet 2
- Chapter Project Scoring Rubric

Developing a Plan

Divide the class into small groups, and have each group brainstorm a list of computer applications they have used or seen. From this list, each group may choose an application to research. This can be done at the library, on the Internet, or by contacting a computer expert or a manufacturer's technical support line. After researching an existing application, groups will create the concept for a new computer application. They will need time to consider the required inputs for their application and the resulting outputs. During this time, they should work on posters, diagrams, descriptions, and other visual information for the presentation of their computer applications to the class.

Possible Materials

Students use paper and pencils for recording information during the research component of the project. For the presentation to the class, groups may want to use poster board, overhead transparencies, markers, and rulers.

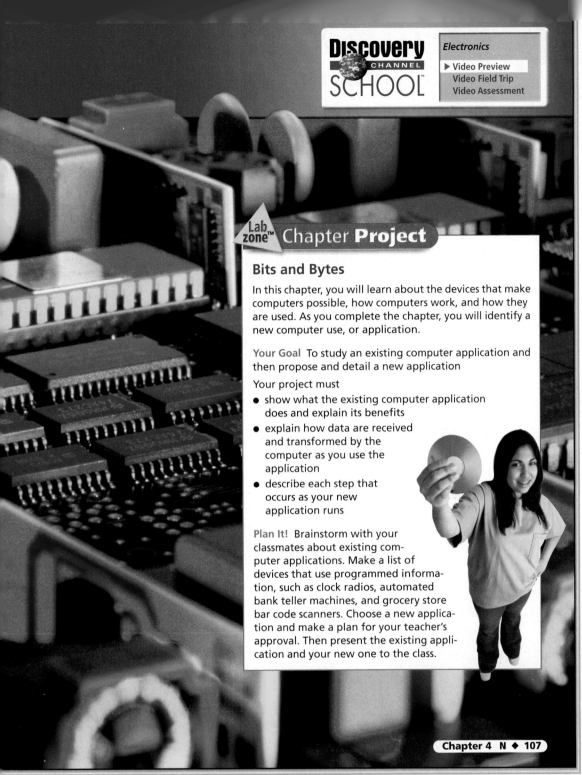

Lab zone™ Chapter Project

Bits and Bytes

In this chapter, you will learn about the devices that make computers possible, how computers work, and how they are used. As you complete the chapter, you will identify a new computer use, or application.

Your Goal To study an existing computer application and then propose and detail a new application

Your project must
- show what the existing computer application does and explain its benefits
- explain how data are received and transformed by the computer as you use the application
- describe each step that occurs as your new application runs

Plan It! Brainstorm with your classmates about existing computer applications. Make a list of devices that use programmed information, such as clock radios, automated bank teller machines, and grocery store bar code scanners. Choose a new application and make a plan for your teacher's approval. Then present the existing application and your new one to the class.

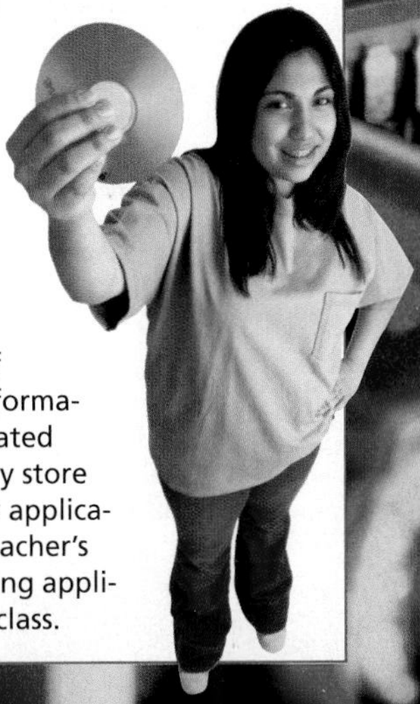

Electronics

Show the Video Preview to introduce the Chapter Project and provide an overview for the chapter content. Discussion question: **What common task helped Farnsworth realize how an image could be scanned electronically?** *(One day when he looked at the parallel rows he had just plowed in his father's potato field, he realized he could use a similar process to use rows of electrons to scan an image.)*

Possible Shortcuts

- You can make this project shorter by having groups research an existing application and then writing a short proposal for a new application.
- For a class project, propose a new computer application, and have groups describe ways in which it could be used.

Launching the Project

To introduce the project, ask: **What kinds of computer applications have you used?** *(Sample answer: Games, word processing programs, e-mail programs)* After students have discussed the function of several existing applications, have them read the description of the Chapter Project. Then encourage discussion of computers, their applications, and possible research materials for the project. Answer any questions students may have. If possible, give students Internet access for researching their computer applications. You may wish to set up a session with the school's computer specialist or computer-class instructor to allow students to practice using Internet search engines.

Performance Assessment

The Chapter Project Scoring Rubric will help you evaluate how well students complete the Chapter Project. You may want to share the scoring rubric with your students so they are clear about what will be expected of them. Students will be assessed on
- how well they understand the origin and operation of an existing computer application
- how well they apply chapter concepts to the development and description of a new computer application
- how effectively they present the existing application and the new application to the class
- how well they participate in their groups

Students can keep their application descriptions in their portfolios.

Section 1 Electronic Signals and Semiconductors

Objectives

After this lesson, students will be able to

N.4.1.1 Describe two types of electronic signals.

N.4.1.2 Explain how semiconductors are used to make electronic components.

Target Reading Skill

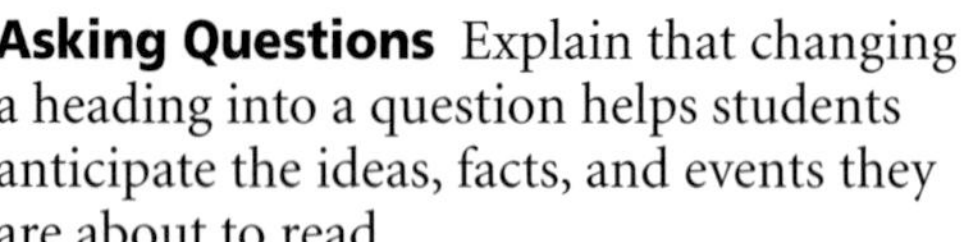

Asking Questions Explain that changing a heading into a question helps students anticipate the ideas, facts, and events they are about to read.

Answers

Sample questions and answers:

What are analog and digital signals? *(Analog signals are currents that are varied smoothly to represent information, while digital signals are pulses of current used to represent information.)* **What are semiconductor devices?** *(Semiconductor devices are electronic devices that use semiconductors to vary the current in a circuit.)*

All in One Teaching Resources

- Transparency N43

Preteach

Build Background Knowledge

L2

Ask: **What are appliances or devices at home that use electrical energy?** *(Sample answer: Refrigerator, lamps, microwave oven)* **What devices use electrical energy and also give you information?** *(Sample answer: Clock, telephone, radio, television, answering machine)* Explain that in this section, students will learn what distinguishes electrical devices from electronic devices.

Section 1 Electronic Signals and Semiconductors

Reading Preview

Key Concepts

- What are two types of electronic signals?
- How are semiconductors used to make electronic components?

Key Terms

- electronics
- electronic signal
- analog signal
- digital signal
- semiconductor
- diode
- transistor
- integrated circuit

Target Reading Skill

Asking Questions Before you read, preview the red headings. In a graphic organizer like the one below, ask a *what* question for each heading. As you read, write the answers to your questions.

Electronic Signals and Devices

Question	Answer
What are analog and digital signals?	Analog signals are . . .

Can You Send Information With a Flashlight?

1. Write a short sentence on a sheet of paper.
2. Morse code is a language that uses dots and dashes to convey information. Convert your sentence to dots and dashes using the International Morse Code chart at the right.
3. Turn a flashlight on and off quickly to represent dots. Leave the flashlight on a little longer to represent dashes. Practice using the flashlight for different letters.
4. Use the flashlight to transmit your sentence to a partner. Ask your partner to translate your message and write down your sentence.

Think It Over

Inferring Were you able to transmit information using light? How does your light message differ from the same message read aloud?

International Morse Code

A •–	B –•••	C –•–•	D –••
E •	F ••–•	G ––•	H ••••
I ••	J •–––	K –•–	L •–••
M ––	N –•	O –––	P •––•
Q ––•–	R •–•	S •••	T –
U ••–	V •••–	W •––	X –••–
Y –•––	Z ––••		

Every day, you use devices that run on electric current. But not all these devices are the same. Light bulbs and toasters are examples of *electrical* devices. An electrical device relies on a continuous supply of electric current.

When you watch television or talk on a cell phone, you are using *electronic* devices. The difference between electronic and electrical devices is in the way that they use electric current.

Electronics is the use of electric current to control, communicate, and process information. How do electronic devices work? Electronics is based on electronic signals. Any information that can be measured or numbered, whether it is electrical or not, can be converted to a signal. An **electronic signal** is a varying electric current that represents information.

◀ Cameras can use electronic signals to take photographs.

Discover Activity

Skills Focus Inferring L2

Materials flashlight

Time 15 minutes

Tips To save time, have students transmit a single word rather than an entire sentence.

Expected Outcome Most students should be able to transmit a message using Morse code.

Think It Over Sample answer: The message was transmitted. A message read aloud would be composed of sounds. The light message uses patterns of flashing light to transmit information.

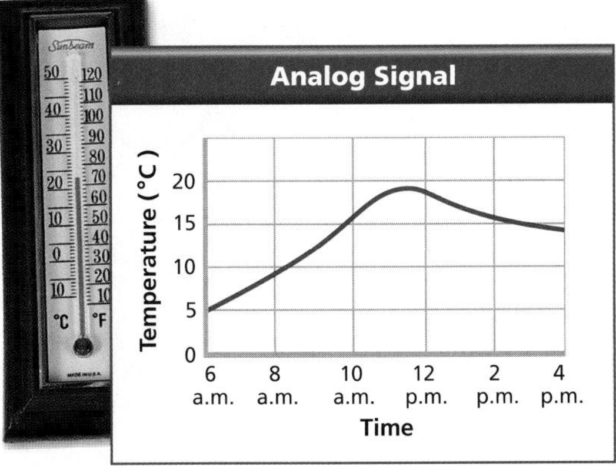

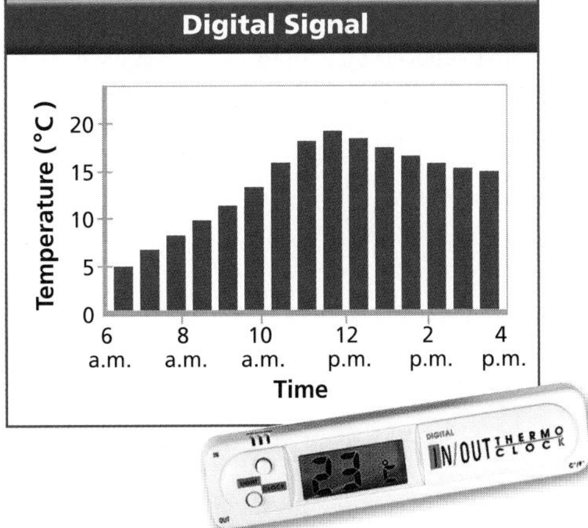

Analog and Digital Signals

There are two basic kinds of electronic signals: analog signals and digital signals. The two types of signals represent information in different ways.

Analog Signals In **analog signals,** a current is varied smoothly to represent information. An analog signal varies in much the same way that temperature varies in a liquid-filled thermometer. This kind of thermometer shows temperature as the height of a liquid in a tube. The height of the liquid rises and falls smoothly with the temperature. The "analog signal" from the liquid-filled thermometer can be represented by a line graph like the one in Figure 1.

Digital Signals In **digital signals,** pulses of current are used to represent information. Rather than varying smoothly to represent information, a digital signal carries information in pulses, or steps. If you did the Discover activity, you used pulses of light to represent letters.

A digital signal varies much the same way the numbers on a digital thermometer vary. You have probably seen a digital thermometer in front of a bank. The number on the thermometer is constant for a while and then changes suddenly by a whole degree. Of course, the temperature doesn't really change so suddenly. But the thermometer can only show the temperature to the nearest degree, and so the temperature seems to jump. The digital signal from a digital thermometer can be represented by a bar graph, as shown in Figure 1.

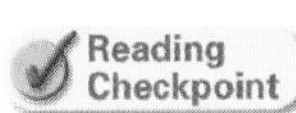
How is the changing temperature on a liquid-filled thermometer like an analog signal?

FIGURE 1
Analog and Digital
An analog signal varies smoothly. A digital signal varies in steps.
Predicting *How would the bar graph be different if it showed temperature measurements made every minute?*

For: Links on electronic signals
Visit: www.SciLinks.org
Web Code: scn-1441

Instruct

Analog and Digital Signals

Teach Key Concepts (L2)

Smooth Variation vs. Pulses

Focus Tell students that two types of signals can represent information in different ways.

Teach Ask: **What are the two kinds of electronic signals?** *(Analog and digital)* **What do digital signals use to represent information?** *(Pulses)* Point out the traditional thermometer in Figure 1. Ask: **How is the way this thermometer shows temperature like an analog signal?** *(The height of the liquid rises and falls smoothly, just as in an analog signal a current is varied smoothly to represent information.)*

Apply Have students study Figure 1. Ask: **Why would a line graph representing the readings of a digital thermometer be misleading?** *(Digital thermometer readings change suddenly by whole degrees, with nothing in between. A line graph implies that temperature readings change smoothly.)* **learning modality: visual**

All in One Teaching Resources
- Transparency N44

For: Links on electronic signals
Visit: www.SciLinks.org
Web Code: scn-1441

Download a worksheet that will guide students' review of Internet sources on electronic signals.

Independent Practice (L2)

All in One Teaching Resources
- Guided Reading and Study Worksheet: *Electronic Signals and Semiconductors*

Student Edition on Audio CD

Monitor Progress (L2)

Writing Ask students to explain the difference between analog and digital signals.

Answers
Figure 1 Sample answer: The bar graph would have 60 bars for each hour instead of 1 bar per hour.

Reading Checkpoint The height of the liquid rises and falls smoothly, just like an analog signal varies smoothly.

Differentiated Instruction

Gifted and Talented (L3)

Testing Thermometers Ask students to investigate whether analog and digital thermometers give the same readings. Each student should design an experiment comparing the two. A typical experiment would involve reading thermometers in the same place at regular intervals. **learning modality: logical/mathematical**

Special Needs (L1)

Diodes and Transistors Take apart an old, nonworking electronic device such as a transistor radio. Show students the diodes and transistors that once made the radio work. As students examine these components, have a volunteer read the text descriptions aloud. **learning modality: visual**

Semiconductor Devices

Teach Key Concepts L2

Conducting Under Certain Conditions

Focus Tell students that an electronic device must be able to vary the current through a circuit to be able to transmit an electronic signal.

Teach Ask: **How is a semiconductor different from a conductor?** *(Current through a conductor is continuous, but a semiconductor conducts current only under certain conditions.)* **What is a diode?** *(An electronic component that consists of an n-type and a p-type semiconductor joined together)* Have students examine the images of a diode and a transistor in Figure 3 to differentiate between the two components. Ask: **What can a transistor do that a diode cannot?** *(Amplify an electronic signal)*

Apply Ask: **What component contains both diodes and transistors?** *(An integrated circuit)* **How is a chip different than an integrated circuit?** *(They aren't different. An integrated circuit and a chip are two names for the same thing.)* **learning modality: verbal**

All in One Teaching Resources

- Transparency N45

L1

Modeling a Semiconductor

Materials flour, sieve or colander, paper towel, mixing bowel, scissors

Time 10 minutes

Focus Tell students that a model can demonstrate the function of a semiconductor.

Teach Fill a sieve lined with a paper towel with flour and hold it over the mixing bowl. Ask: **Does this container "conduct" flour well?** *(No. The flour is contained inside the sieve.)* Using scissors, cut a hole in the center of the paper towel, and then repeat the procedure. Students will observe some of the flour passes through the sieve.

Apply Ask: **How is this sieve like a semiconductor?** *(A semiconductor conducts electricity only under certain conditions. The sieve passes flour through it only under certain conditions.)* **learning modality: visual**

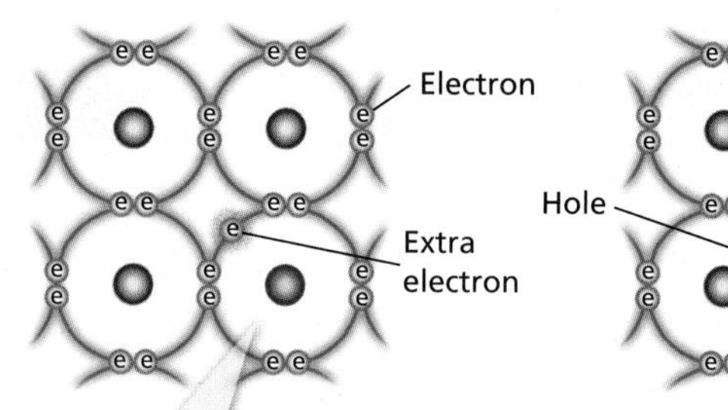

FIGURE 2
Semiconductors
The electrical resistance of pure silicon is reduced by adding atoms of other elements to it.

N-type Semiconductor
Adding an element with an extra electron to silicon creates a n-type semiconductor.

P-type Semiconductor
Adding an element with fewer electrons, or holes, creates a p-type semiconductor.

Semiconductor Devices

How can an electronic device transmit electronic signals? To transmit an electronic signal, an electronic device must be able to vary the current through a circuit. To vary current, electronic devices use semiconductors. A **semiconductor** is a material that conducts current better than insulators but not as well as conductors. A semiconductor conducts current only under certain conditions.

How Semiconductors Work How can a material conduct current only under certain conditions? Silicon and other semiconductors are elements that have extremely high resistance in their pure forms. However, if atoms of other elements are added to semiconductors, the resulting material can conduct current much more easily.

By controlling the number and type of atoms added, scientists produce two types of semiconductors. In Figure 2, you can see that adding atoms with extra electrons to silicon produces an n-type semiconductor. "N," for "negative," indicates that the material can release, or give off, electrons. Look again at Figure 2. Notice that adding atoms with fewer electrons, or holes, to silicon produces a p-type semiconductor. "P," for "positive," indicates that the material has room for and can receive an electron.

Scientists combine n-type and p-type semiconductors in layers. This layered structure allows for the delicate control of current needed for many electronic devices. **The two types of semiconductors can be combined in different ways to make diodes, transistors, and integrated circuits.** These components control current in electronic devices.

Lab zone Skills Activity

Communicating

How do you make someone understand how tiny a chip is or how fast an electronic signal travels? An analogy can help communicate what a measurement means. An analogy uses a similarity between two things that are otherwise unlike each other. For example, "a chip is as small as a baby's fingernail" is an analogy. So is "an electronic signal moves as fast as a bolt of lightning." Write your own analogies to describe how many diodes there are in one integrated circuit chip.

110 ◆ N

Lab zone Skills Activity

Skills Focus Communicating L2

Materials dictionary

Time 15 minutes

Tips You may wish to pair students still mastering English with native speakers for this activity. Advise students to brainstorm a list of possible analogies and write a sentence for each.

Expected Outcome Students' analogies should rely on the idea that a chip may contain hundreds of thousands of components. Sample analogy: There are more diodes in one integrated circuit chip than there are pennies in a million dollars.

Extend Have students choose the best analogies and make a poster about chips with written analogies and cartoon illustrations. **learning modality: verbal**

Diodes An electronic component that consists of an n-type and a p-type semiconductor joined together is a **diode.** A diode, shown in Figure 3, allows current in one direction only. If you connect a diode in a circuit in one direction, there will be a current. But if you turn the diode around, there will not be a current. Diodes can be used to change an alternating current to a direct current. Diodes can also be used as a switch.

Transistors When a layer of one type of semiconductor is sandwiched between two layers of the other type of semiconductor, a transistor is formed. Figure 3 shows the structure of a transistor. A **transistor** has two uses: it either amplifies an electronic signal or switches current on and off.

When electronic signals travel great distances, they gradually grow weak. When they are received, signals must be amplified, or made stronger, so that they can be used. Transistors revolutionized the electronics industry by making amplifiers much cheaper and more reliable.

When a transistor acts as a switch, it either allows a current or cuts it off. Millions of transistors that act as switches are what make computers work.

FIGURE 3
Diodes and Transistors
Diodes (top) allow current in only one direction. Transistors (bottom) can amplify electronic signals or act as switches. **Comparing and Contrasting** *How are diodes and transistors similar? How are they different?*

Diode A diode is a combination of an n-type and a p-type semiconductor.

Transistor A transistor is a combination of three layers of semiconductors.

FIGURE 4
Combining Electronic Components
Diodes and transistors can be combined to carry out specific tasks within electronic devices. The singing fish uses electronics to move and make sounds when a person walks by.

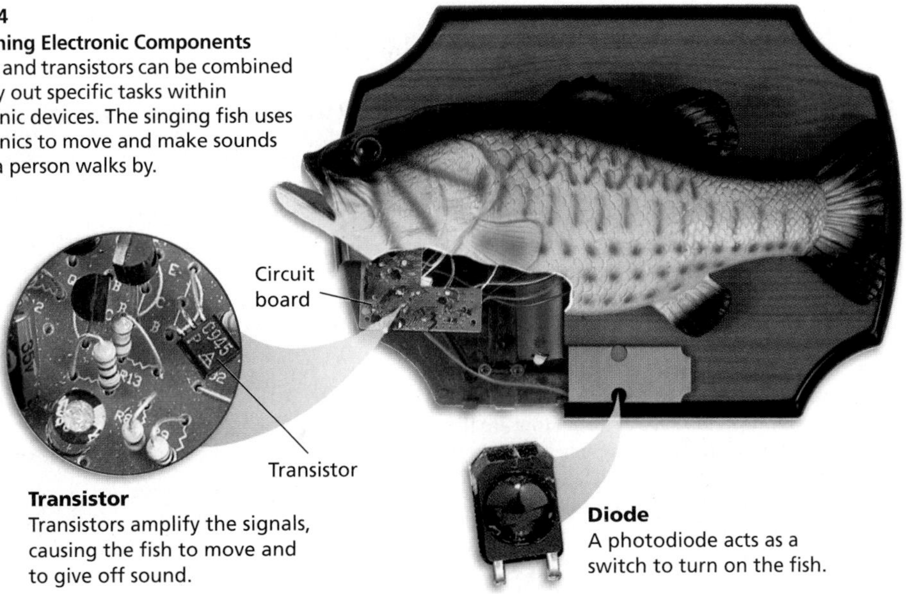

Circuit board

Transistor

Transistor
Transistors amplify the signals, causing the fish to move and to give off sound.

Diode
A photodiode acts as a switch to turn on the fish.

Address Misconceptions L1

Transistors Are Not Radios

Focus Some students may have heard the term *transistor radio* and believe that the radio itself is a transistor.

Teach Explain that a transistor is a component of a radio that amplifies the signal. The use of transistors allowed radios to become much smaller than they once were.

Apply Ask: **What electronic devices are transistors found in other than in radios?** *(Millions of transistors that act as switches are what make computers work.)* **learning modality: verbal**

Monitor Progress L2

Oral Presentation Call on students to explain what a semiconductor is, what diodes are, and what transistors are.

Answer

Figure 3 Both control current, and both can be used as a switch. Diodes can change an alternating current to a direct current. Transistors can amplify electronic signals.

Monitor Progress L2

Answer

Reading Checkpoint A chip is another name for an integrated circuit, which is a thin slice of semiconductor that contains many diodes, transistors, and other electronic components.

Assess

Reviewing Key Concepts

1. a. Analog signals and digital signals
b. Both represent information. Analog signals use smoothly varying current, while digital signals rely on pulses of current.
c. The swinging pendulum represents an analog signal. The pendulum moves continuously and smoothly, much like an analog signal.
2. a. Semiconductors control the current in electronic devices. **b.** A transistor consists of a layer of either n-type or p-type semiconductor sandwiched between two layers of the other type of semiconductor.
c. Transistors could amplify the signals that represent sounds and switch the current that produces sounds on and off.

Reteach L1

Help students make a concept map that shows how the section's key terms are related.

Performance Assessment L2

Writing Ask students to explain in a paragraph why semiconductors are used in electronic devices.

All in One Teaching Resources

- Section Summary: *Electronic Signals and Semiconductors*
- Review and Reinforce: *Electronic Signals and Semiconductors*
- Enrich: *Electronic Signals and Semiconductors*

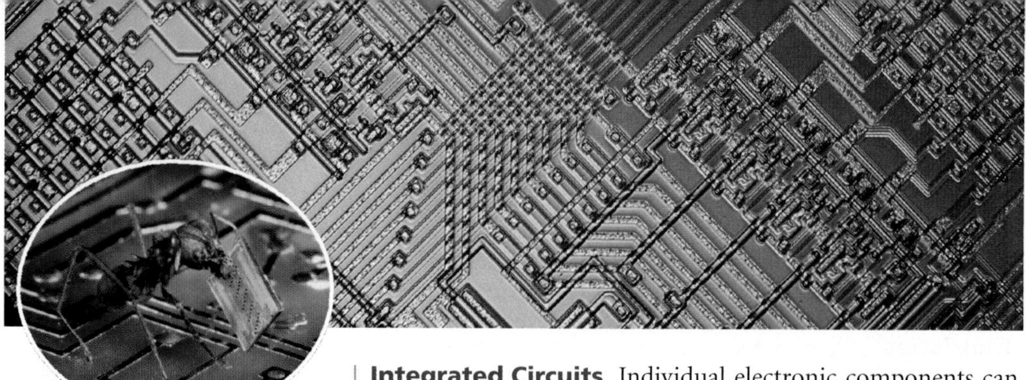

FIGURE 5
Integrated Circuits
An integrated circuit chip is smaller than an ant. Yet the integrated circuit contains hundreds of thousands of diodes and transistors.

Integrated Circuits Individual electronic components can be combined into larger groups, called integrated circuits, to increase their usefulness. An **integrated circuit** is a thin slice of semiconductor that contains many diodes, transistors, and other electronic components. Integrated circuits are also called chips. Figure 5 shows a magnified view of a chip from a computer. A chip smaller than one millimeter on each side can contain hundreds of thousands of components. Electronic signals flow through integrated circuits at tremendous speeds because the various components are so close together. On some chips, the space between two components can be one hundredth as thick as a human hair. The high-speed signals of integrated circuits make possible devices from video games to spacecraft. The small size of integrated circuits has allowed the size of electronic devices such as computers to be greatly reduced.

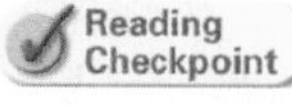 **What is a chip?**

Section 1 Assessment

Target Reading Skill Asking Questions Use the answer to the questions you wrote about the section headings to help you answer the questions below.

Reviewing Key Concepts

1. a. Listing What are the two basic kinds of electronic signals?
   b. Comparing and Contrasting How are the two types of electronic signals similar? How are they different?
   c. Classifying A grandfather clock uses a pendulum that continuously swings to control the clock's hands. What type of signal does the swinging pendulum represent? Explain.
2. a. Reviewing How are semiconductors used in electronic devices?
   b. Explaining What is a transistor?
   c. Relating Cause and Effect A loudspeaker changes electronic signals into sounds. Why would transistors be useful parts of a loudspeaker?

Writing in Science

Directions Review the Morse code at the beginning of the section. Write directions a friend could use to send you messages using light or sound.

112 ◆ N

Lab zone Chapter Project

Keep Students on Track By this point, groups should have brainstormed a list of computer applications and chosen one to research. Encourage students to find out how the application was developed, how it works, and who uses it. Make sure students consider the inputs into the application and the outputs that result. Provide library books on computer applications to help them begin.

Writing in Science

Writing Mode Exposition

Scoring Rubric

4 Exceeds criteria; includes clear and complete directions
3 Meets criteria
2 Meets some criteria; includes confusing directions and/or lacks critical steps
1 Includes inaccurate and/or very incomplete directions

Lab zone **Technology Lab**

• Tech & Design •

Design a Battery Sensor

Problem

How can an LED be used to tell if a battery is installed correctly?

Skills Focus

evaluating the design, redesigning, observing, drawing conclusions

Materials

- 2 D cells
- LED
- bicolor LED (optional)
- flashlight using 2 D-cells
- flashlight bulb and socket
- two insulated wires with alligator clips

Procedure 

PART 1 LED Properties

1. Attach one wire to each terminal of the LED.
2. Tape the two cells together, positive terminal to negative terminal, to make a 3-volt battery.
3. Attach the other ends of the wires to the terminals of the battery and observe the LED.
4. Switch the wires connected to the battery terminals and observe the LED again.
5. Repeat Steps 1–4, but substitute a flashlight bulb in its socket for the LED.

PART 2 Sensor Design

6. Many electrical devices that run on batteries will not run if the batteries are installed backwards (positive where negative should be). Design a device that uses an LED to indicate if batteries are installed backwards.
7. Draw your design. Show how the LED, the device, and the battery are connected. (*Hint:* The LED can be connected either in series or in parallel with the battery and the device.)
8. Make a model of your sensor to see if it works with a flashlight.

Analyze and Conclude

1. **Observing** What did you observe in Part 1 when you connected the LED to the battery the first time? The second time?
2. **Drawing Conclusions** Based on your observations, is the LED a diode? How do you know?
3. **Evaluating the Design** How did your observations of the LED's properties affect your design in Part 2?
4. **Troubleshooting** Describe any problems you had while designing and building your sensor.
5. **Redesigning** In what ways could you improve your sensor?

Communicate

Write a product brochure for your battery sensor. Be sure to describe in detail how your sensor can be used to tell if batteries are installed correctly in electrical devices. Include other possible uses for your sensor. What practical application can you see for such an LED?

Analyze and Conclude

1. Sample answer: The LED lights when there is current in one direction but does not light when the current is reversed.
2. The LED is a diode because it lighted only when there was current in one direction.
3. Sample answer: Based on my observations, I placed the LED in the circuit so it lit when the batteries were installed correctly.
4. The device should be designed so that the LED is connected to allow current only when the battery is installed correctly.
5. Sample answer: The sensor design could be improved by adding another LED of a different color in a parallel circuit. The LEDs would be in opposite directions in the circuit.

Lab zone **Technology Lab**

Design a Battery Sensor 

L2

Prepare for Inquiry

Key Concept

A light-emitting diode (LED) emits light only when there is current in one direction.

Skills Objectives

After this lab, students will be able to:

- observe what happens when an LED is connected to a battery
- draw a conclusion about whether evidence supports the hypothesis
- use their oservations to evaluate the design of their sensor device
- list ways to redesign or improve their battery sensor

Prep Time 15 minutes
Class Time 40 minutes

Advance Planning

Obtain 2 D-cells, a 3-volt flashlight bulb and socket, 2 insulated wires with alligator clips, electrical tape, and an LED for each group.

Safety

Caution students to disconnect the equipment when not in use. Review the safety guidelines in Appendix A.

All in One Teaching Resources

- Lab Worksheet: *Design a Battery Sensor*

Guide Inquiry

Introduce the Procedure

Have students read the procedure, and answer their questions. Review how a diode works.

Expected Outcome

The bulb will light with the current in either direction; the LED will light when there is current in only one direction. The LED is a diode.

Extend Inquiry

Communicate Students' brochures should include a detailed description of how their sensor works. Other possible uses should also be described.

Section 2 Electronic Communication

Objectives

After this lesson, students will be able to

N.4.2.1 Describe how sound is transmitted by telephone.

N.4.2.2 Describe two ways that sound can be reproduced.

N.4.2.3 Explain how electromagnetic waves are involved in the transmission of radio and television signals.

Target Reading Skill

Building Vocabulary Explain that knowing the definitions of key-concept words helps students understand what they read.

Answers

Sample answers:

An **electromagnetic wave** is a wave that is made out of electric and magnetic fields that change. The **amplitude** of a wave is the height of a wave from a line through the center to a crest or a trough. The **frequency** of a wave is the number of times a wave passes a certain point every second. **Amplitude modulation (AM)** is the process of changing the amplitude of a carrier wave so that it matches the wave of a signal. **Frequency modulation (FM)** is the process of changing the frequency of a carrier wave so that it matches the amplitude of a signal.

Preteach

Build Background Knowledge L2

Ask: **How do you think voices are transmitted over telephone lines?** *(Sample answer: Somehow, the voices are turned into electronic signals to send over telephone lines.)* **If that is so, how are the electronic signals turned back into voices at the receiving end?** *(Sample answer: Maybe the process is the same as in a radio.)* Tell students that in this section they will learn how telephones, radios, and television signals are sent and received.

Section 2 Electronic Communication

Reading Preview

Key Concepts

- How is sound transmitted by telephone?
- What are two ways that sounds can be reproduced?
- How are electromagnetic waves involved in the transmission of radio and television signals?

Key Terms

- electromagnetic wave
- amplitude
- frequency
- amplitude modulation (AM)
- frequency modulation (FM)

Target Reading Skill

Building Vocabulary A definition states the meaning of a word or phrase by telling about its most important feature or function. After you read the section, reread the paragraphs that contain definitions of Key Terms. Use all the information you have learned to write a definition of each Key Term in your own words.

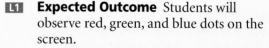

Lab zone Discover Activity

Are You Seeing Spots?

1. Turn on a color television. Hold a hand lens at arm's length up to the television screen.
2. Move the lens closer to and farther from the screen until you can see a clear image through it. What do you see within the image?

Think It Over

Classifying What three colors make up the images on the television screen? How do you think these colors make up the wide range of colors you see on television?

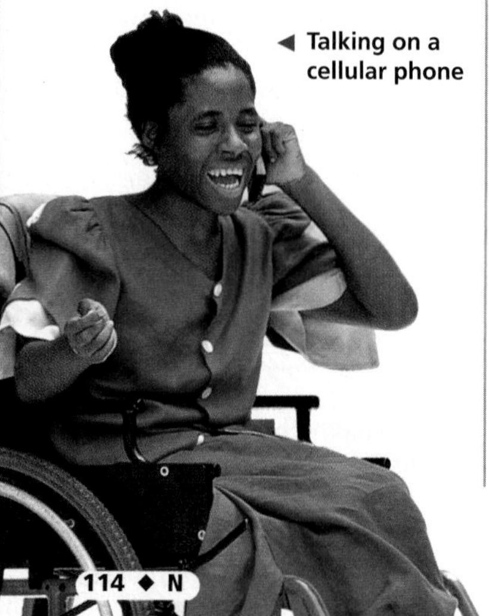

◀ Talking on a cellular phone

Have you ever thought about the amazing technology that enables you to see and hear an event as it happens halfway around the globe? Since the first telegraph message was sent in 1844, people have become accustomed to long distance communication by telephone, radio, and television. Compared with the past, communication today is fast, dependable, and cheap. This is because of advancements in the field of electronics.

Telephones

In a telephone, sound is transformed into an electronic signal that is transmitted and then transformed back into sound. The first telephone was invented by Alexander Graham Bell in 1876. Modern telephones have some of the same main parts as the telephone patented by Bell: a transmitter, a receiver, and a dialing mechanism.

Transmitter Sound is transformed into an electronic signal in the transmitter of a telephone. Transforming sound into an electronic signal is possible because sound travels as a wave. These waves cause a metal disk in the microphone to vibrate, transforming the sound into an electronic signal. The signal can travel through a series of switches and wires to the receiving telephone. Modern telephone equipment can also transform the electronic signals to a pattern of light that travels through optical fibers.

Lab zone Discover Activity

Skills Focus Classifying L1

Materials hand lens, color television

Time 10 minutes

Tips If a color television is unavailable, use a VCR monitor or a computer monitor. Encourage students who need practice seeing through a hand lens to spend extra time using lenses to observe objects around the room.

Expected Outcome Students will observe red, green, and blue dots on the screen.

Think It Over Sample answer: The three colors are red, green, and blue. These three colors combine to form all the other colors on the screen.

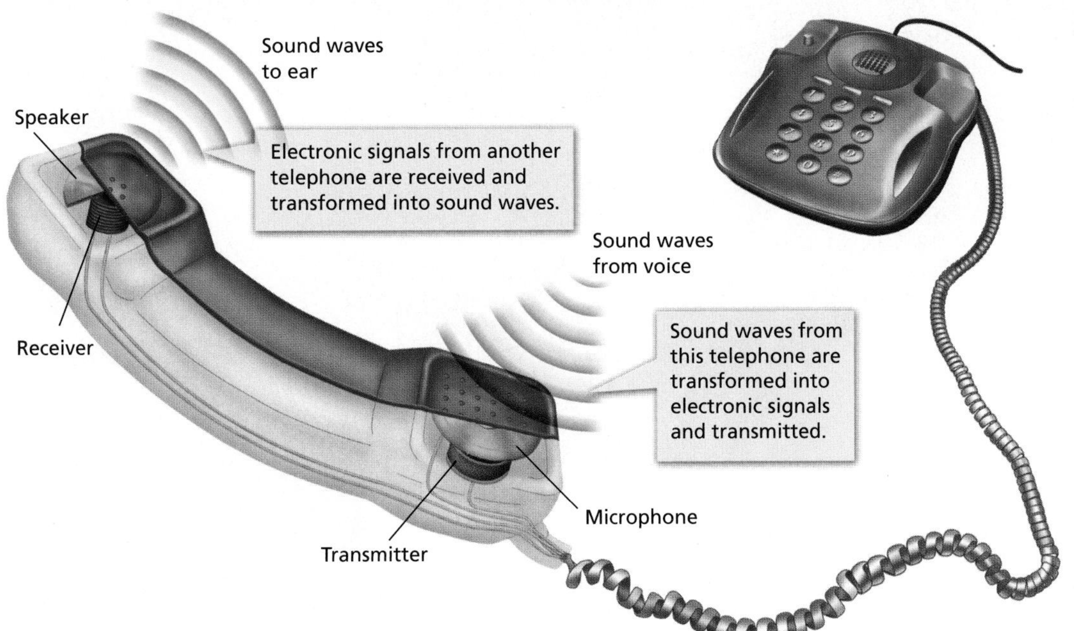
Sound waves to ear
Speaker
Electronic signals from another telephone are received and transformed into sound waves.
Sound waves from voice
Receiver
Sound waves from this telephone are transformed into electronic signals and transmitted.
Microphone
Transmitter

FIGURE 6
How a Telephone Works
When you speak into a telephone, your voice is transformed into electronic signals. The signals are transmitted to the listener's phone, where they are transformed back into sound.
Applying Concepts *How does the dialing mechanism work?*

Receiver The receiver is located in the earpiece of a telephone. The receiver uses a speaker to transform the electronic signal back into sound. A speaker is made up of an electromagnet and a thin metal disk. During a conversation, the amount of electric current in the electromagnet varies with the signal strength. Therefore, the strength of the magnetic field around the electromagnet varies as well. This causes the disk to vibrate in a pattern that matches the electronic signal. These vibrations produce sound waves, which represent the voice on the other telephone. Many modern receivers now use semiconductors instead of electromagnets.

Dialing Mechanism Another part of the telephone is the dialing mechanism. When you dial a telephone number, you are telling the telephone company's switching system where you want the call to go. A dial telephone sends a series of pulses or clicks to the switching network. A push-button device sends different tones. The tones act as signals to the electronic circuits in the switching network. Today, push-button devices have become standard on almost all telephones.

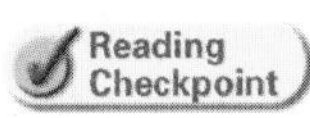
What does a telephone transmitter do?

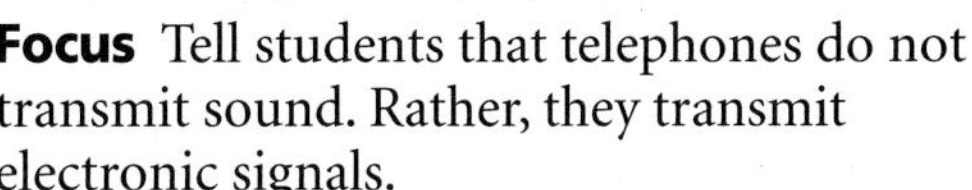

Instruct

Telephones

Teach Key Concepts L2

Focus Tell students that telephones do not transmit sound. Rather, they transmit electronic signals.

Teach Ask: **What do sound vibrations cause to vibrate in a telephone?** *(A metal disk)* **What does the vibration of the metal disk change the sound into?** *(Electronic signals)* **What carries the electronic signals to a receiving telephone?** *(Wires or optical fibers)* **What transforms the electronic signals back into sound in a telephone receiver?** *(A small speaker in the receiver)*

Apply Remind students that cordless phones and cell phones require batteries to function. Ask: **Why do these telephones need batteries to transmit sounds?** *(Sound is transformed into an electronic signal in the transmitter of a telephone. Cordless phones and cell phones need batteries to provide an energy source in the transmitter.)* **learning modality: verbal**

Independent Practice L2

Teaching Resources

- Guided Reading and Study Worksheet: *Electronic Communication*

Student Edition on Audio CD

Monitor Progress L2

Skills Check Have students make a flowchart that explains how a voice spoken into a telephone travels to a receiving telephone.

Answers

Figure 6 The dialing mechanism sends a series of pulses, clicks, or tones to a switching network, telling the network where you want the call to go.

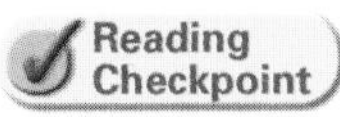
It transforms sound into an electronic signal.

Differentiated Instruction

Less Proficient Readers L1

Parts of Waves Students who need additional help with the concepts of frequency and amplitude may benefit from seeing diagrams of each on an overhead projector. Draw two lines on a blank transparency about 4 cm apart to mark the top and bottom of the waves. Then slowly draw a wave while questioning students about frequency and amplitude. **learning modality: visual**

Special Needs L1

Digital and Analog To help students understand the difference between digital and analog signals, use musical instruments. A slide on a guitar string is analogous to an analog signal. A series of notes on a piano or xylophone are analogous to a digital signal. **learning modality: visual**

Sound Recordings

Teach Key Concepts

L2

Audio Signals

Focus Tell students that sound can be reproduced using both analog devices and digital devices.

Teach Ask: **What do sound recordings use to communicate information?** *(Electronic signals)* **What are the two kinds of electronic signals?** *(Analog signals and digital signals)* Emphasize that just as telephone transmission depends on electronic signals, so too does sound transmission.

Apply Ask: **Is a compact disc an example of analog or digital sound recording?** *(Digital sound recording)* **Does a compact disc, then, send a smooth signal or pulses to an amplifier?** *(Pulses)* **learning modality: verbal**

L1

Playing a Record

Materials turntable, LP records

Time 10 minutes

Focus Explain that before CD players and other music players became common, most people listened to music with records and a turntable.

Teach Hook a turntable up to a receiver, and show students some old records. Have students observe how the stylus, or needle, moves through the continuous groove on the record. Ask: **Is this an analog or digital recording?** *(Analog)* **How do you know?** *(The signal continually changes as the needle runs along the spiral groove.)* Allow students to examine the grooves on the record.

Apply Tell students that when turntables were being replaced by CD players in the early 1990s, people complained that something was being lost from the music they heard on the old LPs. Ask: **What is the difference between analog and digital signals that might explain why some people said sound was missing in CDs?** *(Sample answer: Analog signals are smooth and continuous, while digital signals are pulses. Smooth signals may have translated music more completely than pulses.)* **learning modality: visual**

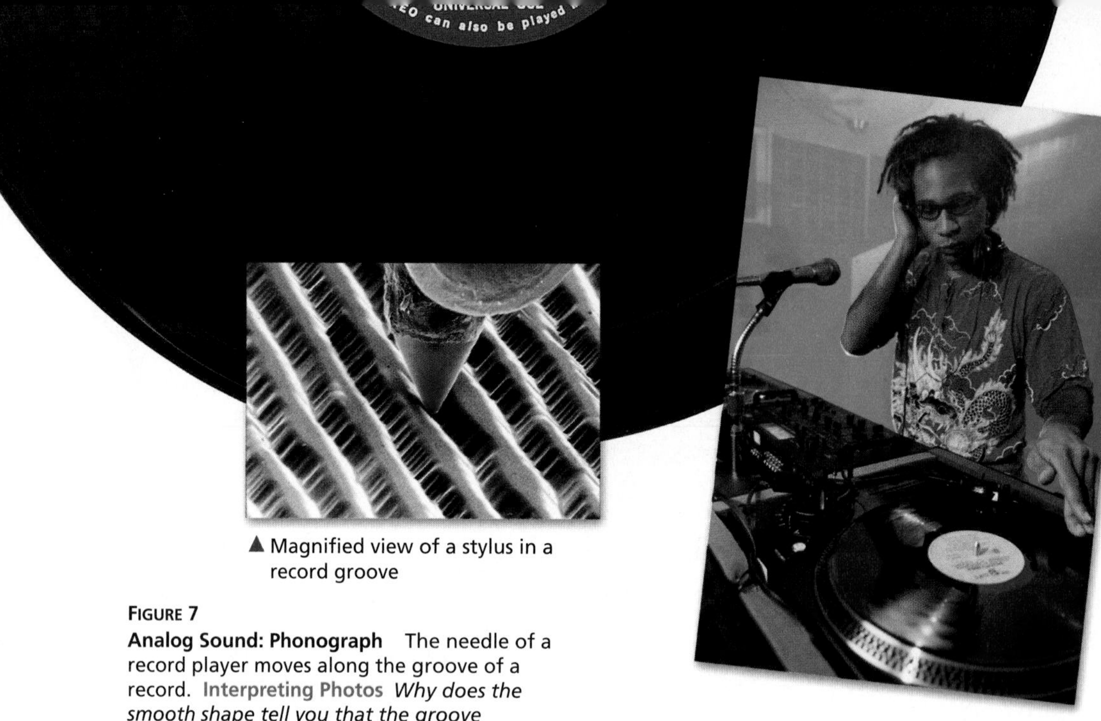

▲ Magnified view of a stylus in a record groove

FIGURE 7
Analog Sound: Phonograph The needle of a record player moves along the groove of a record. **Interpreting Photos** *Why does the smooth shape tell you that the groove represents an analog signal?*

Sound Recordings

Sound recordings also communicate information using electronic signals. **Sound can be reproduced using an analog device such as a phonograph or a digital device such as a CD player.**

Analog Sound Recording When a deejay spins a record by moving it back and forth, the sound varies smoothly. The music the deejay in Figure 7 is playing is stored as analog signals on a plastic record. But how does sound come from a piece of plastic? When you play a record, a needle, or stylus, runs along a spiral groove in the plastic. The wavy pattern of the groove varies in the same way that the sound waves from the musicians did. The needle in the groove follows the groove's wavy pattern. The needle's movement, in turn, moves a tiny magnet that induces an electric current in a coil of wire. This current matches the pattern of the groove in the record.

The current produced by the needle is an analog signal representing the original sounds played by the musicians. The signal varies continuously as it copies the information stored on the record. The analog signal is fed into an amplifier and then into a speaker, which changes the signal back into sound.

Digital Sound Recording As you can see in Figure 8, a CD, or compact disc, is very different from a plastic record. It contains microscopic holes, called pits. The level areas between the pits are called flats. Like the groove on a record, these pits and flats are arranged in a spiral. They allow sound to be stored in steps. Although you can't tell from the photograph, the spiral on a compact disc is divided into pieces of equal time. The arrangement of pits and flats within each piece of the spiral is a code. Each piece of this code represents the sound at one instant.

When the CD spins, a beam of light scans the pits and flats. The light reflects from the flats but not from the pits. This causes the reflected light to form a pattern of tiny flashes of light. The flashes are then transformed into pulses of electric current, or a digital signal. The digital signal is fed into an amplifier and then a speaker, where it is changed back into sound.

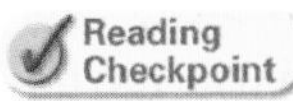
How do the pits and flats on a CD make a digital signal?

FIGURE 8
Digital Sound: CD Player
Each series of 3 pits or flats on this diagram of a CD represents the sound at one instant.

Use Visuals: Figure 8 L2

Digital Sound

Focus Tell students that the inset in Figure 8 shows the magnified surface of a compact disc.

Teach Have students examine the figure, and ask: **What are pits and flats?** *(Pits are microscopic holes on the surface of a CD. Flats are the level areas between the pits.)* **What does the arrangement of pits and flats on a CD represent?** *(Each series of three pits or flats represents the sound at one instant.)* **A beam of light transforms the pits and flats into what?** *(Pulses of electric current)*

Apply Have students compare the inset in Figure 8 with the inset showing the record grooves in Figure 7. Ask: **How can you tell by looking that one produces an analog signal and the other produces a digital signal?** *(The record groove is continuous, just as an analog signal is continuous. The CD contains pits that are separated from one another, just as digital pulses are separate.)* **learning modality: visual**

Monitor Progress L2

Writing Have students write a paragraph that explains the difference between an analog sound recording and a digital sound recording.

Answers

Figure 7 The wavy pattern of the groove in a record varies in the same way that the original sound did.

Reading Checkpoint Light reflects from the flats but not the pits. The pattern of flashes of light is transformed into a digital signal.

Electromagnetic Waves

Teach Key Concepts L2

Carrier Waves

Focus Explain to students that electromagnetic waves carry electronic signals over long distances.

Teach Ask: **What is an electromagnetic wave?** *(A wave that consists of changing electric and magnetic fields)* **What are different types of electromagnetic waves?** *(The light you see, microwaves, and X-rays are all electromagnetic waves.)* **What is the amplitude of a wave?** *(Its height from the center line to a crest or trough)* **What is the frequency of a wave?** *(The number of waves passing a given point each second)*

Apply Explain that a carrier wave is an electromagnetic wave that carries an electronic signal. Ask: **Why is a carrier wave necessary for radio and television transmission?** *(An electromagnetic wave is used to carry electronic signals long distances.)* **learning modality: verbal**

All in One Teaching Resources

- Transparency N46

Math Analyzing Data

Math Skill Making and interpreting graphs

Focus A bar graph is used to display data in a number of distinct categories. In this case, the distinct categories are the separate frequencies of common communication devices.

Teach Ask: **What kind of graph is this?** *(A bar graph)* **What does each bar on the graph indicate?** *(The frequency band of a communication device)* **Which of the communication devices shown has the lowest frequency band?** *(AM Radio)* **What do the top and bottom of each bar indicate?** *(The maximum and minimum frequency for that device)*

Answers

1. Frequency in MHz
2. Cordless phone: 40 MHz to 50 MHz; FM radio: approximately 88 MHz to 108 MHz
3. Sample answer: The frequency bands are mostly separate, with very little overlapping.
4. The frequency band for radio-controlled cars falls within the band for TV channels 2–6. Therefore, radio controlled cars might interfere with television reception.

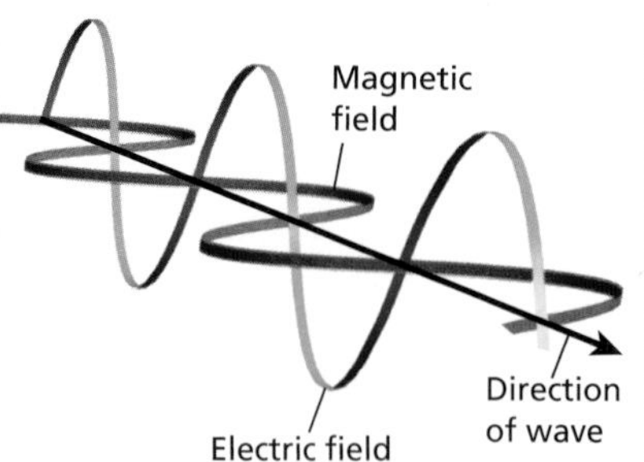

FIGURE 9
Electromagnetic Waves
A changing electric field generates a changing magnetic field. In turn, a changing magnetic field generates a changing electric field.

Electromagnetic Waves

You learned in the last section that electronic signals are transmitted through semiconductors within electronic devices. But, in the case of radio and television, the electronic signal usually has to travel over a long distance from a radio or television station. **Electronic signals can be carried over long distances by electromagnetic waves.**

Electric and Magnetic Fields You already may be familiar with some types of waves, such as water waves or sound waves. Electromagnetic waves share some characteristics with these waves. However, electromagnetic waves do not need to travel through matter. An **electromagnetic wave** is a wave that consists of moving, or changing electric and magnetic fields.

The idea that a wave is made of electric and magnetic fields may sound a little strange at first. But you have already learned that electricity and magnetism are related. You know that a changing magnetic field produces an electric field. The reverse is also true—a changing electric field produces a magnetic field.

If a magnetic field is changing, like the up-and-down movements of a water wave, a changing electric field will form. The changing electric field that is formed then produces a changing magnetic field. The electric and magnetic fields will keep producing each other over and over again, as shown in Figure 9. The result is an electromagnetic wave. The light that you see, the microwaves that heat food in a microwave oven, and the X-rays that a dentist or doctor uses are all types of electromagnetic waves.

Math Analyzing Data

Communication Frequencies

The graph shows the frequency ranges, or bands, for some common communication devices. The top and bottom of each range is the maximum and minimum frequency for that device.

1. **Reading Graphs** What does the *y*-axis of the graph represent?
2. **Reading Graphs** What is the frequency range for a cordless phone? An FM radio?
3. **Interpreting Graphs** What pattern do you see for the frequency bands in the graph? Explain.
4. **Drawing Conclusions** What device might interfere with television reception? Explain.

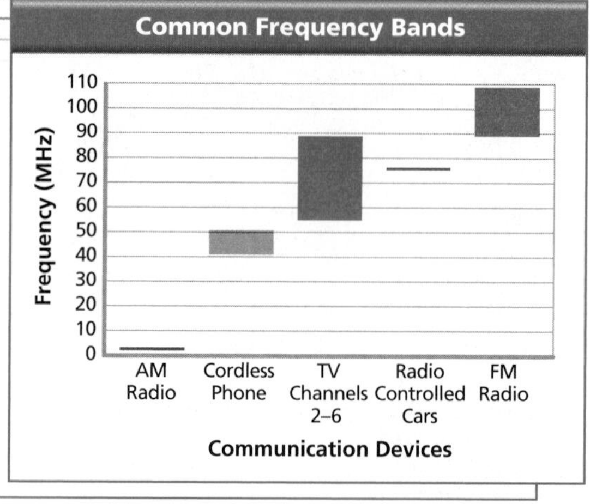

118 ◆ N

Differentiated Instruction

English Learners/Beginning L1
Comprehension: Key Concept On the board, rewrite the boldface sentence under the heading *Electromagnetic Waves.* Circle the term *electronic signals* and the term *electromagnetic waves.* Review the definitions of each. Then circle the word *carried.* Discuss how one wave carries another. **learning modality: verbal**

English Learners/Intermediate L2
Comprehension: Key Concept Read aloud the boldface sentence under the heading *Electromagnetic Waves.* Have students explain which kind of wave carries the other. Then introduce the term *carrier wave.* Ask students which of the waves in the boldface sentence is the carrier wave. **learning modality: verbal**

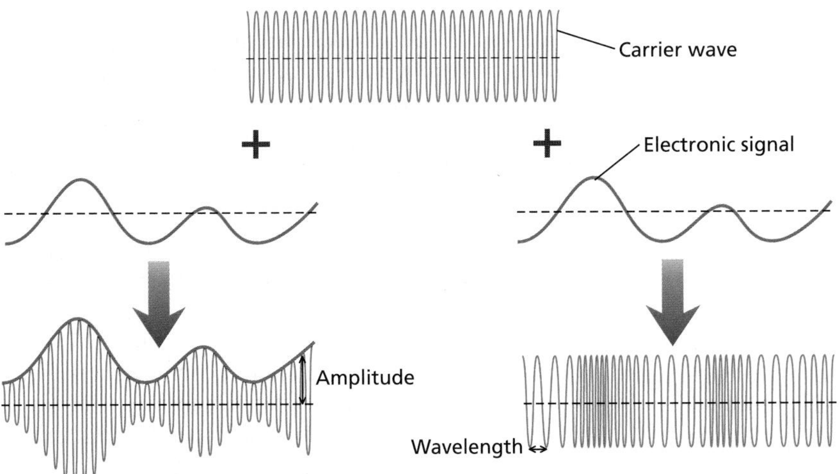

Amplitude Modulation (AM) The amplitude of the carrier wave varies with the strength of the electronic signal.

Frequency Modulation (FM) The frequency of the carrier wave varies with the strength of the electronic signal.

Amplitude and Frequency Modulation All waves have certain basic characteristics. Figure 10 shows a simple wave moving from left to right. The high points are called crests and the low points are called troughs. Waves are described in terms of two quantities, amplitude and frequency. The **amplitude** is the height from the center line to a crest or trough. The **frequency** of a wave is the number of waves passing a given point each second.

The amplitude and frequency of an electromagnetic wave can be changed, or modulated, to carry an electronic signal. The wave that is modulated, shown in red in Figure 10, is called the carrier wave. The electronic signal is shown in blue. In this case, the signal is an analog signal in which the strength, or amplitude, of an electric current changes.

The carrier wave can be modulated to match the electronic signal in two different ways, as shown in Figure 10. One way is to change the amplitude of the carrier wave to match that of the signal. This process is known as **amplitude modulation (AM).** The other way is to change the frequency of the carrier wave to match the amplitude of the signal. Then the space between the waves varies with the strength of the signal. This process is known as **frequency modulation (FM).**

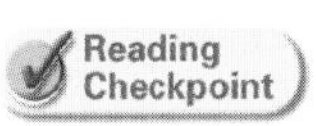
What is amplitude?

FIGURE 10
Modulating Waves
A carrier wave's amplitude and frequency can be modulated to carry an electronic signal.
Interpreting Diagrams *How is a carrier wave modulated to transmit an AM radio signal?*

Go Online

For: Modulating Electromagnetic Waves activity
Visit: PHSchool.com
Web Code: cgp-4042

Use Visuals: Figure 10 

Modulating Waves

Focus Tell students that Figure 10 shows that a carrier wave can be modulated to carry an electronic signal.

Teach Make sure students understand that the carrier wave at the top represents an electromagnetic wave before it has been modulated, and that the two waves below it are electronic signals, not electromagnetic waves. Ask: **What can be modulated to match an electronic signal?** *(A carrier wave)* **What are two ways that it can be modulated?** *(By changing the amplitude of the carrier wave or its frequency or wavelength.)*

Apply For frequency modulation, students can compare the wavelengths of the carrier wave to the places where the signal moves up and down. Ask: **What part of the electronic signal is represented when the wavelengths in the carrier wave are close together?** *(The crests of the electronic signal)* **What part of the electronic signal is represented when the wavelengths in the carrier wave are far apart?** *(The troughs)*

Extend The ***active art*** will show students how a carrier wave's amplitude and frequency can be modulated to carry an electronic signal. **learning modality: visual**

Go Online

For: Modulating Electromagnetic Waves activity
Visit: PHSchool.com
Web Code: cgp-4042

Students can interact with the art of modulating electromagnetic waves online.

All in One Teaching Resources

- Transparency N47

Monitor Progress L2

Drawing Have students draw a carrier wave that is modulated to transmit an AM radio signal and a carrier wave that is modulated to transmit an FM radio signal.

Students can keep their drawings in their portfolios.

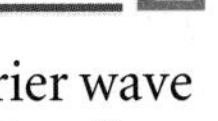

Answers

Figure 10 Its amplitude is modulated.

The height from the center line of a wave to a crest or trough

Radio

Teach Key Concepts

L2

Radio Transmission and Reception

Focus Tell students that transmission of radio sounds depends on electromagnetic waves.

Teach Ask: **At a radio station, what are sounds transformed into?** *(Electronic signals)* **What does the electronic audio signal combine with at a transmitter?** *(A carrier wave)* Remind students that a carrier wave is an electromagnetic wave that carries an electronic signal. Ask: **What does a radio do with the electromagnetic waves it receives?** *(The radio separates different audio signals from the carrier wave.)*

Apply Ask: **When you are listening to a radio, why can adjusting the dial make the sound clearer?** *(Adjusting the dial allows the tuner to receive radio waves at a specific frequency, and the carrier wave that carries the signal has a specific frequency.)* **learning modality: verbal**

Help Students Read

L1

Monitoring Your Understanding Refer to the Content Refresher in this chapter, which provides guidelines for the Monitoring Your Understanding strategy.

Have students look at the visual and read the caption under the heading *Radio.* When they have finished, ask them to write down how processes of transmission and reception allow a radio to work. Then ask: **Did you have any trouble understanding the processes? If so, what can you do to better your understanding?** *(Sample answer: You can reread the passage under the heading, focusing on the concept discussed in the visual. You can read ahead to see whether a process or concept is discussed further as part of another concept.)* Have students come up with their own strategies to improve their understanding, including rereading and adjusting the pace of reading. Have students use these strategies as they continue to look at visuals and read captions.

Radio

Voices or music on an AM or FM radio station are electronic signals carried by an electromagnetic wave. But where do the sounds you hear come from?

Transmission The process begins at a radio station where sounds are generated and transformed into an electronic signal. When a musician plays into a microphone at a radio station, the sound waves produce a varying electric current. This current is an analog signal that represents the sound waves. It is sometimes called an audio signal.

The audio signal is then sent to a transmitter. The transmitter amplifies the audio signal and combines it with a carrier wave. The combined electromagnetic wave is then sent to an antenna, which sends it out in all directions.

Reception Your radio has its own antenna that receives electromagnetic waves from the radio station. The carrier wave has a specific frequency. You tune in to the wave by selecting that frequency on your radio. Your radio amplifies the audio signal and separates it from the carrier wave. The signal is then sent to the radio's speaker, which is the reverse of a microphone. The speaker transforms the audio signal back into sound.

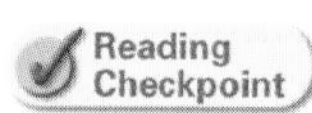

What is an audio signal?

FIGURE 11
How Radios Work
At the radio station, voices and music are transformed into electronic signals and then broadcast. Individual radios pick up the electronic signals and change them back to sound.
Interpreting Photos *What is the role of the transmitter?*

1 Signal Generated A person generates sound waves that are transformed into an audio signal.

2 Transmission The audio signal is sent to a transmitter and combined with a carrier wave that is broadcast at a specific frequency.

3 Reception A radio receives the wave at a specific frequency and separates the audio signal. Speakers transform the audio signal into sound.

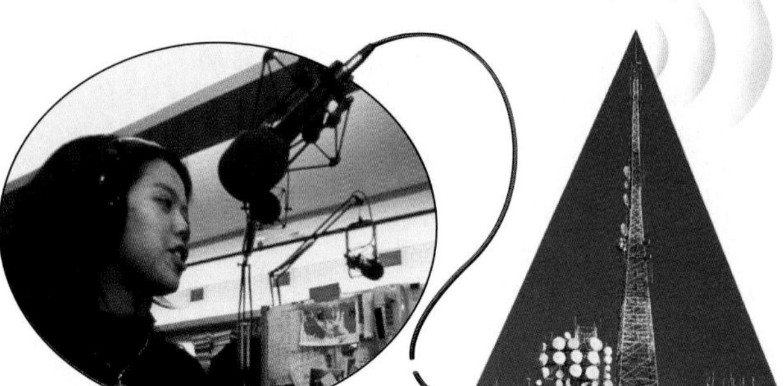

1 Signal Generated At a television station, video and audio signals are recorded and generated by cameras and microphones. The transmitter sends out the signals.

2 Transmission Video and audio signals are carried on electromagnetic waves. The waves travel to a satellite and then to a local cable station.

3 Reception Your television receives the signals from a wire connected to the cable station. You tune into a specific frequency by selecting a television channel.

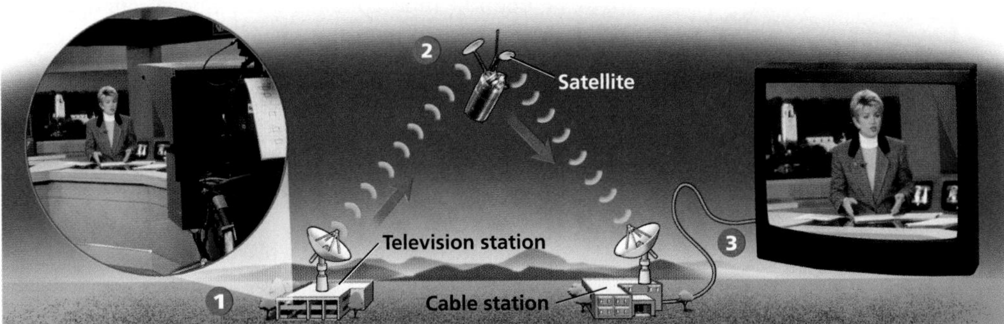

Television

Electromagnetic waves can be used to carry images as well as sound. The transmission of the images and sounds on television is very similar to that of radio sounds.

Transmission The audio and video signals that make up the image on your television screen are generated at a television station. Both signals are carried by electromagnetic waves. The signals are usually sent from transmitting antennas on the ground. But sometimes the signal is blocked by land features or by nearby buildings. Or sometimes a transmitter cannot reach homes that are too far away. To solve these problems, local cable television networks have been developed. These networks distribute television signals through cables from a central receiver to homes.

Communications satellites are also used to relay television signals. A communications satellite orbits Earth, always staying above the same point on the ground. These satellites receive signals from one part of the planet and transmit them to another almost instantly. This enables you to watch events from around the world as they occur.

Reception Each television contains a receiver that accepts video and audio signals. As in a radio, the carrier wave for each television station is at a specific frequency. You tune in the frequency by selecting a channel. Your television amplifies the signal and separates it from the carrier wave. The audio signal is transformed back into sound by the television's speakers.

FIGURE 12
How Televisions Work
Televisions transmit images as well as sound, but they transmit and receive electronic signals in a way similar to radios.
Interpreting Data *What role do satellites play in the transmission of television signals?*

Discovery
CHANNEL
SCHOOL
Electronics
Video Preview
▶Video Field Trip
Video Assessment

Television

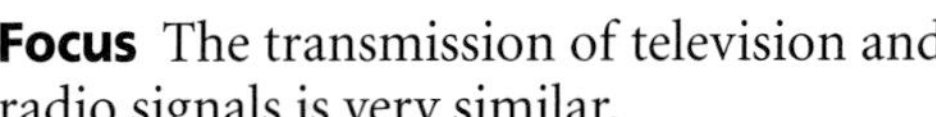

Teach Key Concepts

Images and Sound

Focus The transmission of television and radio signals is very similar.

Teach Ask: **What carries an audio signal from a radio transmitter to a radio?** *(A carrier wave)* **What carries the video and audio signals in a television transmission?** *(The same)* Point out that the main difference between television and radio transmissions is the addition of electronic video signals for television.

Apply Ask: **What does a television's receiver do with the carrier wave it receives?** *(It amplifies the audio and video signals and separates them from the carrier wave.)* **learning modality: verbal**

Electronics

Show the Video Field Trip to let students understand electronics as the basis of modern television. Discussion question: **What role do satellites play in the transmission of television signals?** *(A signal is beamed as an electromagnetic wave up to a relay satellite, and then the signal is relayed in the same form down to a network control room. Then the signal goes back up into space through another satellite link, and is received by local television stations.)*

Monitor Progress L2

Answers

Figure 11 The transmitter amplifies the electronic audio signal and combines it with a carrier wave.

Figure 12 Satellites receive signals from one part of the planet and transmit them to another almost instantly.

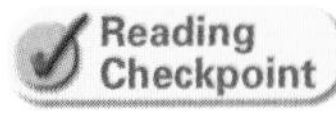

An analog signal that represents sound waves

Monitor Progress L2

Answer

Reading Checkpoint Most televisions use cathode-ray tubes, which contain solid fluorescent material that transforms beams of electrons into tiny, colored dots of light. Some televisions send video signals to a liquid crystal or a mixture of gases called plasma.

Assess

Reviewing Key Concepts

1. a. Transmitter, receiver, and dialing mechanism **b.** The transmitter transforms sound into an electronic signal. The signal travels to the receiving telephone, where a speaker transforms it back into sound. **c.** Sound waves cause a metal disk to vibrate, which transform the sound into an electronic signal.

2. a. Electromagnetic waves are waves consisting of changing electric and magnetic fields. **b.** Amplitude and frequency **c.** Modulating the carrier wave's amplitude produces an AM signal. Modulating the carrier wave's frequency or wavelength produces an FM signal.

3. a. Electromagnetic waves carry electronic signals to radios and televisions. **b.** The television separates the audio and video signals from the carrier wave and transforms them into the images and sounds you see and hear.

Reteach L1

Use Figures 11 and 12 to review concepts related to how radios and televisions work.

Performance Assessment L2

Writing Have students write two short paragraphs describing how sound is transmitted over a telephone and a radio.

All in One Teaching Resources

- Section Summary: *Electronic Communication*
- Review and Reinforce: *Electronic Communication*
- Enrich: *Electronic Communication*

FIGURE 13
Types of Televisions
Traditional televisions use bulky cathode-ray tubes to produce images. Newer technologies permit televisions to be thinner and lighter.

Cathode-ray tube television

Thin screen television

Television Screens How does a television set change a video signal into the picture on a television screen? Today there are several technologies that can do this.

Most televisions use cathode-ray tubes. A cathode-ray tube contains solid fluorescent materials that transform beams of electrons into tiny, colored dots of light. The dots are in the primary colors of light—red, blue, and green. Your eyes combine these three colors to form all of the colors in the images you see.

Newer televisions produce images in other ways. Video signals can be sent to a liquid crystal or to a mixture of gases called a plasma. Both of these technologies can be used to produce a thin screen television like the one shown in Figure 13. A liquid crystal display television produces images in the same way a laptop computer does. In a plasma television, the video signal heats tiny pockets of gases, causing them to glow in different colors.

How are television images produced?

Section 2 Assessment

Target Reading Skill Building Vocabulary
Use your definitions to help you answer the questions.

Reviewing Key Concepts

1. a. Identifying What are the three main parts of a telephone?
   b. Summarizing How is sound transmitted and received during a telephone call?
   c. Relating Cause and Effect In telephones, what causes electric current to vary in the transmitter, producing an electronic signal?
2. a. Defining What are electromagnetic waves?
   b. Describing What are two characteristics of an electromagnetic wave?
   c. Comparing and Contrasting How is an electromagnetic wave changed to produce AM and FM waves?
3. a. Reviewing How is information transmitted to radios and televisions?
   b. Sequencing What happens to an electronic signal when it reaches your television?

Lab zone At-Home Activity

What's a Remote? A remote control uses electromagnetic waves to operate an electronic device—for instance, a television, VCR, radio, or toy—from a distance. Find a device with a remote control. Ask your family members to help you locate the receiver for the remote control on the device. Find out how far away from the device you can stand and still operate it. Find out what objects the waves will travel through. Will they bounce off mirrors? Off walls? Off your hand?

Lab zone At-Home Activity

What's a Remote? L2 Students will discover that the receiver will be a small, round "window" on the device. The effective distance of each remote will depend on the type of sensor and the age of the battery. The waves will travel through clear plastic film but not glass or a student's hand. The waves will bounce off mirrors and walls.

Section 3 Computers

Reading Preview

Key Concepts

- How is information stored and processed in a computer?
- What are the functions of computer hardware and software?

Key Terms

- computer • binary system
- hardware
- central processing unit (CPU)
- input device • output device
- software
- computer programmer

Target Reading Skill

Outlining As you read, make an outline about computers. Use the red headings for the main topics and the blue headings for the subtopics.

Computers
I. What Is a Computer?
  A. The Binary System
  B.
  C.
II. Computer Hardware
  A.

Lab zone Discover Activity

How Fast Are You?

1. Write out ten math problems involving the addition or subtraction of two two-digit numbers.
2. Switch lists with a friend.
3. Take turns timing how long it takes each of you to solve the ten problems by hand.
4. Then time how long it takes each of you to solve the ten problems using a calculator. What is the time difference? Is there a difference in accuracy?

Think It Over
Inferring What are the advantages of using an electronic device to complete calculations?

Over two thousand years ago, the first calculator was invented. This calculating device is called an abacus. For centuries, people in many parts of the world have used the abacus to count by sliding beads along strings. During the twentieth century, mechanical adding machines were developed. Then, in the 1960s, electronic calculators and computers began to be widely used. In just a few decades, these electronic devices changed the way people around the world perform calculations.

What Is a Computer?

A **computer** is an electronic device that stores, processes, and retrieves information. One of the reasons that computers can process and store so much information is that they do not store information in the same form that you see it—numbers, letters, and pictures. **Computer information is represented in the binary system.** The **binary system** uses combinations of just two digits, 0 and 1. Although computers can use analog signals, almost all modern computers are digital.

◀ Calculating with an abacus

Section 3 Computers

Objectives

After this lesson, students will be able to
N.4.3.1 Explain how information is stored and processed in a computer.
N.4.3.2 Describe the functions of computer hardware and software.

Target Reading Skill

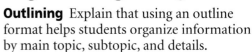

Outlining Explain that using an outline format helps students organize information by main topic, subtopic, and details.

Answer

I. What Is a Computer?
  A. The Binary System
  B. Using the Binary System
  C. Bits and Bytes
II. Computer Hardware
  A. Central Processing Unit (CPU)
  B. Input and Output Devices
  C. Internal Memory
  D. External Memory
III. Computer Software
  A. Two Kinds of Software
  B. Computer Programming

All in One Teaching Resources

- Transparency N48

Preteach

Build Background Knowledge L2

Ask: **What are the parts of the computer system you often use?** *(Sample answer: The computer, the monitor, the mouse, the keyboard, and the printer)* Explain that in this section, students will learn about the components that make up a computer.

Lab zone Discover Activity

Skills Focus Inferring L2

Materials calculator

Time 10 minutes

Tips Make sure students include a variety of different addition and subtraction problems involving numbers up to and including 99.

Expected Outcome Most students will be able to work faster and more accurately with a calculator than by doing the problems by hand.

Think It Over Sample answer: Calculators provide a significant increase in accuracy and speed, especially when dealing with problems more complex than addition.

Instruct

What Is a Computer?

Teach Key Concepts L2

Information in the Binary System

Focus Tell students that a computer uses the binary system to store information.

Teach Ask: **What is the binary system?** *(A number system that uses combinations of only two digits, 0 and 1)* Help students recall what they learned about transistors. A transistor can switch current on and off. Computers contain circuits with transistors that act as switches. Ask: **What does the off position represent?** *(The off position represents a 0.)* **What does the on position represent?** *(The on position represents a 1.)* Emphasize that the binary system allows the computer to process information by switching signals on and off with 1's and 0's.

Apply Have students examine the table in Figure 14. Ask: **In the base-10 number system, what number is the first two-digit number?** *(Number 10)* **In the binary number system, what number is the first two-digit number?** *(The number that equals 2 in base 10)* **Why is that number a two-digit number?** *(Because the binary system has only two numbers—0 and 1—a new place value must begin for any number above 1.)* **In the binary system, what is equal to number 3 in base 10?** *(11)* **learning modality: logical/mathematical**

All in One Teaching Resources

- Transparency N49

Independent Practice L2

All in One Teaching Resources

- Guided Reading and Study Worksheet: *Computers*

Student Edition on Audio CD

FIGURE 14
Binary Switches
To store information, a computer translates binary numbers into electronic switch positions. The background photo shows electronic switches in an enlarged view.
Interpreting Diagrams *What is the base-10 number 5 in the binary system?*

Binary Numbers and Switches

Base-10 Number	Binary Number	Electronic Switch Positions
0	0	
1	1	
2	10	
3	11	
4	100	
5	101	
10	1010	

Key
Switch "off" = 0
Switch "on" = 1

The Binary System How can large numbers be represented using only series of 1's and 0's? Begin by thinking about the numbers with which you are more familiar. You are used to using the base-10 number system. Each place value in a number represents the number 10 raised to some power. The digits 0 through 9 are then multiplied by the place value in each position. For example, the number 327 means 3 × 100 plus 2 × 10 plus 7 × 1.

Using the Binary System The binary system is similar to the base-10 number system, except that the base number is 2. A binary number's place value begins with 1, 2, 4, and 8 instead of 1, 10, 100, and 1,000. In the binary system, only 0 and 1 are multiplied by each place value.

Computers use the binary system because electronic signals can represent the 0's and 1's. Computer chips contain thousands of tiny circuits with transistors that act as switches. A switch in the off position represents a 0 and a switch in the on position represents a 1. Look at Figure 14 to see how switches can represent binary numbers.

Bits and Bytes Each 1 or 0 in the binary system is called a bit, short for binary digit. Arrangements of eight bits are called bytes. Computer memories are rated in kilobytes (one thousand bytes), megabytes (one million bytes), gigabytes (one billion bytes) or even terabytes (one trillion bytes).

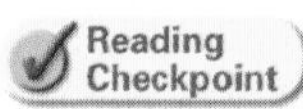
Reading Checkpoint What two digits are used in the binary system?

Lab zone Skills Activity

Calculating

A set of encyclopedias contains 25 volumes with an average of 400 pages per book. Each page contains 1,200 words and the average word is 6 letters long. Suppose each letter requires 1 byte. Could the entire set fit on a single gigabyte chip?

124 ◆ N

Lab zone Skills Activity

Skills Focus Calculating L2

Time 10 minutes

Tips You may need to "walk" students through the calculations. First calculate the number of pages (25 × 400 = 10,000); then calculate the number of words (10,000 × 1,200 = 12,000,000); and then calculate the number of letters (12,000,000 × 6 = 72,000,000).

Expected Outcome Students will realize that the encyclopedias would fit on a single gigabyte chip many times over.

Extend Challenge students to explain how they could estimate how many gigabyte chips would be needed to hold all the information in the school library. **learning modality: logical/mathematical**

Computer Hardware

The physical parts that allow a computer to receive, store, and present information make up the computer's **hardware**. Computer hardware refers to the permanent components of the computer. **Computer hardware includes a central processing unit, input devices, output devices, and memory storage devices.** You can identify the different devices in Figure 15.

Central Processing Unit (CPU) The central processing unit serves as the brain of a computer. The **central processing unit,** or CPU, directs the operation of the computer, performs logical operations and calculations, and directs the storage and retrieval of information.

Input and Output Devices Data are fed to the CPU by an **input device.** There are several different types of input devices. The one most familiar to you is probably the keyboard. A mouse, joystick, light pen, scanner, microphone, and touch-sensitive screen are also input devices.

Data from a computer are presented on an **output device.** A computer monitor, on which you view information, is the most familiar output device. Other output devices are printers and speakers. Some devices, such as modems, may serve as both input and output devices. A modem allows a computer to exchange information with other computers.

FIGURE 15
Computer Hardware
Here are a number of common computer components. The different devices that make up a computer are called hardware.

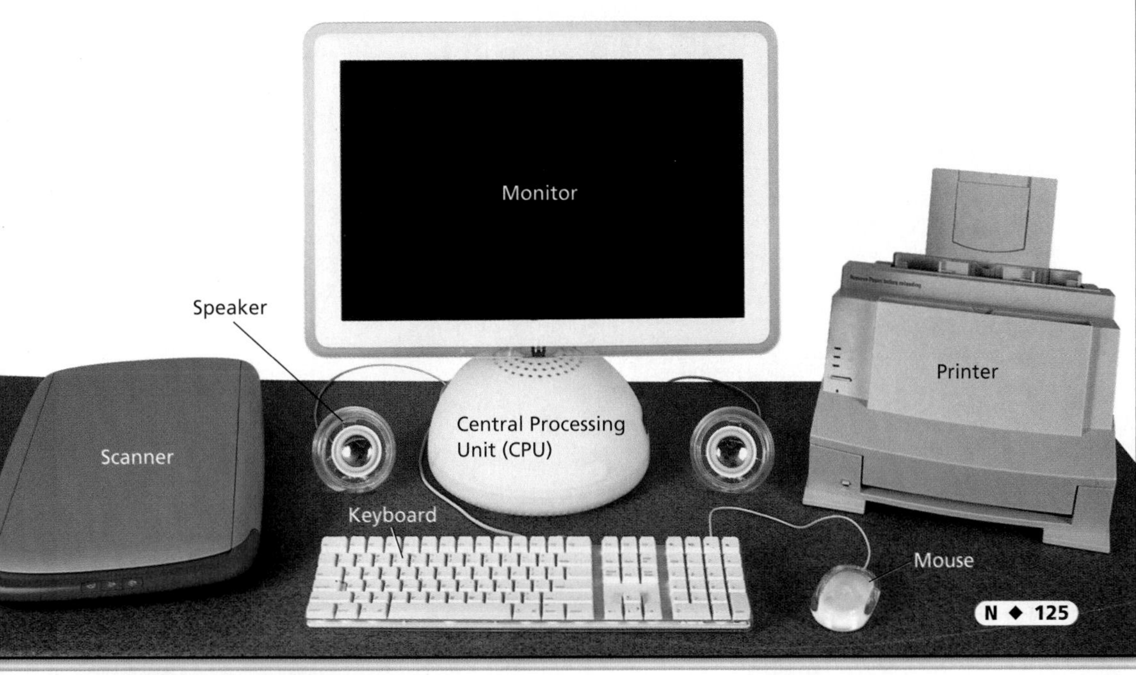

Computer Hardware

Teach Key Concepts L2

The Physical Parts

Focus Tell students that the physical parts of a computer system are called hardware.

Teach Ask: **What is a CPU?** *(The central processing unit, or the brain of the computer)* Explain that when many people think of a computer, they are really thinking of the CPU. The CPU is located inside the housing to which everything else is connected. Ask: **What is an input device?** *(A device that feeds data into the CPU)* **What is an output device?** *(A device on which data from the CPU are presented)*

Apply Ask: **What are the two most common input devices, connected to almost every computer?** *(A keyboard and a mouse)* **What are the two most common output devices, connected to almost every computer?** *(The monitor and the printer)* **learning modality: verbal**

Differentiated Instruction

Less Proficient Readers L1

Identifying Supporting Ideas Have students listen to this section on the **Student Edition Audio CD.** As they listen, they can identify supporting ideas and add them under the appropriate headings and subheadings in their section outlines. **learning modality: verbal**

Gifted and Talented L3

Researching Languages Encourage interested students to investigate computer languages that computer programmers use. Students might make an appointment to talk to a computer programmer at a local college or university. Ask students to prepare a report of their findings. **learning modality: verbal**

Monitor Progress L2

Oral Presentation Call on students to explain the difference between a base-10 system and a binary system and the difference between an input device and an output device.

Answers

Figure 14 101

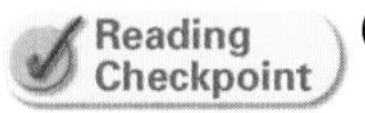

0 and 1

• Tech & Design in History •

Focus Point out that the first entry on the timeline is for 1823. That year, James Monroe was the fifth president of the United States.

Teach Invite volunteers to read aloud the items on the timeline. Guide students through the sequence of the technological developments shown. Ask: **When was the first American computer built?** *(In 1946)* Point out that it was built just after World War II ended. Ask: **How was ENIAC different from a modern computer?** *(Sample answer: It was huge compared to a modern computer. It consisted of thousands of vacuum tubes, while a modern computer is composed of chips and other electronic components.)*

Writing in Science

Writing Mode Description

Scoring Rubric

4 Exceeds criteria; includes a well-written, imaginative, and informative article

3 Meets criteria

2 Meets some criteria; includes a somewhat accurate but incomplete description of an early computer and its applications

1 Includes an inaccurate and/or incomplete description of an early computer

For: Links on computers
Visit: www.SciLinks.org
Web Code: scn-1443

Download a worksheet that will guide students' review of Internet sources on computers.

For: Links on computers
Visit: www.SciLinks.org
Web Code: scn-1443

Internal Memory Computers store information in their memory. There are two general types of computer memory, internal and external. Chips on the main circuit board within the CPU are referred to as internal memory. Random Access Memory (RAM) is the temporary storage area for data while the computer is operating. Information stored in RAM is lost when the computer is turned off.

Information the computer needs to operate properly is stored in Read Only Memory (ROM). The CPU can read these data but cannot change them. Information in ROM is permanently stored and is not lost when the computer is turned off.

• Tech & Design in History •

Development of Computers

Although some modern computers can fit in the palm of your hand, this wasn't always the case. Computers have come a long way in a relatively short period of time.

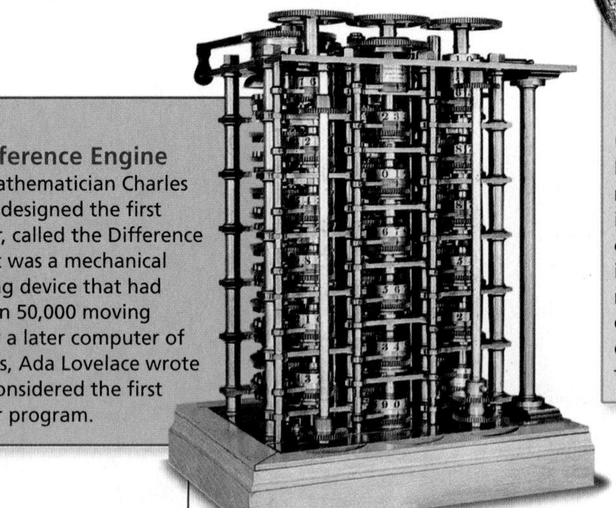

1823
The Difference Engine
British mathematician Charles Babbage designed the first computer, called the Difference Engine. It was a mechanical computing device that had more than 50,000 moving parts. For a later computer of Babbage's, Ada Lovelace wrote what is considered the first computer program.

1890
Census Counting Machine
Herman Hollerith constructed a machine that processed information by allowing electric current to pass through holes in punch cards. With Hollerith's machine, the United States census of 1890 was completed in one fourth the time needed for the 1880 census.

1800 1825 1850 1875

External Memory Neither RAM nor ROM allows you to save information when you turn your computer off. For that reason, devices outside the main CPU circuit are used to store information. They are called external memory. The most widely used form of external storage is the disk. Information is read from a disk or entered onto a disk by a disk drive. Hard disks are rigid magnetic metal disks that stay inside the computer. Information on a hard disk remains in the computer and can be accessed whenever you use the computer. Floppy disks and optical discs can be removed from the computer.

What is read-only memory (ROM)?

Writing in Science

Newspaper Article In 1953 there were only about 100 computers in the entire world. Today, there are hundreds of millions of computers in businesses, homes, government offices, schools, and stores. Select one of the early forms of the computer. Write a newspaper article introducing it and its applications to the public.

1946
ENIAC
The first American-built computer was developed by the United States Army. The Electronic Numerical Integrator and Calculator, or ENIAC, consisted of thousands of vacuum tubes and filled an entire warehouse. To change the program, programmers had to rewire the entire machine.

1974
Personal Computers
The first personal computer (PC) went on the market. Today's personal computer is 400 times faster than the ENIAC, 3,000 times lighter, and several million dollars cheaper.

2000
Personal Data Assistant
Electronic devices have become smaller, and wireless communication has become more common. Hand-held computers can store personal data, send e-mails, and even share images.

1925 1950 1975 2000

Lab zone Teacher Demo

L1

External Storage

Materials computer with a CD drive, CD-R, floppy disk, computer hard drive

Time 10 minutes

Focus Tell students that computer users often save data and files on floppy disks and CD-Rs.

Teach Obtain a nonfunctional computer hard drive from a computer repair shop. Show students the hard drive, and explain that this disk contains the Read Only Memory stored within the computer. Then show students a floppy disk and a recordable CD-R. Demonstrate how to save a file on a floppy disk and on a CD-R. Explain that at one time, a floppy disk was not as rigid as it is today. Ask: **What does this CD-R remind you of?** *(A music CD)* Explain that they are very much the same technology. A CD-R can hold music in a digital form, but it can also hold word-processing and other computer files.

Apply Ask: **Why do people often store computer files on these external-memory devices?** *(In case the computer stops working, the files can be accessed on another computer.)* **learning modality: visual**

Monitor Progress

L2

Skills Check Have students make a concept map of types of computer memory. Students should differentiate between internal memory and external memory and show examples of each.

Answer

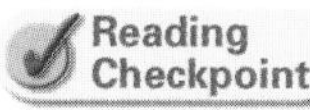

Information the computer needs to operate properly

Computer Software

Teach Key Concepts

L2

A Set of Instructions

Focus Explain that computer software is named to distinguish applications and other instructions from the physical parts of a computer, or the hardware.

Teach Ask: **What is computer software?** *(A set of instructions that directs the computer hardware to perform operations on stored information)* **What are two kinds of software?** *(Operating systems and applications software)* Explain that the most common operating system is called Windows®. Most personal computers have a Windows operating system by which applications software is run.

Apply Ask: **Suppose you buy a computer game that comes with a disc and a joystick. Instructions say that you have to insert the disc and add the joystick to your computer. Where is the software?** *(The software is on the disc, and it is the software that has to be installed.)* **How would you classify the joystick?** *(The joystick is an input device, which is a piece of hardware.)* **learning modality: verbal**

Help Students Read

L2

Monitoring Your Understanding Refer to the Content Refresher in this chapter, which provides guidelines for the Monitoring Your Understanding strategy.

Have students read the subsection *Computer Software*. When they have finished, ask them to write down the main ideas in the subsection. Ask: **Did you have any trouble reading these passages? If so, why?** *(Sample answer: The difference between an operating system and other software is confusing.)* Have students come up with their own strategies to improve their understanding, including rereading, adjusting the pace of reading, and using the visuals and captions. Have students use these strategies as they continue reading.

Computer Software

A computer needs **software,** or instructions, to tell it what to do. **Software is a set of instructions that directs the computer hardware to perform operations on stored information.** The software is also called a computer program. Whenever you use a word processor, solve mathematical problems, or play a computer game, a computer program is instructing the computer to perform in a certain way.

Two Kinds of Software One category of computer software is called the operating system of the computer. An operating system is a set of basic instructions that keep a computer running. Perhaps you have heard of the operating software known as DOS, or disk operating system. Unix is another example of operating software.

A second category of software is usually called applications software. Applications are particular tasks that a computer may carry out. These programs are grouped by their function, such as word processing, graphics, games, or simulations.

FIGURE 16
Computer Software
The electrodes attached to this person's body enable a computer to track the person's movements. Later, artists will used the stored information to create animated game sequences. The instructions for doing this task are contained in a software program.

Computer Programming The people who program computers are called computer programmers. **Computer programmers** use computer languages that convert input information into instructions that the CPU can understand. You may have heard the names of some computer languages, such as Basic, C++, and Java. Each language is designed for a specific purpose. For example, some languages allow users to complete complex calculations. But a program written in such a language may not be practical for word processing.

Programmers create software by using a step-by-step development process. First, they outline exactly what the program will do. Second, they develop a flowchart. A flowchart is a diagram showing the order of computer actions and data flow. Third, they write the instructions for the computer in a particular language. Complicated programs may contain millions of instructions. And finally, they test the program.

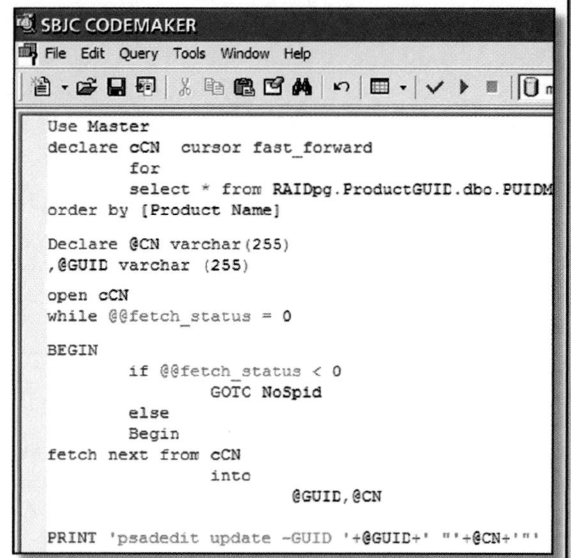

FIGURE 17
Programming a Computer
Programmers use computer languages to write instructions for the CPU.

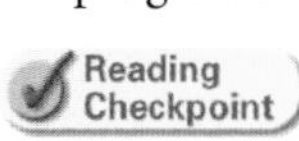
Reading Checkpoint **What is a computer language?**

Section 3 Assessment

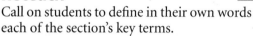

Target Reading Skill Outlining Use the information in your outline about computers to help you answer the questions below.

Reviewing Key Concepts

1. a. Defining What is a computer?
   b. Explaining How do computers store and process information?
   c. Applying Concepts How can electrical off and on switches be combined with numbers to store information?
2. a. Reviewing What is the function of computer hardware? Software?
   b. Comparing and Contrasting Describe the roles of input and output devices.
   c. Sequencing Place the following parts in the correct order for entering, correcting, saving, and then printing a message: CPU, output device, input device, memory storage.

Writing in Science

Software Advertisement Write an advertisement for a new software application. The application should be for word processing, graphics, or simulations. In your ad, give your software application's name, explain what the software does, and describe features that will appeal to customers.

Monitor Progress L2

Answer

Reading Checkpoint Computer languages are what computer programmers use to convert input information into instructions that the CPU can understand.

Assess

Reviewing Key Concepts

1. a. A computer is a device that stores, processes, and retrieves information. **b.** Computer information is represented in the binary system. **c.** A switch in the off position represents a 0, and a switch in the on position represents a 1. 1's and 0's in the place values of the binary system can store information.

2. a. Computer hardware enables the computer to receive, store, and present information. Computer software provides the instructions that tell the computer what to do. **b.** Input devices transmit data to the CPU. Output devices present information from the computer. **c.** Entering—input device; correcting—CPU; saving—memory storage; printing—output device

Reteach L1

Call on students to define in their own words each of the section's key terms.

Performance Assessment L2

Writing Ask students to describe the computer system shown in Figure 15, with definitions of all the labeled components and an explanation of the role of each component in the system.

All in One Teaching Resources
- Section Summary: *Computers*
- Review and Reinforce: *Computers*
- Enrich: *Computers*

Lab zone Chapter Project

Keep Students on Track By this time, groups should have completed their research on an existing computer application and have begun work on the development of a new application. Encourage students to be creative in developing their applications. Suggest they think of ways to make their lives easier or safer, or consider a computer application that would benefit the world.

Writing in Science

Writing Mode Persuasion

Scoring Rubric

4 Exceeds criteria; includes an imaginative and persuasive presentation
3 Meets criteria
2 Meets some criteria; includes a somewhat persuasive presentation
1 Includes an unimaginative and/or limited description of an application

L3

Computer Programming

Prepare for Inquiry

Key Concept

Computer programs are lines of clearly written instructions in a language that a computer can understand.

Skills Objectives

After this lab, students will be able to:

- observe well-written and poorly written lines of instruction
- make a model in the form of a computer program

Prep Time 20 minutes
Class Time 40 minutes

Advance Planning

Obtain large, interlocking plastic brick sets, and use them to put together 2 sets for each student. Each set should have 10 bricks. The 2 sets per student should be identical, though there may be differences in the sets given to different students. A single sheet of newspaper is adequate for each student.

Alternative Materials

If interlocking plastic bricks are unavailable, alternatives include sets of colored blocks, LEGO® sets, and Lincoln Logs®. You could also give each team various items that could be used to make a "sandwich."

All in One Teaching Resources

- Lab Worksheet: *Computer Programming*

Guide Inquiry

Invitation

Ask: **Have you ever had to put something together and had difficulty following the written instructions?** *(Sample answer: Putting together a desk at home was difficult because the instructions didn't seem to match what we had to do.)* **How could those instructions be written better?** *(Sample answer: They could have described the steps we had to do in simple, clear language.)* Have students write instructions for an everyday task, such as brushing teeth. Tell students they should use as few words as possible in their instructions.

Lab zone **Skills Lab**

Computer Programming

Problem

Can you create a model of a computer program?

Skills

observing, forming operational definitions, making models

Materials

- 2 identical sets of 10 interlocking bricks per student
- newspaper
- pencil and paper

Procedure

1. Obtain 2 sets of bricks, a piece of newspaper, and a pencil and paper. Ask your lab partner to do the same.
2. You and your partner should do Steps 3–6 without communicating with each other.
3. Place one brick on a table. On a piece of paper, write the number "1." Next to the number write instructions that someone can follow to place the brick exactly as you did. What you wrote is called a line of instruction. See the example above.

Number each instruction on a separate line.

Lines of Instruction

1. Place a black 8-peg brick on the table so the long side goes left to right.
2. Place a red 2-peg brick on the second level covering the two pegs on the far left end of the black brick.
3. Place a yellow 2-peg brick on the second level covering the two pegs on the far right of the black brick.

Make the instructions accurate and complete.

Include only words and numbers.

4. Select another brick from the same set and attach it to the previous brick. Write a number "2" on your paper and another line of instruction next to the number.
5. Repeat Step 4 eight more times, using the numbers 3 through 10 in front of your instruction lines. You should have one line of instruction for each brick you placed.
6. Cover your structure with the newspaper. Then, trade your second set of bricks and your instruction sheet with your lab partner.
7. Using your partner's instructions and brick set, build the same structure your partner built. Your partner should do the same using your instructions and brick set.
8. When you both are finished, uncover your partner's structure. Compare the structure with the one you built using your partner's instructions. Note any places where your structure is not identical to your partner's.

Introduce the Procedure

Have students read the complete procedure, and then answer any questions they have. Make sure students are familiar with how interlocking plastic bricks fit together. Demonstrate by building a simple wall of bricks. Divide the class into teams of two students. Remind students to keep their brick sets separated from their lab partners' sets.

9. Together, review Line 1 of your partner's instructions. Determine whether the brick was placed exactly as in the original structure. Identify any problems in the line of instruction. (*Hint:* A line of instruction is a problem if it resulted in a brick being placed incorrectly, or if there is more than one way to carry out the instruction.)
10. If the line of instruction has a problem, work with your partner to rewrite it.
11. Review all the remaining lines of instruction one at a time, following the procedures in Steps 9 and 10.
12. Now review the structure you built using your partner's instructions. Repeat the procedures in Steps 8 –11.
13. When you are finished, discuss what you learned about writing lines of instruction.
14. Take apart your brick structures and place the bricks in their containers. Be careful not to mix up your set of bricks with your partner's set.

Analyze and Conclude

1. **Observing** Did you have to rewrite any of your instructions in Step 10? If so, explain why.
2. **Forming Operational Definitions** Write an operational definition of a well-written computer program.
3. **Making Models** During which steps of the lab were you modeling the actions of a computer programmer? In which steps were you modeling the actions of a computer?
4. **Making Models** "Debugging" means examining a computer program to identify instructions that might be a problem. Which steps of this lab modeled debugging?
5. **Communicating** Suppose you are the owner of a small software programming company. Write a newspaper employment advertisement that describes the characteristics of a good programmer.

More to Explore

Build and write instructions for a structure using more than 10 bricks. Create a "computer language" that keeps your instructions as short as possible. For example, replace the word "connect" with a "+" symbol. Use one numbered line of instruction for each brick. With you teacher's permission, plan and carry out a test of your computer language.

Expected Outcome

Most student will have at least one misplaced brick. Rewriting the instruction lines will help students understand how instruction lines in computer programs must be precise.

Analyze and Conclude

1. Answers will vary. A well-written line is often clear and precise. A poorly written line is wordy and ambiguous.

2. Sample answer: A well-written computer program contains single lines of instruction for each task. The lines of instruction are clear and simple.

3. Computer programmer: Steps 3–5; Computer: Step 7.

4. Steps 9–12 modeled debugging.

5. Sample answer: Wanted: Computer programmer with good language skills willing to write and rewrite understandable instructions.

Extend Inquiry

More to Explore Students' computer languages and test plans will vary. The lines of instruction should be clear and concise. Abbreviations and short cuts should be used consistently.

Troubleshooting the Experiment

- Before students begin Step 7, emphasize that they should follow the programming instructions *exactly* as written, and they are not to communicate with anyone else while following the program.
- When students are trying to follow the written programs, make sure the programmers do not interfere.
- Make sure that in Steps 9 through 12—when teams are "debugging"—students understand that they should go through each line of the program to see exactly where any error occurred.
- Encourage students to be imaginative as they write computer languages in More to Explore.

Section 4

The Information Superhighway

Objectives

After this lesson, students will be able to

N.4.4.1 Describe the purpose of a computer network.

N.4.4.2 Explain how people can protect themselves and their property as they use computer networks.

Target Reading Skill

Identifying Main Ideas Explain that identifying main ideas and details helps students sort the facts from the information into groups. Each group can have a main topic, subtopics, and details.

Answers

Sample answers:

Detail: Share personal information only on networks that require authorization and use security software to keep out unwanted users.

Detail: Use software to detect viruses before they cause damage.

Detail: Never give your name, address, or telephone number when using a chat room.

All in One Teaching Resources

- Transparency N50

Preteach

Build Background Knowledge

L2

Ask: **What is the Internet?** *(Sample answer: A huge network of computers)* **Are there different Internets for each country, or is the Internet worldwide?** *(It is worldwide.)* **Are there any dangers in using the Internet?** *(Sample answer: Sometimes criminals use the Internet to find victims.)*

Section 4 • Tech & Design •

The Information Superhighway

Reading Preview

Key Concepts

- What is the purpose of a computer network?
- How can people protect themselves and their property as they use computer networks?

Key Terms

- computer network
- Internet
- World Wide Web
- encryption
- computer virus
- chat room
- intellectual property

Target Reading Skill

Identifying Main Ideas As you read the Using Computers Safely section, write the main idea in a graphic organizer like the one below. Then write three supporting details that further explain the main idea.

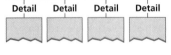

Main Idea

Computer safety practices people can follow include

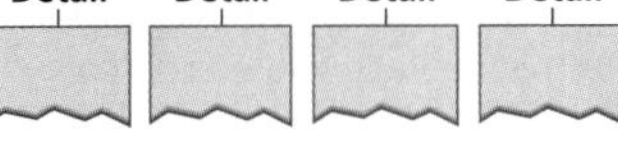

Lab zone Discover Activity

How Important Are Computers?

1. Obtain a local or national newspaper.
2. Look through the newspaper for articles that refer to computers, the Internet, the World Wide Web, or the information superhighway.
3. Write down the topics of the articles. For example, was the article about politics, painting, money, or computers?
4. Create a data table to show your results.

Think It Over

Inferring What can you infer about the kinds of information available through the computer? How much do you think people use computers to obtain information?

Because of the Internet, the world is at your fingertips! You can send an e-mail message to someone on the other side of the planet. Through the World Wide Web, information is yours for the searching as you prepare a school report. The news, sports scores, travel information, and weather reports are all available at any time. How is this possible? The answer is through the use of a computer connected to a network.

Computer Networks

You have traveled on a network of roads and highways that connects cities and towns. A **computer network** is a group of computers connected by cables or telephone lines. **A computer network allows people in different locations to share information and software.**

A global network ▶

Lab zone Discover Activity

Skills Focus Inferring L2

Materials newspapers

Time 15 minutes

Tips Bring in major daily newspapers for students to look through. You may wish to limit the activity to a single page or section.

Expected Outcome Students will find several relevant articles in almost every newspaper. These articles may be about new hardware or software, web sites that contain information, or viruses and other computer problems.

Think It Over Sample answer: All kinds of information are available through the computer. Computers have become important sources of information science, entertainment, politics, business, health, and many other areas.

There are two types of networks. A set of computers connected in one classroom or office building is known as a local area network (LAN). Computers connected across larger distances form a wide area network (WAN). In wide area networks, very powerful computers serve as a support connection for hundreds of less powerful computers.

The Internet The most significant wide area network is the Internet. The **Internet** is a global network that links millions of computers in businesses, schools, and research organizations. The Internet is a network of host computers that extends around the world. You might say that the Internet is a network of networks. The Internet, along with other smaller networks, sometimes is called the information superhighway.

The Internet began in 1969 as a military communications system. Colleges and universities were later added to the Internet so that scientists could exchange data. Beginning in 1993, businesses were allowed to sell Internet connections to individuals. These businesses are known as Internet service providers (ISPs). With easy access available, use of the Internet has grown at an incredible rate.

World Wide Web The World Wide Web (www) was developed in 1989. The **World Wide Web** is a system that allows you to display and view files, called pages, on the Internet. A Web page can include text, pictures, video, or sound. Prior to the development of the World Wide Web, Internet users could only view information in the form of words and numbers. Through the World Wide Web, users can look at images similar to those you might see on television or videos. Software programs called search engines allow people to search through the Web for information.

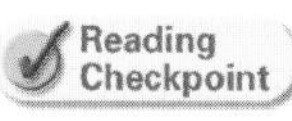
How has the World Wide Web changed the Internet?

What a Web You Weave

Many businesses and individuals have home pages on the World Wide Web. Such pages usually describe the characteristics of the business or person.

Communicating Design your own home page that describes your interests, hobbies, and achievements. A home page usually allows a user to click on certain words to find out more information about a particular topic. Be sure to include text, photographs, and art in your design.

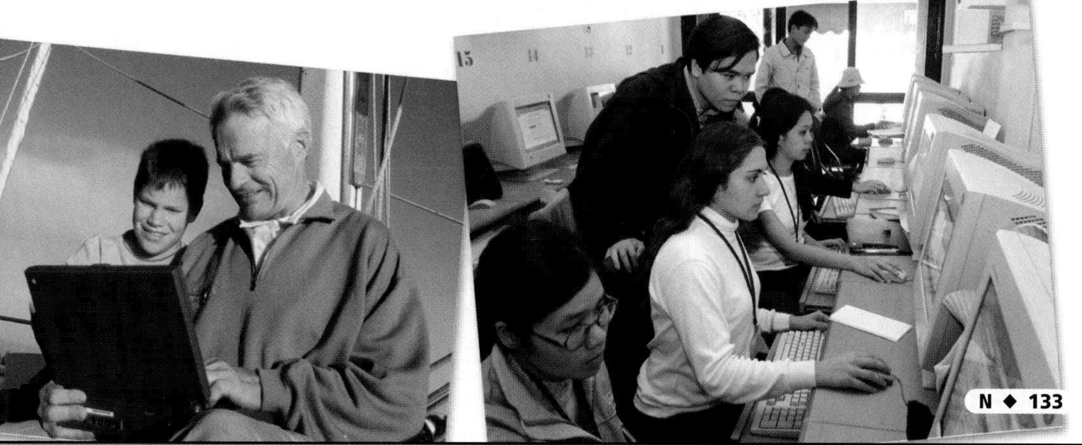

Instruct

Computer Networks

Teach Key Concepts L2

Connected Computers

Focus Tell students that the Internet is a worldwide network of connected computers.

Teach Ask: **What is a computer network?** *(A group of computers connected by cables or telephone lines)* **What does a computer network allow people to do?** *(It allows people in different locations to share information and software.)* **What is the World Wide Web?** *(A system that allows you to display and view files on the Internet)* Explain that the World Wide Web is not a computer network. Rather, it's more like the system of traffic laws that allows people to drive safely on the road.

Apply Ask: **If an Internet service provider sends you a letter offering to sell you its service, what is it that you would be buying?** *(A connection to the Internet)* **learning modality: verbal**

Independent Practice L2

All in One Teaching Resources

- Guided Reading and Study Worksheet: *The Information Superhighway*

Student Edition on Audio CD

Lab zone Try This Activity

Skills Focus Communicating L1

Materials poster board, markers, colored pencils, magazines, scissors, glue

Time 30 minutes

Tips Encourage students to design home pages that include several photos and links. Tell them to used colored pencils to write words that serve as buttons to more information. Provide magazines from which students can cut photos.

Expected Outcome Students will design a variety of home pages that include photos and information.

Extend Encourage students to work together to design a home page for the class, using web-page design software, if possible. **learning modality: visual**

Monitor Progress L2

Writing Ask students to write a paragraph that explains the difference between the Internet and the World Wide Web.

Answer

Reading Checkpoint Prior to the development of the World Wide Web, Internet users could only view information in the form of words and numbers. Through the World Wide Web, users can look at images similar to those you might see on television or videos.

Using Computers Safely

Teach Key Concepts L2

Protecting Self and Property

Focus Tell students that using a computer on a network can open the door to problems.

Teach Ask: **Why should you be careful about sharing personal information on a computer network?** *(Sample answer: Unscrupulous companies and criminals can take the information and use it for their benefit, not yours.)* **Why shouldn't you give your name and address whey you're in a chat room?** *(Sample answer: You can't know for sure who you're giving the information to.)*

Apply Have students consider this scenario: You meet someone online with whom you share a lot of interests, and you're considering meeting in person. Ask: **Why should you be careful about arranging to meet this person?** *(Sample answer: You can't really tell who this person is or what the motives are for wanting to meet you.)* **learning modality: verbal**

Teacher **Demo** L1

Antivirus Software

Focus Tell students that the school's computers are protected from damage by computer viruses with antivirus software.

Teach Demonstrate the antivirus program on a school computer. Show how the software scans the computer for viruses. If the computer also has a firewall to protect against worms and parasites, demonstrate this software for students.

Apply Ask: **Why is the expense of antivirus software a good investment?** *(A computer virus can damage a computer. Computers are very expensive to purchase, and with antivirus software the school is protecting its investment.)* **learning modality: visual**

For: Links on computer networks
Visit: www.SciLinks.org
Web Code: scn-1444

Download a worksheet that will guide students' review of Internet sources on computer networks.

FIGURE 18
Safety First
People can protect themselves and their property by using computer networks properly.
Interpreting Diagrams *How does encryption protect communications within a network?*

Using Computers Safely

Computer networks provide great benefits. But they also pose potential problems. By following careful practices, people can protect themselves and their property as they use computer networks. Here are four issues to consider.

Protect Private Data People may use networks to share personal information such as financial records, credit card numbers, medical data, and business records. It is essential to guard that kind of information from misuse. **Share personal information only on networks that require authorization and use security software to keep out unwanted users.** Look for networks that encrypt information. **Encryption** is a mathematical process of coding information so that only the intended user can read it.

Avoid Viruses Computer viruses are a form of vandalism. **Computer viruses** are programs that interfere with the normal operation of a computer. Like a living virus, a computer virus enters a computer and reproduces itself. It can destroy stored data or even disable a computer. **Use software to detect viruses before they cause damage.** When you download a file, run virus-checking software. Store downloaded programs on a floppy disk or CD.

For: Links on computer networks
Visit: www.SciLinks.org
Web Code: scn-1444

Differentiated Instruction

Special Needs L1

Computer Network If you have a local area network in your school, students may not realize that the computers are connected by cables. Explain that cables are often run through walls and ceilings, just as electrical wiring is. Arrange for the school's computer technician to show students these cables and connections. **learning modality: visual**

Gifted and Talented L3

Computer Viruses Have students prepare a presentation to the class about computer viruses. Ask that they do research to find out what computer viruses are, how they spread, what effect they have on computers, and how they can be prevented. Tell students they might also investigate computer worms and parasites. **learning modality: verbal**

Protect Personal Safety Many people enjoy chat rooms. **Chat rooms** allow multiple users to exchange messages simultaneously. However, users are not screened, so you do not know who is using the chat room with you. **Never give your name, address, or telephone number.** Do not respond to offensive messages, and do not accept files from strangers.

Respect Intellectual Property A computer program is a piece of intellectual property. **Intellectual property** can be an idea or creative work, such as a book or musical performance. Governments protect intellectual property by granting copyrights and patents. When you buy a copyrighted program, you buy a license for your own use. **Do not make copies for friends to use.** Violating copyrights or patents can result in fines or other penalties.

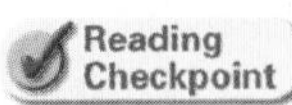
What kind of information does encryption protect?

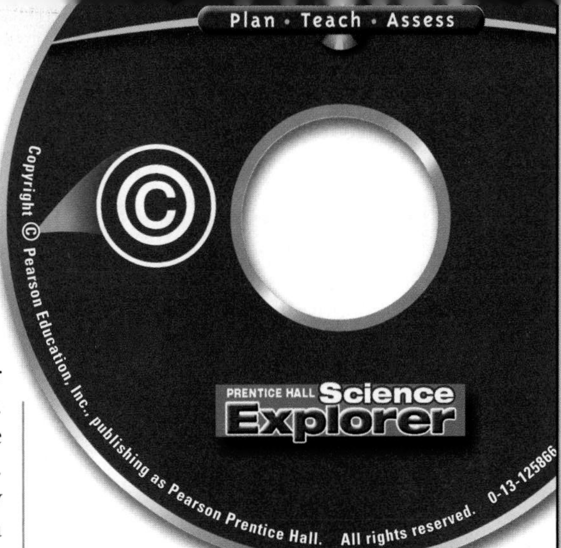

FIGURE 19
Intellectual Property
The copyright symbol on this CD protects the intellectual property rights of the company that produced it. Predicting *What might happen to the software and music industries if too many people copy CDs rather than buy them?*

Section 4 Assessment

Target Reading Skill Using Prior Knowledge Review your graphic organizer about computer networks and revise it based on what you just learned in the section.

Reviewing Key Concepts

1. a. Reviewing What is a computer network?
   b. Describing Give an example of a computer network.
   c. Making Judgments What are the advantages of computer networks?
2. a. Identifying What are three kinds of personal information that might be shared on a computer network?
   b. Explaining What is one way to protect personal information when using a network?
   c. Summarizing Write three simple rules that would help protect your family and your family's property when using computer networks.

Lab zone At-Home Activity

Conduct an Interview Although computers are commonplace today, this was not always the case. Interview a family member who grew up before computers were common. Prepare a list of questions for the interview. Find out whether that person has used a computer, what he or she thinks about computers, and how computers might have changed his or her life. Ask if the large number of applications for computers has come as a surprise.

Lab zone At-Home Activity

Conduct an interview L2 Encourage students to talk to older adults who grew up before computers were available. Students can make a list of everyday applications that now rely on computers and then research how people performed those tasks before computers were common. Students can present their findings to the class.

Lab zone Chapter Project

Keep Students on Track
As groups prepare to make their presentations, suggest ways in which they could better organize their descriptions of the existing and new computer applications. Make sure groups are making diagrams and preparing posters to explain their applications.

Monitor Progress L2

Answers
Figure 18 Encryption is a mathematical process of coding information so that only the intended user can read it.
Figure 19 Sample answer: Parts of the software and music industries might go bankrupt.

Reading Checkpoint Personal information, such as financial records, credit card numbers, medical data, and business records

Assess

Reviewing Key Concepts

1. a. A computer network is a group of computers connected by cables or telephone lines. **b.** Sample answer: The Internet is a global computer network. **c.** People in different locations can use computer networks to share information and software.
2. a. Sample answer: People might share personal information such as medical data, business records, and credit card information through a computer network. **b.** Sample answer: Use only networks that encrypt information. **c.** Sample answer: Share personal information only on networks that require authorization and use security software. Use computer virus protection software, and update it regularly. When using chat rooms, do not answer offensive messages, do not accept files from strangers, and do not give personal information such as your name, address, and phone number.

Reteach L1

Ask students to explain the difference between the Internet and the World Wide Web.

Performance Assessment L2

Writing Ask students to write a newspaper article that explains to readers the dangers that computer users can face online.

All in One Teaching Resources
- Section Summary: *The Information Superhighway*
- Review and Reinforce: *The Information Superhighway*
- Enrich: *The Information Superhighway*

Science and Society

When Seeing ISN'T Believing

Key Concept

Digital photographs can be easily manipulated. This provides advantages and disadvantages in modern society.

Build Background Knowledge

Film and Digital Photography

Help students recall what they know about photography. Ask: **What is the difference between film photography and digital photography?** *(Sample answer: Film photography uses light-sensitive film to take images. Digital photography translates light into digital signals.)* **What is the process used to turn the film in a camera into a photograph?** *(Sample answer: Film is developed in a darkroom using chemicals.)* **What is the process used to turn a digital photo into a photograph you can handle?** *(Sample answer: A computer simply prints out the digital photo on special paper.)* **Which do you think is easier to manipulate?** *(Sample answer: Digital photos are easier to manipulate because they exist as digital signals, which can be easily manipulated.)*

Introduce the Debate

Point out that digital photography is becoming more and more common. The problem is that a digital photograph can be manipulated much easier than a traditional film photograph can. Tell students they will debate this proposition: "Some digitally manipulated photographs can be misleading and cause a great deal of harm. Consequently, all altered photographs must be labeled as such." Inform students that a debate is not an argument. In a debate, two groups discuss a proposition by presenting reasons that support their positions.

Science and **Society**

When Seeing ISN'T Believing

Combining photography and computers can produce visual magic. A computer can turn a photo's objects and colors into a code. Then, using a computer to change the codes, a person can change a photo in amazing ways. Changing photos with computers is called digital manipulation.

The Issues

Advantages of Photo Manipulation

Computers allow people to greatly improve a photograph. Images of objects or people can be added, removed, or moved around. Fuzzy pictures can become sharper. Colors can be brightened. Unclear or tiny details can be made easy to see. Old or damaged photos can be made to look like new.

▲ Original image

Facilitate the Debate

- Have students read the feature and answer the You Decide questions individually as a homework assignment. The next day, organize the class into small groups for discussion. Have students discuss whether or not all altered photos should be labeled as such.
- Separate the class into two groups. Arbitrarily assign one group to support the proposition and the other group to oppose it. Both groups should critically and constructively support their viewpoints. Alternately call on students from each group to state the group's position or refute an idea from someone in the other group.
- Remind students that arguments should be succinct, without using harsh language.

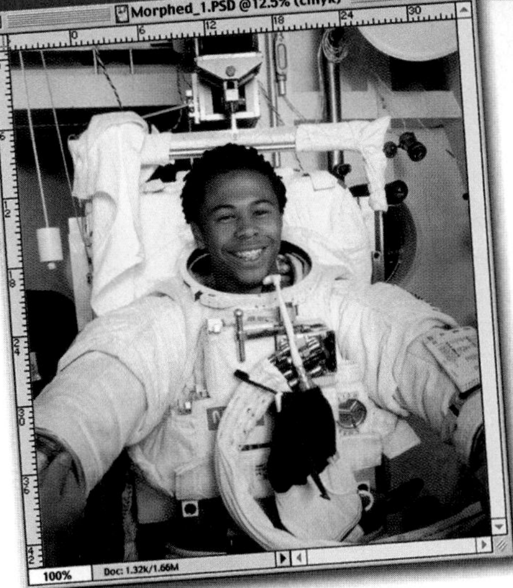

▲ Photos can be combined using digital manipulation.

▲ Digital manipulation can change your image in realistic ways.

Disadvantages of Photo Manipulation

It's nearly impossible to tell the difference between a changed and unchanged photo. Some people worry that digital manipulation could be used to harm or cheat people. Personal or family photos could be changed to a person's disadvantage. Newspapers, magazines, and TV stations could mislead the public about individuals and stories. Faked photos might be presented as evidence in court cases.

What Safeguards Are Needed?

Should governments pass laws against changing photographs? Such laws would be hard to enforce, and they might make it difficult to use digital manipulation for useful purposes. Such laws might also violate the right of free speech, since the courts consider photos a kind of speech, or expression. Should photographers or organizations police themselves? They could write codes of conduct. For example, it could be considered acceptable to make photos clearer digitally, but not to add, take away, or move around parts of a photo. Some photographers who work for newspapers have suggested such a code. Another safeguard might be to put a symbol on any digitally manipulated photo.

You Decide

1. **Identify the Problem**
   Summarize the problems created by digital manipulation of photos.
2. **Analyze the Options**
   Research this topic further at the library or on the Internet. List additional arguments for and against manipulating photos, and explain possible remedies.
3. **Find a Solution**
   You run a TV station. Your assistants want to use two digitally changed photos, one in a commercial and one in a news story about an individual. Will you let them use one, or both, or neither? Explain.

For: More on photo manipulation
Visit: PHSchool.com
Web Code: cgh-4040

You Decide

1. Sample answer: The main problem created by digital manipulation of photos is that an observer cannot tell whether a photo has been changed or not. News organizations could mislead readers and viewers by publishing fake photos. Manipulated photos might also be used to convict an innocent person in court.
2. Sample answer: An additional argument for photo manipulation is that artists have another way to create artistic images as they interpret reality. An additional argument against photo manipulation is that photos can no longer be taken for granted as historical documentation, since a digital photo may not reflect what really happened.
3. Sample answer: A digitally changed photo may be used for a commercial, as long as it is done in fun or it's obvious that the photo has been manipulated. A digitally changed photo may never be used in a news story, because using a fake photo would make the news story dishonest and would mislead the public.

For: More on photo manipulation
Visit: PHSchool.com
Web Code: cgh-4040

Students can research this issue online.

Extend

Encourage students to contact a local graphic or computer artist. Have them arrange a viewing of digitally altered images. Tell students to prepare questions in advance. Students could also use a search engine to search the Internet for other ways in which this issue affects society.

Background

Facts and Figures Photographs have not always been accepted as evidence in court because they are a representation of a thing, not the thing itself. The principal requirement for admitting a photograph in a trial is that both sides agree that the photo is an accurate representation of the scene or whatever the photo purports to be. This requirement may mean that someone must testify that the photo accurately portrays reality as witnessed by that person. Because defense attorneys often question the validity of digital photographs, many police departments have not gone fully digital. Traditional film photography is easier to defend on the witness stand. Digital photos are too easily manipulated, and juries don't trust them as much as film photos.

- Complete student edition
- Section and chapter self-assessments
- Assessment reports for teachers

Help Students Read L1

Building Vocabulary

Word/Parts Analysis To help distinguish among the words *electricity, electrical,* and *electronics,* have students examine the suffixes of the three terms. Ask them to think of other words that end in *-al, -ity,* and *-ics.* Examples are *individual, conductivity,* and *phonics*. Have students use a dictionary to find out what each suffix means. They will discover that *-al* means "related to," *-ity* means "a state or quality," and *-ics* means "the science or art of." Have students write definitions of the three terms using the meanings of the suffixes.

Words in Context Help students learn the meaning of new terms by examining context. Tell students to look for familiar words or phrases that are near the new term. These are clues to the new term's meaning. Have them read the paragraphs that introduce the key terms *hardware* and *software* in the section *Computers*. Ask: **Which words that appear in the same paragraph as *hardware* and the same paragraph as *software* can help you remember what each term means?** *(The word* physical *in the paragraph that introduces* hardware; *the word* program *in the paragraph that introduces* software*)*

Chapter 4 Study Guide

1 Electronic Signals and Semiconductors

Key Concepts

- There are two basic kinds of electronic signals: analog signals and digital signals.
- The two types of semiconductors can be combined in different ways to make diodes, transistors, and integrated circuits.

Key Terms

electronics
electronic signal
analog signal
digital signal
semiconductor
diode
transistor
integrated circuit

2 Electronic Communication

Key Concepts

- In a telephone, sound is transformed into an electronic signal that is transmitted and then transformed back into sound.
- Sound can be reproduced using an analog device such as a phonograph or a digital device such as a CD player.
- Electronic signals can be carried over long distances by electromagnetic waves.
- Voices and music on an AM or FM radio station are electronic signals carried by an electromagnetic wave.
- Electromagnetic waves can be used to carry images as well as sound.

Key Terms

electromagnetic wave
amplitude
frequency
amplitude modulation (AM)
frequency modulation (FM)

3 Computers

Key Concepts

- Computer information is represented in the binary system.
- Computer hardware includes a central processing unit, input devices, output devices, and memory storage devices.
- Software is a set of instructions that directs the computer hardware to perform operations on stored information.

Key Terms

computer
binary system
hardware
central processing unit (CPU)
input device
output device
software
computer programmer

4 The Information Superhighway

Key Concepts

- A computer network allows people in different locations to share information and software.
- Share personal information only on networks that require authorization and use security software to keep out unwanted users.
- Use software to detect viruses before they cause damage.
- Never give your name, address, or telephone number in chat rooms.
- Do not make copies of intellectual property or copyrighted material for friends to use.

Key Terms

computer network
World Wide Web
computer virus
intellectual property
Internet
encryption
chat room

138 ◆ N

Connect Concepts

Concept Maps Help students develop one way to show how the information in this chapter is related. Have students brainstorm to identify the key concepts, key terms, details, and examples. Ask students to write these suggestions in their notebooks.

Tell students that this concept map will be organized in hierarchical order and to begin at the top with key concepts or key terms. Ask students these questions to guide them to categorize the information in their notebooks: **What are two types of electronic signals? How are electromagnetic waves involved in the transmission of electronic signals? What are examples of computer hardware and software? What is a computer network?**

Prompt students by using connecting words or phrases, such as "includes" and "consists of," to indicate the basis for the organization of the map. The phrases should form a sentence between or among a set of concepts.

Answer Accept logical presentations by students.

All in One Teaching Resources

- Key Terms Review: *Electronics*
- Connecting Concepts: *Electronics*

Review and Assessment

For: Self-Assessment
Visit: PHSchool.com
Web Code: cga-4040

Organizing Information

Flowcharts Copy the flowchart about telephone communication onto a separate sheet of paper. Then complete it and add a title. (For more on flowcharts, see the Skills Handbook.)

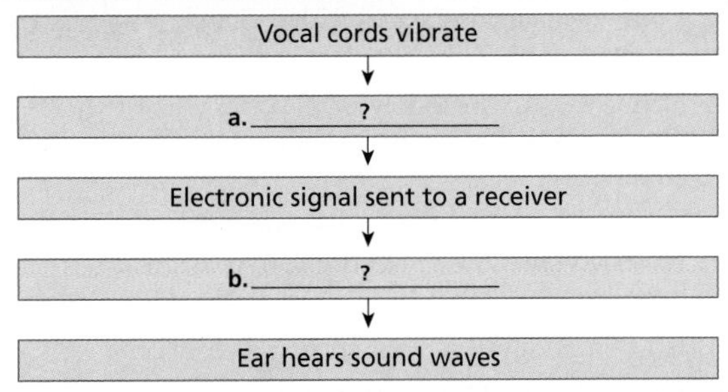

Reviewing Key Terms

Choose the letter of the best answer.

1. The use of electric current to communicate information is
   a. encryption.
   b. amplitude modulation.
   c. electrical communication.
   d. electronics.
2. A sandwich of three layers of semiconductor that is used to amplify an electric signal is known as a(n)
   a. diode.
   b. modem.
   c. transistor.
   d. integrated circuit.
3. An electromagnetic wave consists of
   a. changing electric and magnetic fields.
   b. AM and FM waves.
   c. electrons and protons.
   d. beams of electrons.
4. An example of an output device is a
   a. transistor.
   b. printer.
   c. hard disk.
   d. diskette.
5. A group of computers connected by cables or telephone lines is a
   a. microprocessor.
   b. CPU.
   c. modem.
   d. network.

If the statement is true, write *true*. If it is false, change the underlined word or words to make the statement true.

6. A <u>transistor</u> changes alternating current into direct current.
7. Before <u>computers</u>, electronic devices used vacuum tubes to control electric current.
8. <u>Input</u> devices feed data into a computer.
9. Computer programs are also called <u>hardware.</u>
10. A(n) <u>virus</u> is a program that interferes with the normal operation of a computer.

Writing in Science

Sequence of Events Imagine that you are a director in charge of televising a live music concert. Describe the sequence of events through which the images will be transmitted from a camera on stage to the television screens in people's homes.

Electronics
Video Preview
Video Field Trip
▶ Video Assessment

Go Online PHSchool.com
For: Self-Assessment
Visit: PHSchool.com
Web Code: cga-4040

Students can take a practice test online that is automatically scored.

All in One Teaching Resources
- Transparency N51
- Chapter Test
- Performance Assessment Teacher Notes
- Performance Assessment Student Worksheet
- Performance Assessment Scoring Rubric

***ExamView®* Computer Test Bank CD-ROM**

Review and Assessment

Organizing Information
How Telephones Work
a. Sound waves transformed into electronic signals
b. Electronic signals transformed into sound waves

Reviewing Key Terms
1. d **2.** c **3.** a **4.** b **5.** d
6. diode
7. semiconductors
8. true
9. software
10. true

Writing in Science

Writing Mode Sequencing

Scoring Rubric
4 Exceeds criteria; includes a detailed and accurate description of each step in the transmission and reception of television signals
3 Meets criteria
2 Meets some criteria; includes somewhat accurate descriptions
1 Includes inaccurate and/or incomplete descriptions

Electronics

Show the Video Assessment to review chapter content and as a prompt for the writing assignment. Discussion questions: **How do television stations transmit signals?** *(The transmission of television signals involves light energy being transformed to electronic signals and electromagnetic waves, and it even involves satellites in space.)* **How is analog television different from digital television?** *(Until recently, information was transmitted in a continuous wave representing the vibrations of sound and video. Digital technology eliminates many of the problems associated with analog signals such as poor picture and sound quality.)*

Checking Concepts

11. An analog signal involves continuous change. In electronics, this might mean changing the strength of a signal to match changes in the strength of a sound. A digital signal involves pulses of current. Digital information is recorded in a binary system.

12. Diode—device that allows current in one direction only; transistor—device that amplifies a signal or switches current on and off; integrated circuit—device that contains thousands of electronic components on a thin slice of semiconductor

13. Students' illustrations should show that electromagnetic waves are composed of changing electric and magnetic fields. An electromagnetic wave is produced when a changing electric field generates a changing magnetic field or when a changing magnetic field generates a changing electric field.

14. Sounds are transformed into electronic signals at the radio station. The signals are broadcast as an electromagnetic wave. The signals are transformed back into sounds in the speakers of a radio.

15. The Internet is a world-wide network of connected computers. The World Wide Web is a system that allows you to display and view files, on the Internet.

Thinking Critically

16. Semiconductors have made electronic components smaller, lighter, and faster.

17. 54,000 images

18. Students' programs should describe each step involved in the activity and list the steps in the sequence in which they should be performed. Students may revise their descriptions to break down more complex steps into simpler steps

19. Computer programs are protected by copyright laws, just as books or other intellectual products are. This allows the author of the program to profit from his or her work.

20. The device is a transistor, because it has three layers of semiconductors.

Review and Assessment

Checking Concepts

11. Compare an analog signal with a digital signal.

12. Define each of the following in your own words: diode, transistor, and integrated circuit.

13. Draw an illustration of an electromagnetic wave. Explain how an electromagnetic wave is generated.

14. How is a radio show broadcast and received?

15. How is the World Wide Web different from the Internet?

Thinking Critically

16. **Relating Cause and Effect** What are some advantages of semiconductors and the electronic components made from semiconductors?

17. **Calculating** The television pictures people enjoy are composed of images shown very quickly. Each image on a traditional television screen lasts for $\frac{1}{30}$ of a second. How many images appear on the screen during a 30-minute program?

18. **Applying Concepts** A computer program is a list of instructions that tells a computer exactly how to perform a task. Write a program that describes the steps involved in some small task, such as walking your dog, taking out the trash, setting the table, or playing a game. Reread and revise your description so that a person could use it to correctly perform the task.

19. **Making Judgments** Why does a government protect a computer program as the intellectual property of the author?

20. **Classifying** What type of semiconductor device is shown in the diagram below? How can you tell?

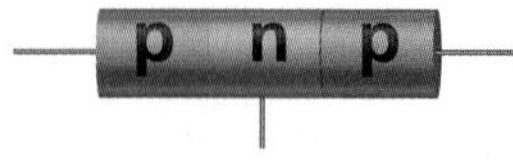

Applying Skills

Use the illustrations below to answer Questions 21–24.

Examine the waves diagrammed below. The diagrams may not all show a variation of the same wave.

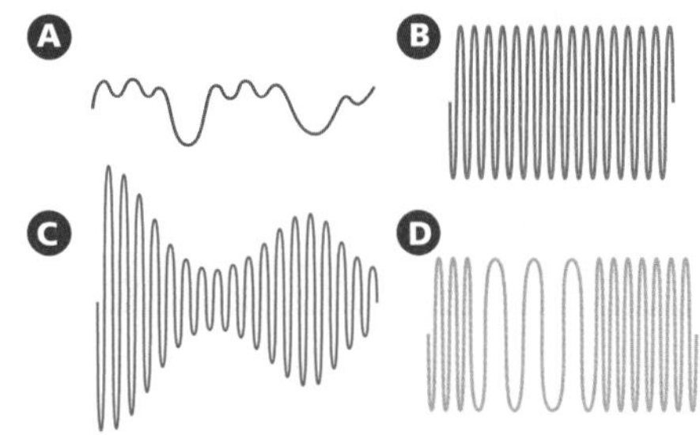

21. **Predicting** Diagram A represents an audio signal. What would that signal look like if it were converted to an AM radio signal? Draw a sketch to illustrate your answer.

22. **Interpreting Diagrams** Which of these waves might be a carrier wave? Describe the role of a carrier wave in electronic communication.

23. **Classifying** Two radio transmitters send out electronic signals shown as diagram C and diagram D. Which represents an AM wave? Which represents an FM wave? How can you tell?

24. **Comparing and Contrasting** Could the wave in diagram C be a modulated version of the wave in diagram A? Explain how you know.

Lab zone Chapter Project

Performance Assessment Present both the existing computer application and the new one you invented to the class. Provide diagrams of each and describe their operation. You might want to pretend to sell your new invention to the class. Prepare a poster describing the task that your new application will accomplish. Show yourself enjoying the benefits!

Lab zone Chapter Project

L3

Performance Assessment Talk with each student or group before the presentation. Offer encouragement, and make suggestions about how to present the existing and new computer applications. As groups present their applications, encourage their classmates to take brief notes about the characteristics of the applications. If a group presents a sales pitch for the new application, invite other students to ask relevant questions about how the application might benefit them. Assess the presentations on the quality and organization of the information presented, the description of the new application, and the design of the visual aids used.

Standardized Test Prep

Test-Taking Tip

Sequencing Events

Some test questions require you to arrange a series of events in order. You might be asked to arrange events in order, or to identify which event in a series happens first or last. Or a question might ask you which event comes before or after another event. Before looking at the answer choices, first try to recall the correct sequence in which the events occur.

Sample Question

When you speak into a telephone transmitter, which of the following events happens first?

A An electronic signal travels through a series of wires.
B A vibrating disk creates sound waves.
C Sound vibrations are changed into electronic signals.
D Electronic signals are changed into vibrations.

Answer

The correct answer is **C.** The events described in **A, B,** and **D** all happen after sound vibrations are converted into electronic signals.

Choose the letter of the best answer.

1. Each of the events listed below happens in the process of producing an image and sound in a television set. Which event happens last?
A A communication satellite receives electromagnetic signals.
B Electronic signals are converted into sound and light.
C Electromagnetic signals are sent out from an antenna.
D Light and sound are converted into electronic signals.

2. In the binary number system, the number 8 would be written as
F 2.
G 8.
H 100.
J 1000.

Use the graphs and your knowledge of science to answer Question 3.

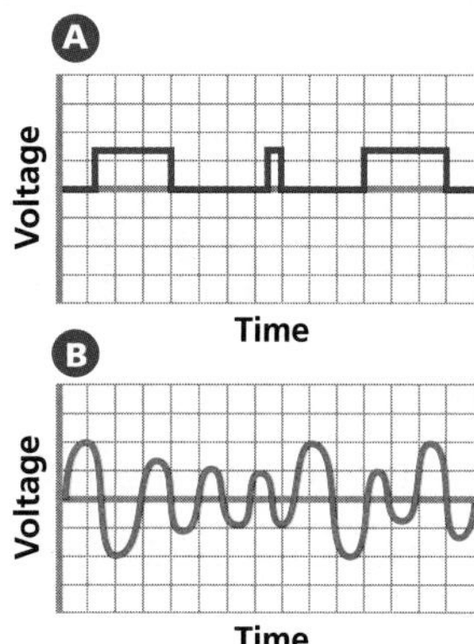

3. Which of the following statements about graphs A and B is correct?
A Graph A shows an analog signal and graph B shows a digital signal.
B Graph A shows a digital signal and graph B shows an analog signal.
C Both graphs show analog signals.
D Neither graph shows an analog signal.

4. Which of the following is not a good way to protect yourself and your property while using a computer network?
F Use computer software that detects viruses.
G Store downloaded programs on floppy disks or CDs.
H Use your real name when you visit a chat room.
J Do not accept electronic files from strangers.

5. Which of the following items is an input device?
A computer monitor
B hard disk
C mouse
D central processing unit

Constructed Response

6. Explain what an integrated circuit is. Also explain why integrated circuits are useful devices.

Applying Skills

21. Students' sketches should show an electromagnetic wave with an amplitude pattern that matches the shape of the wave in A.

22. B might be a carrier electromagnetic wave because its frequency and amplitude do not vary. A carrier wave's amplitude and frequency can be modulated to carry an electronic signal.

23. C represents an AM wave, because the amplitude of the wave is modulated. D represents an FM wave, because the frequency has been modulated.

24. It could not be, because the amplitude pattern in C does not match the signal in A.

Standardized Test Prep

1. B **2.** J **3.** B **4.** H **5.** C

6. An integrated circuit is a thin slice of semiconductor that contains many diodes, transistors, and other electronic components. The high-speed signals of integrated circuits make possible devices from video games to spacecraft. The small size of integrated circuits has allowed the size of electronic devices such as computers to be greatly reduced.

Interdisciplinary Exploration

Edison—Genius of Invention

This interdisciplinary feature presents the central theme of Thomas Edison as a genius of invention by connecting four different disciplines: science, language arts, mathematics, and social studies. The four explorations are designed to capture students' interest and help them see how the content they are studying in science relates to other school subjects and to real-world events. Share with others for a team-teaching experience.

All in One Teaching Resources

- Interdisciplinary Exploration: *Science*
- Interdisciplinary Exploration: *Language Arts*
- Interdisciplinary Exploration: *Mathematics*
- Interdisciplinary Exploration: *Social Studies*

Build Background Knowledge

Technology Powered by Electricity

Help students recall what they have previously learned about electric charges and electric currents. Ask: **What causes a current to flow through an electric circuit?** *(Voltage)* **What are examples of voltage sources?** *(Batteries and generators)* **How do series and parallel circuits differ?** *(In a series circuit, there is only one path for the charges to follow. In a parallel circuit, there are several paths.)* **What is resistance?** *(Resistance is something that slows down the flow of charge.)*

Introduce the Exploration

Ask: **Have you ever been without electricity? What was it like?** *(Sample answer: The electricity went out in a storm and stayed out for hours. It was scary without electric lights.)* **Have you ever had to make do using only candles or oil lamps? How is electricity better?** *(Sample answer: During electric outages, candles and oil lamps have provided some light. Electric lights are much brighter. They also seem safer, because they provide light without a flame.)* Then, tell students a little about Thomas Edison, including that he received little school education and was mostly home schooled.

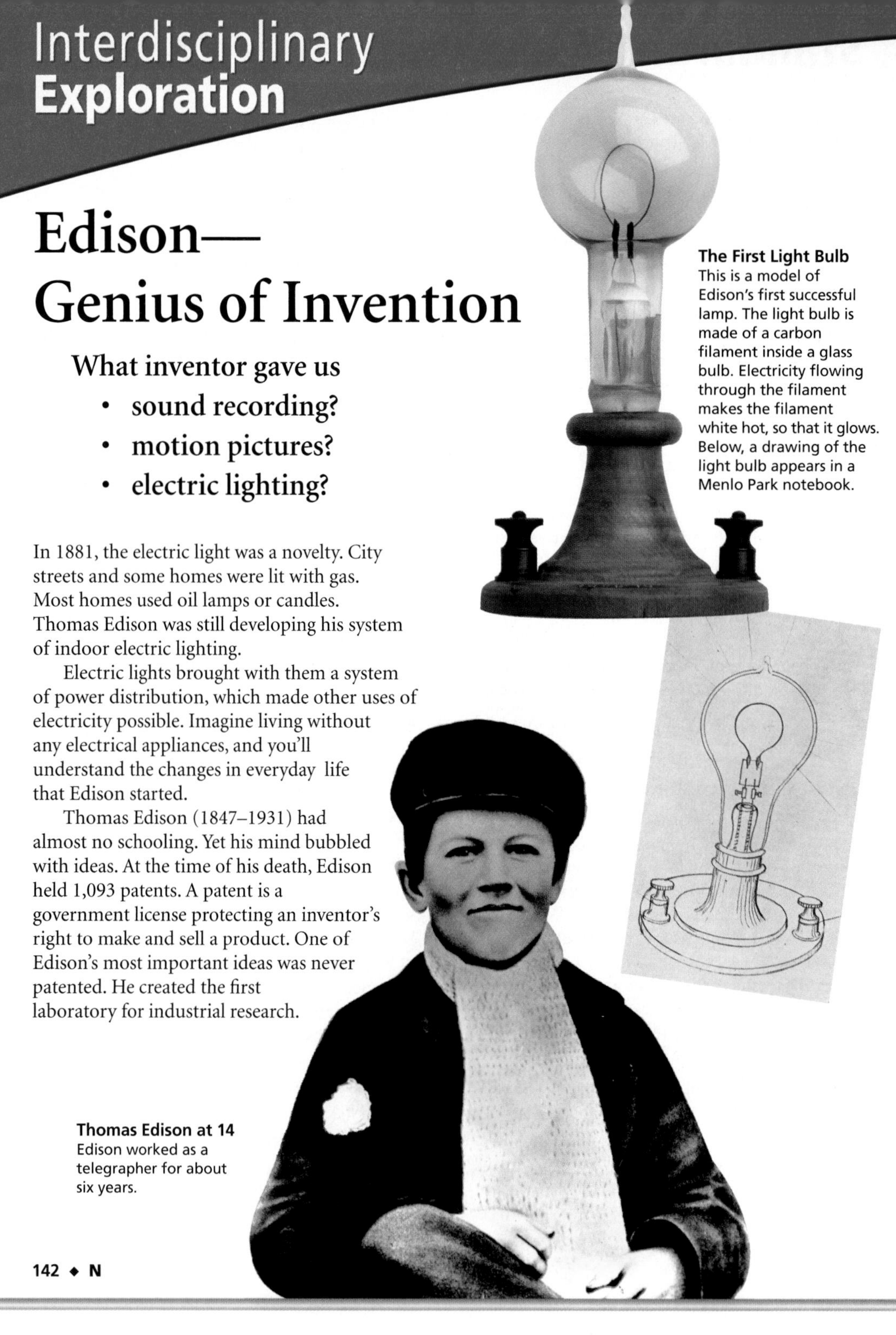

Interdisciplinary
Exploration

Edison—
Genius of Invention

What inventor gave us
- sound recording?
- motion pictures?
- electric lighting?

In 1881, the electric light was a novelty. City streets and some homes were lit with gas. Most homes used oil lamps or candles. Thomas Edison was still developing his system of indoor electric lighting.

Electric lights brought with them a system of power distribution, which made other uses of electricity possible. Imagine living without any electrical appliances, and you'll understand the changes in everyday life that Edison started.

Thomas Edison (1847–1931) had almost no schooling. Yet his mind bubbled with ideas. At the time of his death, Edison held 1,093 patents. A patent is a government license protecting an inventor's right to make and sell a product. One of Edison's most important ideas was never patented. He created the first laboratory for industrial research.

The First Light Bulb This is a model of Edison's first successful lamp. The light bulb is made of a carbon filament inside a glass bulb. Electricity flowing through the filament makes the filament white hot, so that it glows. Below, a drawing of the light bulb appears in a Menlo Park notebook.

Thomas Edison at 14 Edison worked as a telegrapher for about six years.

142 ◆ N

The Wizard of Menlo Park

Before 1900, most inventors worked alone. Edison, in contrast, depended on a strong team of research co-workers to carry out his ideas. Edison had an unusual ability to inspire those who worked for him. Some of his original team stayed with him for years. A very hard worker himself, Edison demanded that everyone on his team also work long hours.

By 1876, Edison had enough money to set up an "invention factory." He chose the small town of Menlo Park, New Jersey. His Menlo Park laboratory became the world's first industrial research laboratory.

Edison's team often made improvements on other people's inventions. The light bulb is an example. Other scientists had invented electric lamps, but their light bulbs burned rapidly. The problem was to find a material for the filament that would not overheat or burn out quickly.

The Menlo Park team spent months testing hundreds of materials. First, they rolled each material into a long, thin strand. Then, they carbonized it, which meant baking it until it turned to charcoal. Finally, they tested it in a vacuum, or in the absence of air. Most materials failed in only a few minutes or a few hours. The breakthrough came in 1879. The first successful filament was a length of ordinary cotton thread, carefully carbonized. The newspapers carried the headlines "Success in a Cotton Thread" and "It Makes a Light, Without Gas or Flame."

Edison's Lab
Edison set up his research laboratory in Menlo Park.

Science Activity

Work together as a team to invent a new electrical device.

- What could a new electrical device help you do? How could it make your life easier?
- Brainstorm for possible products that would help you in some way. Write down all possible ideas.
- Evaluate each solution and agree on the best one.
- Plan your design and make a labeled drawing. List the supplies you will need. Note any new skills you should learn.
- Write down the steps you will use to build your device.

Background

History After having scarlet fever as a child, Edison began to lose his hearing. Eventually he was completely deaf in one ear and had only slight hearing in the other. Edison felt this was a benefit because he could not hear what he called "foolish small talk" and had more time to think. Despite ear surgeries, Edison's hearing continued to decline.

Possibly because of his hearing loss, Edison did poorly in school. One of Edison's teachers was very strict and punished students for asking questions. Because Edison liked to ask questions, he was punished. The teacher declared Edison was too confused to be able to learn. Edison's mother met with the teacher and became very angry. She then decided to teach Edison at home.

Explore Science Concepts

Discuss Ask: **Why do you think many inventors work alone?** *(Sample answer: An inventor is often a creative person who might not accomplish anything for a while and then suddenly have an inspiration that works out.)* Point out that Edison worked long hours with a loyal team of employees. **Why do you think people worked so hard for Edison?** *(Sample answer: People worked hard because Edison set an example by working hard himself.)*

Use Visuals Have students look at the photo and diagram of an early light bulb, and ask a student to read the caption aloud. Ask: **What is a light bulb's filament?** *(A long, thin strand of material or wire)* **What causes the light produced by a light bulb?** *(Electricity flowing through the filament makes the filament white hot, producing light.)* Explain that most material from living things is made of molecules that contain carbon. Baking a carbon material can turn it into a kind of charcoal, a process called carbonization. Ask: **What was Edison's first successful filament?** *(A length of ordinary cotton thread, carefully carbonized)*

Science Activity

Focus Ask: **What are some electrical devices that you think don't work very well?** *(Sample answer: A toaster that burns the bread. A clock alarm that doesn't go off on time.)* Ask students to suggest ways to improve these devices.

Teach Preview the activity with students, and then divide the class into teams. Give teams 10–15 minutes to brainstorm a list of possible products. Review the list with each team, making suggestions. Encourage each team to choose one idea and proceed on to the design phase.

Expected Outcome Students on each team should specifically describe how a new electrical device could make life easier. A design for a new device should be detailed, with a labeled drawing that shows the different parts and the electrical circuitry. Each team should have a list of supplies they would need, as well as a procedure that could be used to build the device.

Extend Encourage students to work with older students or adults to build their devices. Students might investigate whether a device could be patented and how they could apply for a patent.

Language Arts

Explore Language Arts Concepts

Use Maps Some students may not know where Manhattan is. Use a large map of the United States to show students the location of New York state and New York City. Use a road atlas of the United States to show students the location of Manhattan within New York City.

Oral Presentation Ask a volunteer to read the *Times* article from 1882. Help students understand the context of the article. Point out that this period was before the invention of the automobile. Ask: **What kind of artificial light does the writer compare the electric lamps to?** *(Gas burners)* Explain that big cities at the time had gas-burning lamps to light the streets and buildings. **How did the writer describe the quality of the light from the electric lamps?** *("Light was soft, mellow, and grateful to the eye.")* **What does the writer mean by the phrase "without a particle of flicker"?** *(Light was steady and not flickering like a flame flickers.)*

Language Arts Activity

Focus Show students a junk-mail letter that attempts to persuade the reader to buy a product or pay for a service. Ask: **What are some strategies such letters use to persuade the reader to try the product or service?** *(They describe in glowing detail how the product or service will improve the reader's life.)*

Teach Before students tackle the writing activity, ask: **What advantages could Edison relate about electric light bulbs that might persuade readers of his time?** *(Sample answer: The warm, steady glow of an electric light; the convenience and safety of light bulbs versus gas lamps)* Point out that people are often suspicious of new technologies. Ask students to imagine the fears people might have had about having electricity at home.

Writing Mode Persuasion

Scoring Rubric

4 Exceeds criteria; provides accurate details about the Edison's light bulbs and power system in an imaginative and persuasive context

3 Meets criteria

2 Meets some criteria; is only somewhat descriptive and/or persuasive

1 Includes few details about the electric lights and/or fails in writing persuasively about Edison's product

Language Arts

Lighting Manhattan

Edison recognized the value of publicity. Besides being a productive inventor, he knew how to promote himself. He made glowing predictions about his new electric system. Electricity would soon be so cheap, he said, that "only the rich would be able to afford candles."

When he built his first neighborhood generating station, Edison made a shrewd choice of location. The Pearl Street power station brought light and power to about 2.6 square kilometers of downtown Manhattan. It supplied businesses and factories, as well as private homes. The circuits could light 400 light bulbs. Some of those lights were in the offices of J. P. Morgan, the leading banker and financier of the time. Other lights were located in the offices of *The New York Times*. Here's what the *Times* reporter wrote on September 5, 1882.

New York City
This photo shows Broadway in the 1880s.

SEPTEMBER 5, 1882—Yesterday for the first time The Times Building was illuminated by electricity. Mr. Edison had at last perfected his incandescent light, had put his machinery in order, and had started up his engines, and last evening his company lighted up about one-third of the lower City district in which The Times Building stands.

It was not until about seven o'clock, when it began to grow dark, that the electric light really made itself known and showed how bright and steady it is. It was a light that a man could sit down under and write for hours without the consciousness of having any artificial light about him. There was a very slight amount of heat from each lamp, but not nearly as much as from a gas-burner—one-fifteenth as much as from gas, the inventor says. The light was soft, mellow, and grateful to the eye, and it seemed almost like writing by daylight to have a light without a particle of flicker and with scarcely any heat to make the head ache. The decision was unanimously in favor of the Edison electric lamp as against gas.

———Excerpted with permission from *The New York Times.*

Language Arts Activity

The reporter who wrote the newspaper story observed details carefully and used them to write about an event—the first lights in his office. Look back at the story. Now write about the event as Edison would have told it to convince people to buy light bulbs and install electrical power systems. You could make an advertisement. Inform your readers about the product and persuade them to buy it.

Background

History Edison's mother loved to read, and he adopted her love of reading. Before he was 10 years old, his mother gave him a basic science book. He began performing the experiments he found in the book. Soon he was spending his pocket money on chemical supplies to use in more experiments. By the time he was 12, he got a job selling newspapers and candy to passengers on the train in order to buy books and supplies for a chemistry laboratory in the basement.

Solving Practical Problems

As he grew older, Edison worried that American students were not learning mathematics well enough. To motivate students, he suggested using problems that related to real-life situations. In 1925, when he was 78, he proposed these problems below as recorded in his notebooks. Note that light bulbs were called lamps. Tungsten is a metal used in light bulbs.

Edison Lamp
This advertisement promotes reading by Edison's Mazda lamp.

Problem 1
American power plants now serve 9,500,000 homes. The estimated number of homes in the United States is 21,000,000. What percentage receives electric power?

Problem 2
It needs about 280,000,000 tungsten lamps [bulbs] each year to supply the market today. And yet the first lamp factory in the world—the Edison Lamp Works. . .—was not started until 1880, and I was told it would never pay. The output for our first year was about 25,000 globes [bulbs]. How many times that figure would be required for the present market?

Problem 3
A household using 21 lamps requires about 7 new lamps each year. What percentage is this?

Problem 4
If these lamps had been bought at the retail prices of the first year of the lamp factory, they would have cost $1.25 each. How much would the family save by the decreased prices of today?

Inventor Thomas Edison
Edison stands next to his original light bulb invention. In his hand, he holds a smaller model.

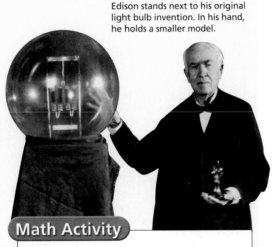

Math Activity

Solve the four math problems that Edison wrote. To solve Problem 4, use 1902 prices. That year, incandescent light bulbs (or lamps) cost $.30 each.

Background

Facts and Figures The incandescent light bulb is not the only type of lighting available. Electric-discharge lamps were developed in the early 1900s. These lamps produced light by applying a voltage to two electrodes at either end of a tube filled with a small amount of gas, such as mercury or sodium. Lights filled with mercury give off a bright, whitish, blue-green light. These lights found use as street lighting in the early part of the twentieth century in the United States. Lights filled with sodium vapor give off a yellow-orange glow. They are used to light streets, highways, and tunnels all over the world. Fluorescent lighting is another type of electric-discharge lamp. Fluorescent lights are used as interior lighting in factories, schools, and office buildings.

Explore Mathematics Concepts

Show Examples If possible, bring to class some very old math textbooks. Have students examine the pages to see how rarely real-world problems were featured in such texts. Ask: **Do you think real-life problems motivate students to learn? Justify your answer.** *(Sample answer: Real-life problems would motivate students by showing them that learning math skills will help in everyday activities.)* Invite students to think of other ways math textbooks could motivate students to learn. Then ask: **What do you think Edison would think of today's math books?** *(Sample answer: He would think they are much more colorful and lively than the old books. There are now more questions that relate to real life.)*

Review Help students recall their understanding of how to calculate percentages. Explain that to find a percentage of a portion of a whole, divide the portion by the whole. The answer is a decimal to the hundredths. For example, suppose there are 14 boys in a class of 30. To calculate the percentage of boys in the class, divide 14 by 30. The result is 0.47. Multiply by 100 to determine the percentage, or 47%.

Extend Invite students to make a display of math questions that relate to real-life problems. Challenge students to write problems that they think would motivate others to learn math.

Math Activity

Focus Tell students that part of marketing a new product is determining how large the market is and what people would pay for the product.

Teach Point out that Problem 2 has extraneous information—the year 1882—that has no bearing on the math problem. Explain that part of problem solving is identifying what data you need and don't need to determine an answer. Point out that for Problem 4 students should calculate how much a family would save per lamp.

Answers
1. 45%
2. 11,200
3. 33%
4. $0.95 per lamp

Social Studies

Explore Social Studies Concepts

Discuss Explain that it is a common misconception that Thomas Edison invented the electric light. Point out that Edison invented the first practical incandescent light bulb. Have students look at other Edison inventions shown here. Ask: **How has the technology for these inventions changed in the last hundred years?** *(It's become a vast movie and recording industry)* **How have these technologies affected people's lives today?** *(It enables more people to have access to entertainment.)*

Use Visuals Have students look at the satellite image of the United States showing electric lights at night. Ask: **How do you think this image might differ from a similar image of a less-developed country in Asia or Africa?** *(many fewer lights in such a country.)* **How do you think this will change in the future?** *(Electric lights will become more common.)*

Social Studies Activity

Focus Tell students that electric lights are so bright that they can be seen from satellites orbiting Earth. A satellite image can show population distribution.

Teach Provide students with a large wall map of the United States, or provide several smaller maps. Explain that students should compare the satellite image to the map of the United States and find where lighted areas on the image correlate with large cities on the map. Demonstrate how to do this with New York City or Los Angeles.

Expected Outcome Students' answers may vary because it is difficult to judge where state lines are. With the exception of coastal California and a few scattered cities, the eastern half of the country is more brightly lit and thus more populated than the western half.

According to the U.S. Census Bureau, the population of the United States in April, 2000, was 281,421,906. According to the 2000 census, the top five cities were: New York City, 8 million; Los Angeles, 3.7 million; Chicago, 2.9 million; Houston, 2 million; and Philadelphia, 1.3 million. These are populations for cities proper.

Social Studies

Daily Life Transformed

Edison's inventions in the late 1800s helped spark a technological and social revolution. Some of these inventions forever transformed the way people live, play, and work.

Edison's light bulb made indoor lighting practical. Along with the light bulb, he developed the idea of a central power system to distribute electricity to homes and businesses. That system included generators, underground cables, junction boxes, and meters. Other inventors improved on Edison's ideas for lights and electricity.

Other Edison inventions influenced ways that people entertain themselves. Edison created the phonograph, a rotating disk that could record and play back sounds. About that same time, Edison invented the first movie camera, a device that could store pictures. These inventions spurred the development of the recording and film industries.

Edison Movie
This poster advertises one of Edison's early movies.

EDISON PHOTO-PLAY
ZEB'S MUSICAL CAREER
COMEDY
EDISON

Phonograph
In 1878, Edison demonstrated his phonograph, which recorded sound on a rotating cylinder. A needle attached to a thin metal disk played the sound.

Improved Phonograph
A later version of Edison's phonograph included a horn to project the sound.

Background

Facts and Figures Light pollution is a problem faced by amateur and professional astronomers when gazing at the night sky. The amount of illumination from street lamps, buildings, billboards, and other light sources pointing toward the sky masks stars that should be visible.

Light pollution is caused by poorly designed or improperly installed light fixtures. It is estimated that in the United States, $1.5 billion per year in electricity bills is wasted on light going upward into the sky.

Because of light pollution, only a few hundred stars of the more than 320,000 stars that should be visible over North America can be seen in the night sky from most cities and towns in the United States.

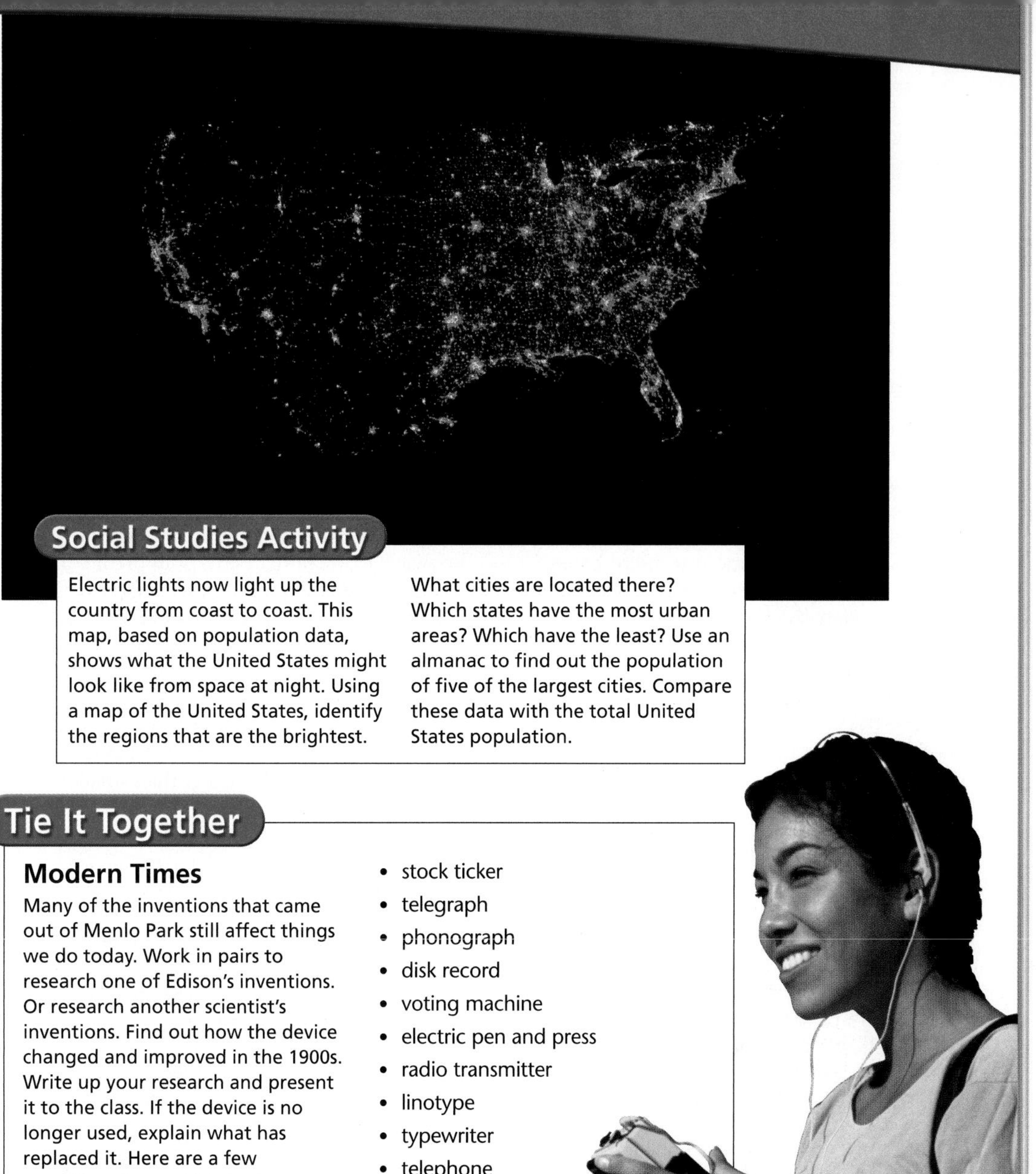

Social Studies Activity

Electric lights now light up the country from coast to coast. This map, based on population data, shows what the United States might look like from space at night. Using a map of the United States, identify the regions that are the brightest. What cities are located there? Which states have the most urban areas? Which have the least? Use an almanac to find out the population of five of the largest cities. Compare these data with the total United States population.

Tie It Together

Modern Times

Many of the inventions that came out of Menlo Park still affect things we do today. Work in pairs to research one of Edison's inventions. Or research another scientist's inventions. Find out how the device changed and improved in the 1900s. Write up your research and present it to the class. If the device is no longer used, explain what has replaced it. Here are a few inventions from which to choose. (Not all of them were Edison's.)

- stock ticker
- telegraph
- phonograph
- disk record
- voting machine
- electric pen and press
- radio transmitter
- linotype
- typewriter
- telephone
- automobile
- vacuum tube
- mechanical music

Cassette Player
Is this device related to Edison's invention?

Tie It Together

Modern Times

Time 3 days (2 days for research; 1 day for presentations)

Tips Encourage students to choose any invention from Edison's time that interests them. Display a sheet in the classroom where students can record the invention they will research to ensure that different groups research different inventions.

• Encourage students to make photocopies or flag the pages of books that show illustrations of the inventor, early versions of the invention, or other interesting graphics. Tell students to research enough material to be able to give a five-minute presentation.

• In the research stage, suggest that students visit a local historical museum or center of science and technology to see some of these inventions firsthand.

Other Resources Many excellent books have been published about inventors and inventions. Encyclopedias, both print and online, are also good sources of information. In addition, using the term *inventions* in an Internet search engine will yield a number of informative web sites. Your school media specialist can help you plan this activity and work with students to help them develop their information literacy skills as they locate resources, conduct research, and prepare their presentations.

Extend Students may wish to combine their research findings to make a classroom display or hall display for the school.

• Some students may want to research the lives of other inventors who lived during Edison's time period. Encourage these students to present their findings as biographies.

• Suggest that students find out about present-day inventors by researching one of the organizations that help inventors. Students may also be able to find information on web sites or in magazines published by these organizations. Have these students present their findings to the class.

Think Like a Scientist

The Skills Handbook is designed as a reference for students to use whenever they need to review inquiry, reading, or math skills. You can use the activities in this part of the Skills Handbook to teach or reinforce inquiry skills.

Observing

Focus Remind students that an observation is what they can see, hear, smell, taste, or feel.

Teach Invite students to make observations of the classroom. List these observations on the board. Challenge students to identify the senses they used to make each observation. Then, ask: **Which senses will you use to make observations from the photograph on this page?** *(Sight is the only sense that can be used to make observations from the photograph.)*

Activity

Some observations that students might make include that the boy is skateboarding, wearing a white helmet, and flying in the air. Make sure that students' observations are confined to only things that they can actually see in the photograph.

Inferring

Focus Choose one or two of the classroom observations listed on the board, and challenge students to interpret them. Guide students by asking why something appears as it does.

Teach Encourage students to describe their thought processes in making their inferences. Point out where they used their knowledge and experience to interpret the observations. Then invite students to suggest other possible interpretations for the observations. Ask: **How can you find out whether an inference is correct?** *(By further investigation)*

Activity

One possible inference is that the boy just skated off a ramp at a skate park. Invite students to share their experiences that helped them make the inference.

Predicting

Focus Discuss the weather forecast for the next day. Point out that this prediction is an inference about what will happen in the future based on observations and experience.

Teach Help students differentiate between a prediction and an inference. You might organize the similarities and differences in a Venn diagram on the board. Both are interpretations of observations using experience and knowledge, and both can be incorrect. Inferences describe current or past events. Predictions describe future events.

Activity

Students might predict that the boy will land and skate to the other side. Others might predict that the boy will fall. Students should also describe the evidence or experience on which they based their predictions.

SKILLS Handbook

Think Like a Scientist

Scientists have a particular way of looking at the world, or scientific habits of mind. Whenever you ask a question and explore possible answers, you use many of the same skills that scientists do. Some of these skills are described on this page.

Observing

When you use one or more of your five senses to gather information about the world, you are **observing.** Hearing a dog bark, counting twelve green seeds, and smelling smoke are all observations. To increase the power of their senses, scientists sometimes use microscopes, telescopes, or other instruments that help them make more detailed observations.

An observation must be an accurate report of what your senses detect. It is important to keep careful records of your observations in science class by writing or drawing in a notebook. The information collected through observations is called evidence, or data.

Inferring

When you interpret an observation, you are **inferring,** or making an inference. For example, if you hear your dog barking, you may infer that someone is at your front door. To make this inference, you combine the evidence—the barking dog—and your experience or knowledge—you know that your dog barks when strangers approach—to reach a logical conclusion.

Notice that an inference is not a fact; it is only one of many possible interpretations for an observation. For example, your dog may be barking because it wants to go for a walk. An inference may turn out to be incorrect even if it is based on accurate observations and logical reasoning. The only way to find out if an inference is correct is to investigate further.

Predicting

When you listen to the weather forecast, you hear many predictions about the next day's weather—what the temperature will be, whether it will rain, and how windy it will be. Weather forecasters use observations and knowledge of weather patterns to predict the weather. The skill of **predicting** involves making an inference about a future event based on current evidence or past experience.

Because a prediction is an inference, it may prove to be false. In science class, you can test some of your predictions by doing experiments. For example, suppose you predict that larger paper airplanes can fly farther than smaller airplanes. How could you test your prediction?

Activity

Use the photograph to answer the questions below.

Observing Look closely at the photograph. List at least three observations.

Inferring Use your observations to make an inference about what has happened. What experience or knowledge did you use to make the inference?

Predicting Predict what will happen next. On what evidence or experience do you base your prediction?

Classifying

Could you imagine searching for a book in the library if the books were shelved in no particular order? Your trip to the library would be an all-day event! Luckily, librarians group together books on similar topics or by the same author. Grouping together items that are alike in some way is called **classifying.** You can classify items in many ways: by size, by shape, by use, and by other important characteristics.

Like librarians, scientists use the skill of classifying to organize information and objects. When things are sorted into groups, the relationships among them become easier to understand.

Activity

Classify the objects in the photograph into two groups based on any characteristic you choose. Then use another characteristic to classify the objects into three groups.

Making Models

Have you ever drawn a picture to help someone understand what you were saying? Such a drawing is one type of model. A model is a picture, diagram, computer image, or other representation of a complex object or process. **Making models** helps people understand things that they cannot observe directly.

Scientists often use models to represent things that are either very large or very small, such as the planets in the solar system, or the parts of a cell. Such models are physical models—drawings or three-dimensional structures that look like the real thing. Other models are mental models—mathematical equations or words that describe how something works.

Activity

This student is using a model to demonstrate what causes day and night on Earth. What do the flashlight and the tennis ball in the model represent?

Communicating

Whenever you talk on the phone, write a report, or listen to your teacher at school, you are communicating. **Communicating** is the process of sharing ideas and information with other people. Communicating effectively requires many skills, including writing, reading, speaking, listening, and making models.

Scientists communicate to share results, information, and opinions. Scientists often communicate about their work in journals, over the telephone, in letters, and on the Internet. They also attend scientific meetings where they share their ideas with one another in person.

Activity

On a sheet of paper, write out clear, detailed directions for tying your shoe. Then exchange directions with a partner. Follow your partner's directions exactly. How successful were you at tying your shoe? How could your partner have communicated more clearly?

Inquiry Skills

Classifying

Focus Encourage students to think of common things that are classified.

Teach Ask: **What things at home are classified?** *(Clothing might be classified in order to place it in the appropriate dresser drawer; glasses, plates, and silverware are grouped in different parts of the kitchen; screws, nuts, bolts, washers, and nails might be separated into small containers.)* **What are some things that scientists classify?** *(Scientists classify many things they study, including organisms, geological features and processes, and kinds of machines.)*

Activity

Some characteristics students might use include color, pattern of color, use of balls, and size. Students' criteria for classification should clearly divide the balls into two, and then three, distinct groups.

Making Models

Focus Ask: **What are some models you have used to study science?** *(Students might have used human anatomical models, solar system models, maps, or stream tables.)* **How have these models helped you?** *(Models can help you learn about things that are difficult to study because they are very large, very small, or highly complex.)*

Teach Be sure students understand that a model does not have to be three-dimensional. For example, a map is a model, as is a mathematical equation. Have students look at the photograph of the student modeling the causes of day and night on Earth. Ask: **What quality of each item makes this a good model?** *(The flashlight gives off light, and the ball is round and can be rotated by the student.)*

Activity

The flashlight represents the sun and the ball represents Earth.

Communicating

Focus Have students identify the methods of communication they have used today.

Teach Ask: **How is the way you communicate with a friend similar to and different from the way scientists communicate about their work to other scientists?** *(Both may communicate using various methods, but scientists must be very detailed and precise, whereas communication between friends may be less detailed and precise.)* Encourage students to communicate like a scientist as they carry out the activity.

Activity

Students' answers will vary but should identify a step-by-step process for tying a shoe. Help students identify communication errors such as leaving out a step, putting steps in the wrong order, or disregarding the person's handedness.

Making Measurements

Students can refer to this part of the Skills Handbook whenever they need to review how to make measurements with SI units. You can use the activities here to teach or reinforce SI units.

Measuring in SI

Focus Review SI units with students. Begin by providing metric rulers, graduated cylinders, balances, and Celsius thermometers. Use these tools to reinforce that the meter is the unit of length, the liter is the unit of volume, the gram is the unit of mass, and the degree Celsius is the unit of temperature.

Teach Ask: **If you want to measure the length and the width of the classroom, which SI unit would you use?** *(Meter)* **Which unit would you use to measure the amount of mass in your textbook?** *(Gram)* **Which would you use to measure how much water a drinking glass holds?** *(Liter)* **When would you use the Celsius scale?** *(To measure the temperature of something)* Then use the measuring equipment to review SI prefixes. For example, ask: **What are the smallest units on the metric ruler?** *(Millimeters)* **How many millimeters are there in one centimeter?** *(10 millimeters)* **How many in 10 centimeters?** *(100 millimeters)* **How many centimeters are there in one meter?** *(100 centimeters)* **What does 1,000 meters equal?** *(One kilometer)*

Activity

Length The length of the shell is 7.8 centimeters, or 78 millimeters. If students need more practice measuring length, have them use meter sticks and metric rulers to measure various objects in the classroom.

Activity

Liquid Volume The volume of water in the graduated cylinder is 62 milliliters. If students need more practice, have them use a graduated cylinder to measure different volumes of water.

SKILLS Handbook

Making Measurements

By measuring, scientists can express their observations more precisely and communicate more information about what they observe.

Measuring in SI

The standard system of measurement used by scientists around the world is known as the International System of Units, which is abbreviated as SI (**Système International d'Unités,** in French). SI units are easy to use because they are based on multiples of 10. Each unit is ten times larger than the next smallest unit and one tenth the size of the next largest unit. The table lists the prefixes used to name the most common SI units.

Common SI Prefixes		
Prefix	**Symbol**	**Meaning**
kilo-	k	1,000
hecto-	h	100
deka-	da	10
deci-	d	0.1 (one tenth)
centi-	c	0.01 (one hundredth)
milli-	m	0.001 (one thousandth)

Length To measure length, or the distance between two points, the unit of measure is the **meter (m).** The distance from the floor to a doorknob is approximately one meter. Long distances, such as the distance between two cities, are measured in kilometers (km). Small lengths are measured in centimeters (cm) or millimeters (mm). Scientists use metric rulers and meter sticks to measure length.

Common Conversions
1 km = 1,000 m
1 m = 100 cm
1 m = 1,000 mm
1 cm = 10 mm

Activity

The larger lines on the metric ruler in the picture show centimeter divisions, while the smaller, unnumbered lines show millimeter divisions. How many centimeters long is the shell? How many millimeters long is it?

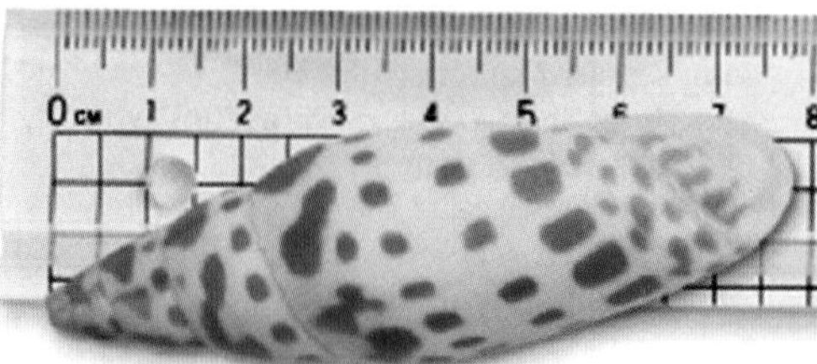

Liquid Volume To measure the volume of a liquid, or the amount of space it takes up, you will use a unit of measure known as the **liter (L).** One liter is the approximate volume of a medium-size carton of milk. Smaller volumes are measured in milliliters (mL). Scientists use graduated cylinders to measure liquid volume.

Activity

The graduated cylinder in the picture is marked in milliliter divisions. Notice that the water in the cylinder has a curved surface. This curved surface is called the *meniscus*. To measure the volume, you must read the level at the lowest point of the meniscus. What is the volume of water in this graduated cylinder?

Common Conversion
1 L = 1,000 mL

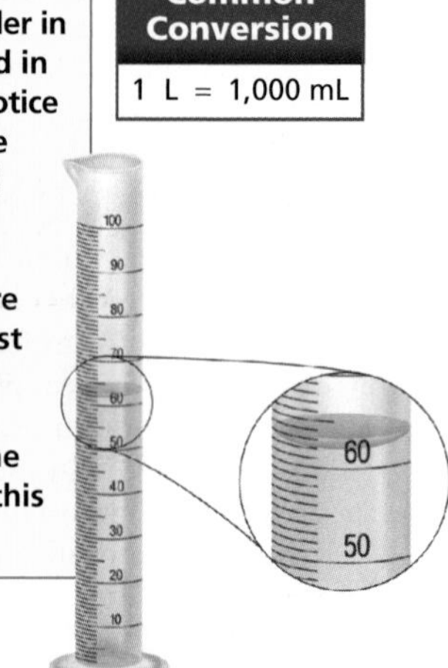

Mass To measure mass, or the amount of matter in an object, you will use a unit of measure known as the **gram (g).** One gram is approximately the mass of a paper clip. Larger masses are measured in kilograms (kg). Scientists use a balance to find the mass of an object.

Common Conversion
1 kg = 1,000 g

Activity

The mass of the potato in the picture is measured in kilograms. What is the mass of the potato? Suppose a recipe for potato salad called for one kilogram of potatoes. About how many potatoes would you need?

Temperature To measure the temperature of a substance, you will use the **Celsius scale.** Temperature is measured in degrees Celsius (°C) using a Celsius thermometer. Water freezes at 0°C and boils at 100°C.

Time The unit scientists use to measure time is the **second (s).**

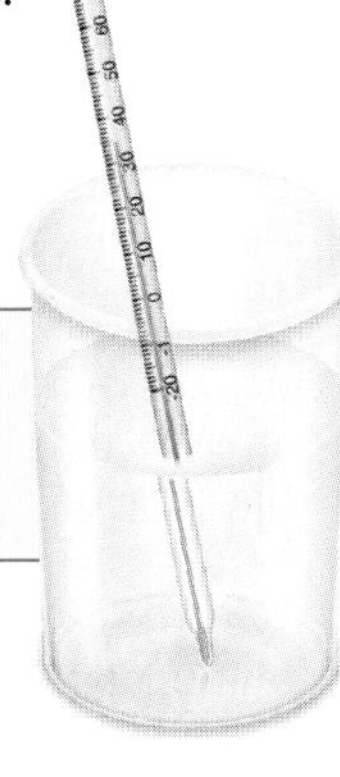

Activity

What is the temperature of the liquid in degrees Celsius?

Converting SI Units

To use the SI system, you must know how to convert between units. Converting from one unit to another involves the skill of **calculating,** or using mathematical operations. Converting between SI units is similar to converting between dollars and dimes because both systems are based on multiples of ten.

Suppose you want to convert a length of 80 centimeters to meters. Follow these steps to convert between units.

1. Begin by writing down the measurement you want to convert—in this example, 80 centimeters.
2. Write a conversion factor that represents the relationship between the two units you are converting. In this example, the relationship is 1 meter = 100 centimeters. Write this conversion factor as a fraction, making sure to place the units you are converting from (centimeters, in this example) in the denominator.
3. Multiply the measurement you want to convert by the fraction. When you do this, the units in the first measurement will cancel out with the units in the denominator. Your answer will be in the units you are converting to (meters, in this example).

Example

80 centimeters = ■ meters

$$80 \text{ centimeters} \times \frac{1 \text{ meter}}{100 \text{ centimeters}} = \frac{80 \text{ meters}}{100}$$

$$= 0.8 \text{ meters}$$

Activity

Convert between the following units.

1. 600 millimeters = ■ meters
2. 0.35 liters = ■ milliliters
3. 1,050 grams = ■ kilograms

Activity

Mass The mass of the potato is 0.25 kilograms. You would need 4 potatoes to make one kilogram. If students need more practice, give them various objects, such as coins, paper clips, and books, to measure mass.

Activity

Temperature The temperature of the liquid is 35°C. Students who need more practice can measure the temperatures of various water samples.

Converting SI Units

Focus Review the steps for converting SI units, and work through the example with students.

Teach Ask: **How many millimeters are in 80 centimeters?** *(With the relationship 10 millimeters = 1 centimeter, students should follow the steps to calculate that 80 centimeters is equal to 800 millimeters.)* Have students do the conversion problems in the activity.

Activity

1. *600 millimeters = 0.6 meters*
2. *0.35 liters = 350 milliliters*
3. *1,050 grams = 1.05 kilograms*

If students need more practice converting SI units, have them make up conversion problems to trade with partners.

Conducting a Scientific Investigation

Students can refer to this part of the Skills Handbook whenever they need to review the steps of a scientific investigation. You can use the activities here to teach or reinforce these steps.

Posing Questions

Focus Ask: **What do you do when you want to learn about something?** *(Answers might include asking questions about it or looking for information in books or on the Internet.)* Explain that scientists go through the same process to learn about something.

Teach Tell students that the questions scientists ask may have no answers or many different answers. To answer their questions, scientists often conduct experiments. Ask: **Why is a scientific question important to a scientific investigation?** *(It helps the scientist decide if an experiment is necessary; the answer might already be known. It also helps focus the idea so that the scientist can form a hypothesis.)* **What is the scientific question in the activity on the next page?** *(Is a ball's bounce affected by the height from which it is dropped?)*

Developing a Hypothesis

Focus Emphasize that a hypothesis is one possible explanation for a set of observations. It is *not* a guess. It is often based on an inference.

Teach Ask: **On what information do scientists base their hypotheses?** *(Their observations and previous knowledge or experience)* Point out that a hypothesis does not always turn out to be correct. Ask: **When a hypothesis turns out to be incorrect, do you think the scientist wasted his or her time? Explain.** *(No. The scientist learned from the investigation and will develop another hypothesis that could prove to be correct.)*

Designing an Experiment

Focus Have a volunteer read the Experimental Procedure in the box. Invite students to identify the manipulated variable *(amount of salt)*, the variables kept constant *(amount and temperature of water, location of containers)*, the control *(Container 3)*, and the responding variable *(time required for the water to freeze)*.

Conducting a Scientific Investigation

In some ways, scientists are like detectives, piecing together clues to learn about a process or event. One way that scientists gather clues is by carrying out experiments. An experiment tests an idea in a careful, orderly manner. Although experiments do not all follow the same steps in the same order, many follow a pattern similar to the one described here.

Posing Questions

Experiments begin by asking a scientific question. A scientific question is one that can be answered by gathering evidence. For example, the question "Which freezes faster—fresh water or salt water?" is a scientific question because you can carry out an investigation and gather information to answer the question.

Developing a Hypothesis

The next step is to form a hypothesis. A **hypothesis** is a possible explanation for a set of observations or answer to a scientific question. In science, a hypothesis must be something that can be tested. A hypothesis can be worded as an *If . . . then . . .* statement. For example, a hypothesis might be *"If I add salt to fresh water, then the water will take longer to freeze."* A hypothesis worded this way serves as a rough outline of the experiment you should perform.

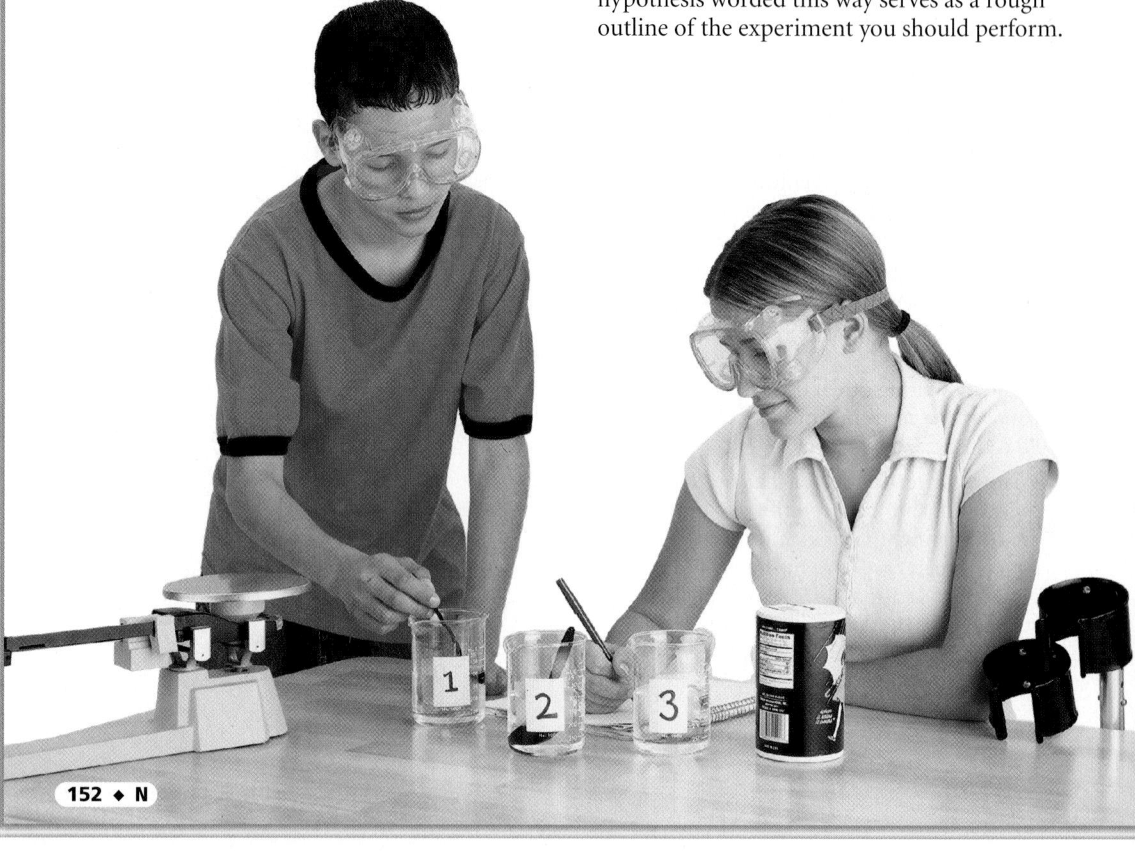

Teach Ask: **How might the experiment be affected if Container 1 had only 100 milliliters of water?** *(It wouldn't be an accurate comparison with the containers that have more water.)* Also make sure that students understand the importance of the control. Then, ask: **What operational definition is used in this experiment?** *("Frozen" means the time at which a wooden stick can no longer move in a container.)*

Designing an Experiment

Next you need to plan a way to test your hypothesis. Your plan should be written out as a step-by-step procedure and should describe the observations or measurements you will make.

Two important steps involved in designing an experiment are controlling variables and forming operational definitions.

Controlling Variables In a well-designed experiment, you need to keep all variables the same except for one. A **variable** is any factor that can change in an experiment. The factor that you change is called the **manipulated variable.** In this experiment, the manipulated variable is the amount of salt added to the water. Other factors, such as the amount of water or the starting temperature, are kept constant.

The factor that changes as a result of the manipulated variable is called the **responding variable.** The responding variable is what you measure or observe to obtain your results. In this experiment, the responding variable is how long the water takes to freeze.

An experiment in which all factors except one are kept constant is called a **controlled experiment.** Most controlled experiments include a test called the control. In this experiment, Container 3 is the control. Because no salt is added to Container 3, you can compare the results from the other containers to it. Any difference in results must be due to the addition of salt alone.

Forming Operational Definitions Another important aspect of a well-designed experiment is having clear operational definitions. An **operational definition** is a statement that describes how a particular variable is to be measured or how a term is to be defined. For example, in this experiment, how will you determine if the water has frozen? You might decide to insert a stick in each container at the start of the experiment. Your operational definition of "frozen" would be the time at which the stick can no longer move.

Experimental Procedure	
1.	Fill 3 containers with 300 milliliters of cold tap water.
2.	Add 10 grams of salt to Container 1; stir. Add 20 grams of salt to Container 2; stir. Add no salt to Container 3.
3.	Place the 3 containers in a freezer.
4.	Check the containers every 15 minutes. Record your observations.

Interpreting Data

The observations and measurements you make in an experiment are called **data.** At the end of an experiment, you need to analyze the data to look for any patterns or trends. Patterns often become clear if you organize your data in a data table or graph. Then think through what the data reveal. Do they support your hypothesis? Do they point out a flaw in your experiment? Do you need to collect more data?

Drawing Conclusions

A **conclusion** is a statement that sums up what you have learned from an experiment. When you draw a conclusion, you need to decide whether the data you collected support your hypothesis or not. You may need to repeat an experiment several times before you can draw any conclusions from it. Conclusions often lead you to pose new questions and plan new experiments to answer them.

Activity

Is a ball's bounce affected by the height from which it is dropped? Using the steps just described, plan a controlled experiment to investigate this problem.

Interpreting Data

Focus Ask: **What kind of data would you collect from the experiment with freezing salt water?** *(Time and state of the water)*

Teach Ask: **What if you forgot to record some data during an investigation?** *(You wouldn't be able to draw valid conclusions because some data are missing.)* Then, ask: **Why are data tables and graphs a good way to organize data?** *(They make it easier to record data accurately, as well as compare and analyze data.)* **What kind of data table and graph might you use for this experiment?** *(A table would have columns for each container with a row for each time interval in which the state of water is recorded. A bar graph would show the time elapsed until water froze for each container.)*

Drawing Conclusions

Focus Help students understand that a conclusion is not necessarily the end of a scientific investigation. A conclusion about one experiment may lead right into another experiment.

Teach Point out that in scientific investigations, a conclusion is a summary and explanation of the results of an experiment. For the Experimental Procedure described on this page, tell students to suppose that they obtained the following results: Container 1 froze in 45 minutes, Container 2 in 80 minutes, and Container 3 in 25 minutes. Ask: **What conclusions can you draw from this experiment?** *(Students might conclude that water takes longer to freeze as more salt is added to it. The hypothesis is supported, and the question of which freezes faster is answered—fresh water.)*

Activity

You might wish to have students work in pairs to plan the controlled experiment. Students should develop a hypothesis, such as, "If I increase the height from which a ball is dropped, then the height of its bounce will increase." They can test the hypothesis by dropping a ball from varying heights (the manipulated variable). All trials should be done with the same kind of ball and on the same surface (constants). For each trial, they should measure the height of the bounce (responding variable). After students have designed the experiment, provide rubber balls, and invite them to carry out the experiment so they can collect and interpret data and draw conclusions.

Technology Design Skills

Students can refer to this part of the Skills Handbook whenever they need to review the process of designing new technologies. You can use the activities here to teach or reinforce the steps in this process.

Identify a Need

Focus Solicit from students any situations in which they have thought that a tool, machine, or other object would be really helpful to them or others. Explain that this is the first step in the design of new products.

Teach Point out that identifying specific needs is very important to the design process. Ask: **If it was specified that the toy boat be wind-powered, how might that affect the design?** *(The boat would likely be designed with sails.)*

Research the Problem

Focus Explain that research focuses the problem so that the design is more specific.

Teach Ask: **What might happen if you didn't research the problem before designing the solution?** *(Answers include developing a design that has already been found to fail, using materials that aren't the best, or designing a solution that already exists.)* **What would you research before designing your toy boat?** *(Students might research designs and materials.)*

Design a Solution

Focus Emphasize the importance of a design team. Ask: **Why are brainstorming sessions important in product design?** *(A group will propose more new ideas than one person.)*

Teach Divide the class into teams to design the toy boat. Instruct them to brainstorm design ideas. Then, ask: **Why do you think engineers evaluate constraints after brainstorming?** *(Evaluating constraints while brainstorming often stops the flow of new ideas.)* **What design constraints do you have for your toy boat?** *(Materials must be readily available and teacher-approved. The boat must be 15 centimeters or less in length and must travel 2 meters in a straight line carrying a load of 20 pennies)*

Technology Design Skills

Engineers are people who use scientific and technological knowledge to solve practical problems. To design new products, engineers usually follow the process described here, even though they may not follow these steps in the exact order. As you read the steps, think about how you might apply them in technology labs.

Identify a Need

Before engineers begin designing a new product, they must first identify the need they are trying to meet. For example, suppose you are a member of a design team in a company that makes toys. Your team has identified a need: a toy boat that is inexpensive and easy to assemble.

Research the Problem

Engineers often begin by gathering information that will help them with their new design. This research may include finding articles in books, magazines, or on the Internet. It may also include talking to other engineers who have solved similar problems. Engineers often perform experiments related to the product they want to design.

For your toy boat, you could look at toys that are similar to the one you want to design. You might do research on the Internet. You could also test some materials to see whether they will work well in a toy boat.

Drawing for a boat design ▼

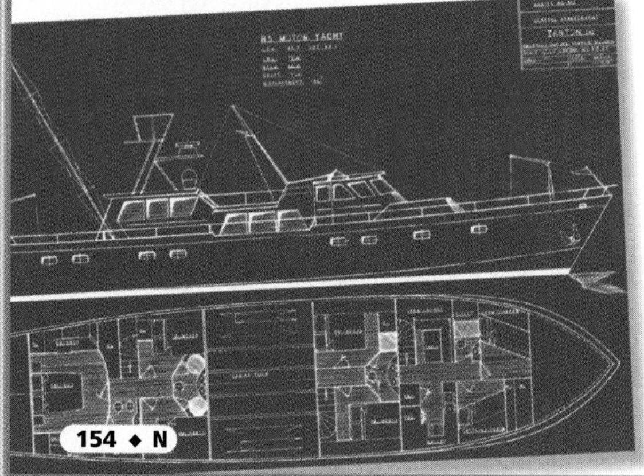

Design a Solution

Research gives engineers information that helps them design a product. When engineers design new products, they usually work in teams.

Generating Ideas Often design teams hold brainstorming meetings in which any team member can contribute ideas. **Brainstorming** is a creative process in which one team member's suggestions often spark ideas in other group members. Brainstorming can lead to new approaches to solving a design problem.

Evaluating Constraints During brainstorming, a design team will often come up with several possible designs. The team must then evaluate each one.

As part of their evaluation, engineers consider constraints. **Constraints** are factors that limit or restrict a product design. Physical characteristics, such as the properties of materials used to make your toy boat, are constraints. Money and time are also constraints. If the materials in a product cost a lot, or if the product takes a long time to make, the design may be impractical.

Making Trade-offs Design teams usually need to make trade-offs. In a **trade-off,** engineers give up one benefit of a proposed design in order to obtain another. In designing your toy boat, you will have to make trade-offs. For example, suppose one material is sturdy but not fully waterproof. Another material is more waterproof, but breakable. You may decide to give up the benefit of sturdiness in order to obtain the benefit of waterproofing.

Build and Evaluate a Prototype

Once the team has chosen a design plan, the engineers build a prototype of the product. A **prototype** is a working model used to test a design. Engineers evaluate the prototype to see whether it works well, is easy to operate, is safe to use, and holds up to repeated use.

Think of your toy boat. What would the prototype be like? Of what materials would it be made? How would you test it?

Troubleshoot and Redesign

Few prototypes work perfectly, which is why they need to be tested. Once a design team has tested a prototype, the members analyze the results and identify any problems. The team then tries to **troubleshoot,** or fix the design problems. For example, if your toy boat leaks or wobbles, the boat should be redesigned to eliminate those problems.

Communicate the Solution

A team needs to communicate the final design to the people who will manufacture and use the product. To do this, teams may use sketches, detailed drawings, computer simulations, and word descriptions.

Activity

You can use the technology design process to design and build a toy boat.

Research and Investigate

1. Visit the library or go online to research toy boats.
2. Investigate how a toy boat can be powered, including wind, rubber bands, or baking soda and vinegar.
3. Brainstorm materials, shapes, and steering for your boat.

Design and Build

4. Based on your research, design a toy boat that
   - is made of readily available materials
   - is no larger than 15 cm long and 10 cm wide
   - includes a power system, a rudder, and an area for cargo
   - travels 2 meters in a straight line carrying a load of 20 pennies
5. Sketch your design and write a step-by-step plan for building your boat. After your teacher approves your plan, build your boat.

Evaluate and Redesign

6. Test your boat, evaluate the results, and troubleshoot any problems.
7. Based on your evaluation, redesign your toy boat so it performs better.

Activity

The design possibilities are endless. Students might use small plastic containers, wood, foil, or plastic drinking cups for the boat. Materials may also include toothpicks, straws, or small wooden dowels. Brainstorm with students the different ways in which a toy boat can be propelled. The boats may be any shape, but must be no longer than 15 centimeters.

As student groups follow the steps in the design process, have them record their sources, brainstorming ideas, and prototype design in a logbook. Also give them time to troubleshoot and redesign their boats. When students turn in their boats, they should include assembly directions with a diagram, as well as instructions for use.

Build and Evaluate a Prototype

Focus Explain that building a prototype enables engineers to test design ideas.

Teach Relate building and testing a prototype to conducting an experiment. Explain that engineers set up controlled experiments to test the prototype. Ask: **Why do you think engineers set up controlled experiments?** *(From the data, they can determine which component of the design is working and which is failing.)* **How would you test your prototype of the toy boat?** *(Answers will vary depending on the toy boat's propulsion system.)*

Troubleshoot and Redesign

Focus Make sure students know what it means to troubleshoot. If necessary, give an example. One example is a stapler that isn't working. In that case, you would check to see if it is out of staples or if the staples are jammed. Then you would fix the problem and try stapling again. If it still didn't work, you might check the position of staples and try again.

Teach Explain that engineers often are not surprised if the prototype doesn't work. Ask: **Why isn't it a failure if the prototype doesn't work?** *(Engineers learn from the problems and make changes to address the problems. This process makes the design better.)* Emphasize that prototypes are completely tested before the product is made in the factory.

Communicate the Solution

Focus Inquire whether students have ever read the instruction manual that comes with a new toy or electronic device.

Teach Emphasize the importance of good communication in the design process. Ask: **What might happen if engineers did not communicate their design ideas clearly?** *(The product might not be manufactured correctly or used properly.)*

Creating Data Tables and Graphs

Students can refer to this part of the Skills Handbook whenever they need to review the skills required to create data tables and graphs. You can use the activities provided here to teach or reinforce these skills.

Data Tables

Focus Emphasize the importance of organizing data. Ask: **What might happen if you didn't use a data table for an experiment?** *(Possible answers include that data might not be collected or they might be forgotten.)*

Teach Have students create a data table to show how much time they spend on different activities during one week. Suggest that students first list the main activities they do every week. Then they should determine the amount of time they spend on each activity each day. Remind students to give the data table a title. A sample data table is shown below.

Bar Graphs

Focus Have students compare and contrast the data table and the bar graph on this page. Ask: **Why would you make a bar graph if the data are already organized in a table?** *(The bar graph organizes the data in a visual way that makes them easier to interpret.)*

Teach Students can use the data from the data table they created to make a bar graph that shows the amount of time they spend on different activities during a week. The vertical axis should be divided into units of time, such as hours. Remind students to label both axes and give their graph a title. A sample bar graph is shown below.

Creating Data Tables and Graphs

How can you make sense of the data in a science experiment? The first step is to organize the data to help you understand them. Data tables and graphs are helpful tools for organizing data.

Data Tables

You have gathered your materials and set up your experiment. But before you start, you need to plan a way to record what happens during the experiment. By creating a data table, you can record your observations and measurements in an orderly way.

Suppose, for example, that a scientist conducted an experiment to find out how many Calories people of different body masses burn while doing various activities. The data table shows the results.

Calories Burned in 30 Minutes

Body Mass	Experiment 1: Bicycling	Experiment 2: Playing Basketball	Experiment 3: Watching Television
30 kg	60 Calories	120 Calories	21 Calories
40 kg	77 Calories	164 Calories	27 Calories
50 kg	95 Calories	206 Calories	33 Calories
60 kg	114 Calories	248 Calories	38 Calories

Notice in this data table that the manipulated variable (body mass) is the heading of one column. The responding variable (for Experiment 1, the number of Calories burned while bicycling) is the heading of the next column. Additional columns were added for related experiments.

Bar Graphs

To compare how many Calories a person burns doing various activities, you could create a bar graph. A bar graph is used to display data in a number of separate, or distinct, categories. In this example, bicycling, playing basketball, and watching television are the three categories.

To create a bar graph, follow these steps.

1. On graph paper, draw a horizontal, or *x*-, axis and a vertical, or *y*-, axis.
2. Write the names of the categories to be graphed along the horizontal axis. Include an overall label for the axis as well.
3. Label the vertical axis with the name of the responding variable. Include units of measurement. Then create a scale along the axis by marking off equally spaced numbers that cover the range of the data collected.
4. For each category, draw a solid bar using the scale on the vertical axis to determine the height. Make all the bars the same width.
5. Add a title that describes the graph.

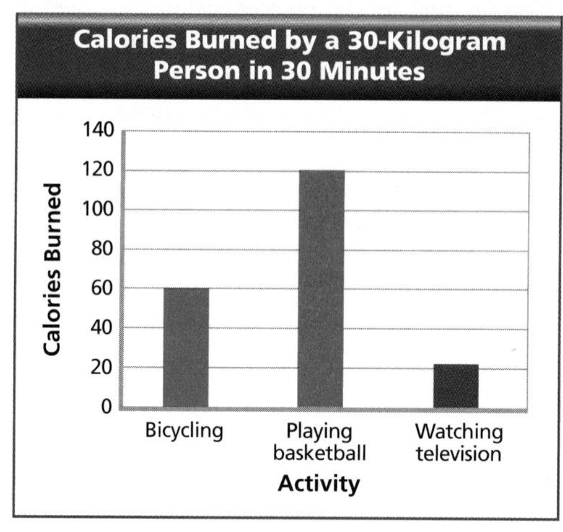

Time Spent on Different Activities in a Week

	Going to Classes	Eating Meals	Playing Soccer	Watching Television
Monday	6	2	2	0.5
Tuesday	6	1.5	1.5	1.5
Wednesday	6	2	1	2
Thursday	6	2	2	1.5
Friday	6	2	2	0.5
Saturday	0	2.5	2.5	1
Sunday	0	3	1	2

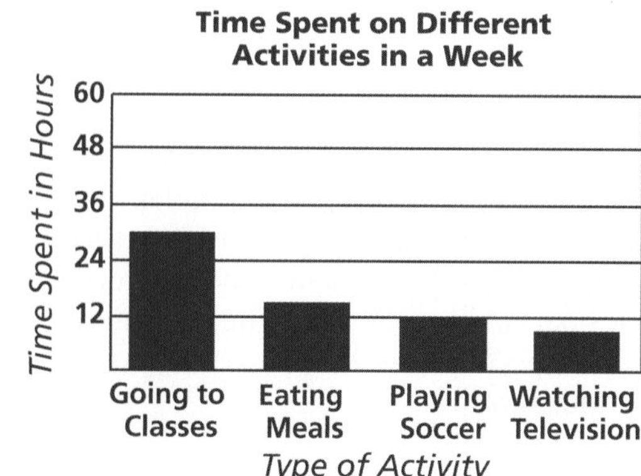

Line Graphs

To see whether a relationship exists between body mass and the number of Calories burned while bicycling, you could create a line graph. A line graph is used to display data that show how one variable (the responding variable) changes in response to another variable (the manipulated variable). You can use a line graph when your manipulated variable is **continuous,** that is, when there are other points between the ones that you tested. In this example, body mass is a continuous variable because there are other body masses between 30 and 40 kilograms (for example, 31 kilograms). Time is another example of a continuous variable.

Line graphs are powerful tools because they allow you to estimate values for conditions that you did not test in the experiment. For example, you can use the line graph to estimate that a 35-kilogram person would burn 68 Calories while bicycling.

To create a line graph, follow these steps.

1. On graph paper, draw a horizontal, or *x*-, axis and a vertical, or *y*-, axis.
2. Label the horizontal axis with the name of the manipulated variable. Label the vertical axis with the name of the responding variable. Include units of measurement.
3. Create a scale on each axis by marking off equally spaced numbers that cover the range of the data collected.
4. Plot a point on the graph for each piece of data. In the line graph above, the dotted lines show how to plot the first data point (30 kilograms and 60 Calories). Follow an imaginary vertical line extending up from the horizontal axis at the 30-kilogram mark. Then follow an imaginary horizontal line extending across from the vertical axis at the 60-Calorie mark. Plot the point where the two lines intersect.

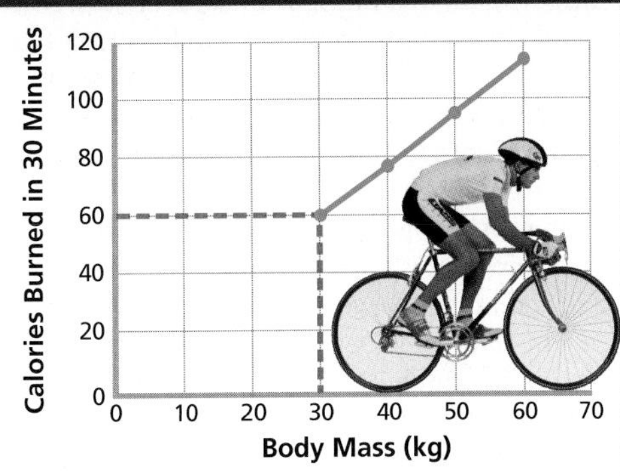

5. Connect the plotted points with a solid line. (In some cases, it may be more appropriate to draw a line that shows the general trend of the plotted points. In those cases, some of the points may fall above or below the line. Also, not all graphs are linear. It may be more appropriate to draw a curve to connect the points.)
6. Add a title that identifies the variables or relationship in the graph.

Activity

Create line graphs to display the data from Experiment 2 and Experiment 3 in the data table.

Activity

You read in the newspaper that a total of 4 centimeters of rain fell in your area in June, 2.5 centimeters fell in July, and 1.5 centimeters fell in August. What type of graph would you use to display these data? Use graph paper to create the graph.

Line Graphs

Focus Ask: **Would a bar graph show the relationship between body mass and the number of Calories burned in 30 minutes?** *(No. Bar graphs can only show data in distinct categories.)* Explain that line graphs are used to show how one variable changes in response to another variable.

Teach Walk students through the steps involved in creating a line graph using the example illustrated on the page. For example, ask: **What is the label on the horizontal axis? On the vertical axis?** *(Body Mass (kg); Calories Burned in 30 Minutes)* **What scale is used on each axis?** *(10 kg on the x-axis and 20 Calories on the y-axis)* **What does the second data point represent?** *(77 Calories burned for a body mass of 40 kg)* **What trend or pattern does the graph show?** *(The number of Calories burned in 30 minutes of cycling increases with body mass.)*

Activity

Students should make a different graph for each experiment. Each graph should have a different *x*-axis scale that is appropriate for the data. See sample graphs below.

Activity

Students should conclude that a bar graph would be best for displaying the data.

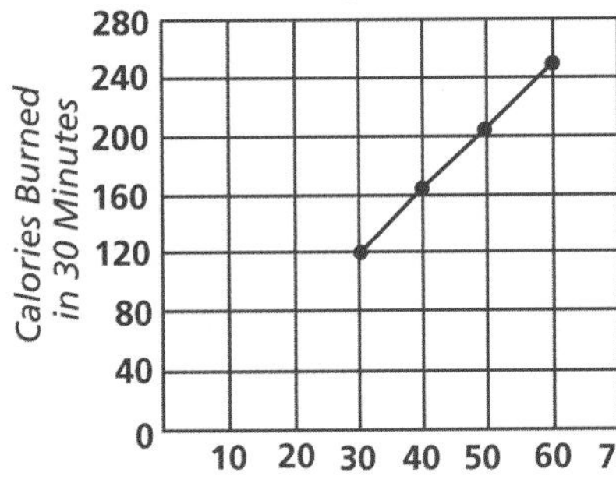

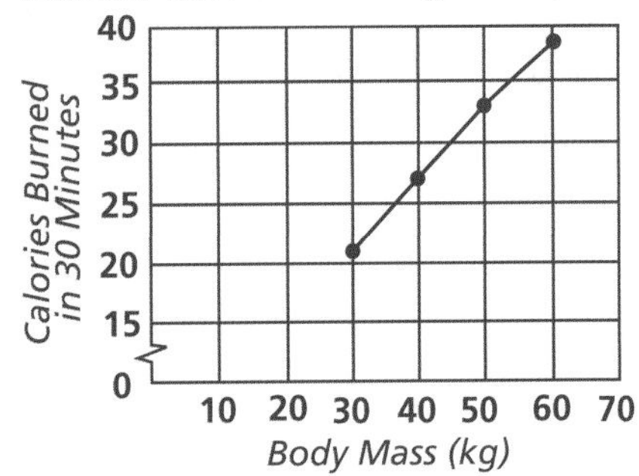

Circle Graphs

Focus Emphasize that a circle graph must include 100 percent of the categories for the topic being graphed. For example, ask: **Could the data in the bar graph titled "Calories Burned by a 30-kilogram Person in Various Activities" (on the previous page) be shown in a circle graph? Why or why not?** *(No. It does not include all the possible ways a 30-kilogram person can burn Calories.)*

Teach Walk students through the steps for making a circle graph. If necessary, help them with the compass and the protractor. Use the protractor to illustrate that a circle has 360 degrees. Make sure students understand the mathematical calculations involved in making a circle graph.

Activity

You might have students work in pairs to complete the activity. Students' circle graphs should look like the graph below.

Ways Students Get to School

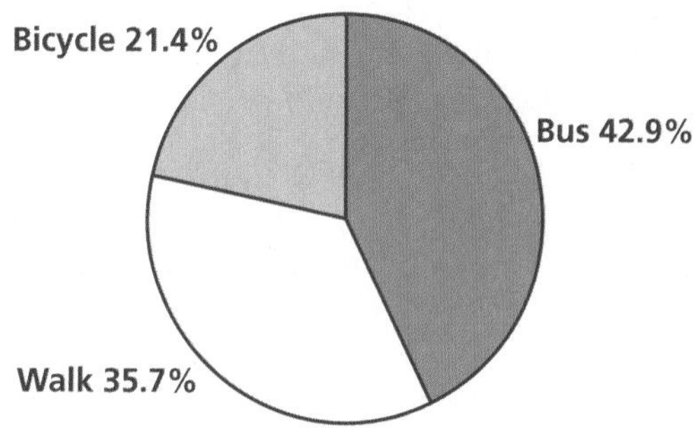

Circle Graphs

Like bar graphs, circle graphs can be used to display data in a number of separate categories. Unlike bar graphs, however, circle graphs can only be used when you have data for *all* the categories that make up a given topic. A circle graph is sometimes called a pie chart. The pie represents the entire topic, while the slices represent the individual categories. The size of a slice indicates what percentage of the whole a particular category makes up.

The data table below shows the results of a survey in which 24 teenagers were asked to identify their favorite sport. The data were then used to create the circle graph at the right.

Favorite Sports

Sport	Students
Soccer	8
Basketball	6
Bicycling	6
Swimming	4

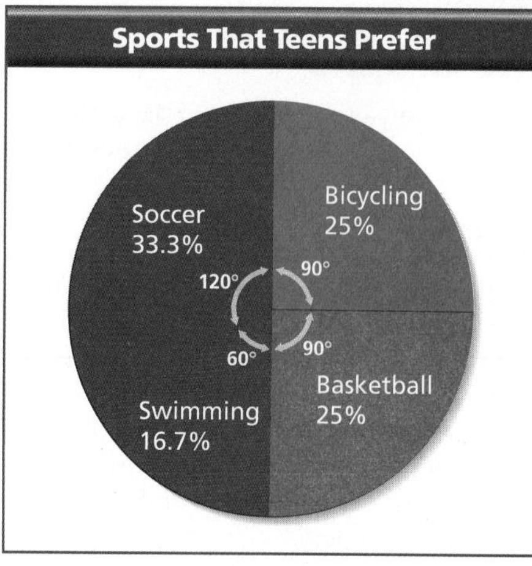

To create a circle graph, follow these steps.

1. Use a compass to draw a circle. Mark the center with a point. Then draw a line from the center point to the top of the circle.
2. Determine the size of each "slice" by setting up a proportion where x equals the number of degrees in a slice. (*Note:* A circle contains 360 degrees.) For example, to find the number of degrees in the "soccer" slice, set up the following proportion:

$$\frac{\text{Students who prefer soccer}}{\text{Total number of students}} = \frac{x}{\text{Total number of degrees in a circle}}$$

$$\frac{8}{24} = \frac{x}{360}$$

Cross-multiply and solve for x.

$$24x = 8 \times 360$$
$$x = 120$$

The "soccer" slice should contain 120 degrees.

3. Use a protractor to measure the angle of the first slice, using the line you drew to the top of the circle as the 0° line. Draw a line from the center of the circle to the edge for the angle you measured.
4. Continue around the circle by measuring the size of each slice with the protractor. Start measuring from the edge of the previous slice so the wedges do not overlap. When you are done, the entire circle should be filled in.
5. Determine the percentage of the whole circle that each slice represents. To do this, divide the number of degrees in a slice by the total number of degrees in a circle (360), and multiply by 100%. For the "soccer" slice, you can find the percentage as follows:

$$\frac{120}{360} \times 100\% = 33.3\%$$

6. Use a different color for each slice. Label each slice with the category and with the percentage of the whole it represents.
7. Add a title to the circle graph.

Activity

In a class of 28 students, 12 students take the bus to school, 10 students walk, and 6 students ride their bicycles. Create a circle graph to display these data.

Math Review

Scientists use math to organize, analyze, and present data. This appendix will help you review some basic math skills.

Mean, Median, and Mode

The **mean** is the average, or the sum of the data divided by the number of data items. The middle number in a set of ordered data is called the **median.** The **mode** is the number that appears most often in a set of data.

Example

A scientist counted the number of distinct songs sung by seven different male birds and collected the data shown below.

Male Bird Songs							
Bird	A	B	C	D	E	F	G
Number of Songs	36	29	40	35	28	36	27

To determine the mean number of songs, add the total number of songs and divide by the number of data items—in this case, the number of male birds.

$$\text{Mean} = \frac{231}{7} = 33 \text{ songs}$$

To find the median number of songs, arrange the data in numerical order and find the number in the middle of the series.

27 28 29 35 36 36 40

The number in the middle is 35, so the median number of songs is 35.

The mode is the value that appears most frequently. In the data, 36 appears twice, while each other item appears only once. Therefore, 36 songs is the mode.

Practice

Find out how many minutes it takes each student in your class to get to school. Then find the mean, median, and mode for the data.

Probability

Probability is the chance that an event will occur. Probability can be expressed as a ratio, a fraction, or a percentage. For example, when you flip a coin, the probability that the coin will land heads up is 1 in 2, or $\frac{1}{2}$, or 50 percent.

The probability that an event will happen can be expressed in the following formula.

$$P(\text{event}) = \frac{\text{Number of times the event can occur}}{\text{Total number of possible events}}$$

Example

A paper bag contains 25 blue marbles, 5 green marbles, 5 orange marbles, and 15 yellow marbles. If you close your eyes and pick a marble from the bag, what is the probability that it will be yellow?

$$P(\text{yellow marbles}) = \frac{\text{15 yellow marbles}}{\text{50 marbles total}}$$

$$P = \frac{15}{50}, \text{ or } \frac{3}{10}, \text{ or } 30\%$$

Practice

Each side of a cube has a letter on it. Two sides have *A*, three sides have *B*, and one side has *C*. If you roll the cube, what is the probability that *A* will land on top?

Math Skills

Math Review

Students can refer to this part of the Skills Handbook whenever they need to review some basic math skills. You can use the activities provided here to teach or reinforce these skills.

Mean, Median, and Mode

Focus Remind students that data from an experiment might consist of hundreds or thousands of numbers. Unless analyzed, the numbers likely will not be helpful.

Teach Work through the process of determining mean, median, and mode using the example in the book. Make sure students realize that these three numbers do not always equal each other. Point out that taken together, these three numbers give more information about the data than just one of the numbers alone.

Practice

Answers will vary based on class data. The mean should equal the total number of minutes divided by the number of students. The median should equal the number in the middle after arranging the data in numerical order. The mode should equal the number of minutes that is given most frequently.

Probability

Focus Show students a coin and ask: **What is the chance that I will get tails when I flip the coin?** *(Some students might know that there is a 1 in 2, or 50 percent, chance of getting tails.)*

Teach Set up a bag of marbles like the one in the example. Allow students to practice determining the probabilities of picking marbles of different colors. Then, encourage them to actually pick marbles and compare their actual results with those results predicted by probability.

Practice

$P(A) = 2$ sides with $\frac{A}{6}$ sides total

$P = \frac{2}{6}$, or $\frac{1}{3}$, or 33%

Area

Focus Ask: **Who knows what area is?** *(Area is equal to the number of square units needed to cover a certain shape or object.)* On the board, write the formulas for the area of a rectangle and a circle.

Teach Give students various objects of different shapes. Have them measure each object and determine its area based on the measurements. Point out that the units of the answer are squared because they are multiplied together. If students are interested, you might also explain that π is equal to the ratio of the circumference of a circle to its diameter. For circles of all sizes, π is approximately equal to the number 3.14, or $\frac{22}{7}$.

Practice

The area of the circle is equal to 21 m × 21 m × $\frac{22}{7}$, or 1,386 m^2.

Circumference

Focus Draw a circle on the board. Then trace the outline with your finger and explain that this is the circumference of the circle, or the distance around it.

Teach Show students that the radius is equal to the distance from the center of the circle to any point on it. Point out that the diameter of a circle is equal to two times the radius. Give students paper circles of various sizes, and have them calculate the circumference of each.

Practice

The circumference is equal to 2 × 28 m × $\frac{22}{7}$, or 176 m.

Volume

Focus Fill a beaker with 100 milliliters of water. Ask: **What is the volume of water?** *(100 milliliters)* Explain that volume is the amount of space that something takes up. Then point out that one milliliter is equal to one cubic centimeter (cm^3).

Teach Write on the board the formulas for calculating the volumes of a rectangle and a cylinder. Point out that volume is equal to the area of an object multiplied by its height. Then measure the beaker to show students the relationship between liquid volume (100 milliliters) and the number of cubic units it contains (100 cubic centimeters).

Area

The **area** of a surface is the number of square units that cover it. The front cover of your textbook has an area of about 600 cm^2.

Area of a Rectangle and a Square To find the area of a rectangle, multiply its length times its width. The formula for the area of a rectangle is

$$A = \ell \times w, \text{ or } A = \ell w$$

Since all four sides of a square have the same length, the area of a square is the length of one side multiplied by itself, or squared.

$$A = s \times s, \text{ or } A = s^2$$

Example

A scientist is studying the plants in a field that measures 75 m × 45 m. What is the area of the field?

$A = \ell \times w$

$A = 75 \text{ m} \times 45 \text{ m}$

$A = 3{,}375 \text{ m}^2$

Area of a Circle The formula for the area of a circle is

$$A = \pi \times r \times r, \text{ or } A = \pi r^2$$

The length of the radius is represented by *r*, and the value of π is approximately $\frac{22}{7}$.

Example

Find the area of a circle with a radius of 14 cm.

$A = \pi r^2$

$A = 14 \times 14 \times \frac{22}{7}$

$A = 616 \text{ cm}^2$

Practice

Find the area of a circle that has a radius of 21 m.

Circumference

The distance around a circle is called the circumference. The formula for finding the circumference of a circle is

$$C = 2 \times \pi \times r, \text{ or } C = 2\pi r$$

Example

The radius of a circle is 35 cm. What is its circumference?

$C = 2\pi r$

$C = 2 \times 35 \times \frac{22}{7}$

$C = 220 \text{ cm}$

Practice

What is the circumference of a circle with a radius of 28 m?

Volume

The volume of an object is the number of cubic units it contains. The volume of a wastebasket, for example, might be about 26,000 cm^3.

Volume of a Rectangular Object To find the volume of a rectangular object, multiply the object's length times its width times its height.

$$V = \ell \times w \times h, \text{ or } V = \ell wh$$

Example

Find the volume of a box with length 24 cm, width 12 cm, and height 9 cm.

$V = \ell wh$

$V = 24 \text{ cm} \times 12 \text{ cm} \times 9 \text{ cm}$

$V = 2{,}592 \text{ cm}^3$

Practice

What is the volume of a rectangular object with length 17 cm, width 11 cm, and height 6 cm?

Practice

The volume of the rectangular object is equal to 17 cm × 11 cm × 6 cm, or 1,122 cm^3.

Fractions

A **fraction** is a way to express a part of a whole. In the fraction $\frac{4}{7}$, 4 is the numerator and 7 is the denominator.

Adding and Subtracting Fractions To add or subtract two or more fractions that have a common denominator, first add or subtract the numerators. Then write the sum or difference over the common denominator.

To find the sum or difference of fractions with different denominators, first find the least common multiple of the denominators. This is known as the least common denominator. Then convert each fraction to equivalent fractions with the least common denominator. Add or subtract the numerators. Then write the sum or difference over the common denominator.

Example

$$\frac{5}{6} - \frac{3}{4} = \frac{10}{12} - \frac{9}{12} = \frac{10-9}{12} = \frac{1}{12}$$

Multiplying Fractions To multiply two fractions, first multiply the two numerators, then multiply the two denominators.

Example

$$\frac{5}{6} \times \frac{2}{3} = \frac{5 \times 2}{6 \times 3} = \frac{10}{18} = \frac{5}{9}$$

Dividing Fractions Dividing by a fraction is the same as multiplying by its reciprocal. Reciprocals are numbers whose numerators and denominators have been switched. To divide one fraction by another, first invert the fraction you are dividing by—in other words, turn it upside down. Then multiply the two fractions.

Example

$$\frac{2}{5} \div \frac{7}{8} = \frac{2}{5} \times \frac{8}{7} = \frac{2 \times 8}{5 \times 7} = \frac{16}{35}$$

Practice

Solve the following: $\frac{3}{7} \div \frac{4}{5}$.

Decimals

Fractions whose denominators are 10, 100, or some other power of 10 are often expressed as decimals. For example, the fraction $\frac{9}{10}$ can be expressed as the decimal 0.9, and the fraction $\frac{7}{100}$ can be written as 0.07.

Adding and Subtracting With Decimals To add or subtract decimals, line up the decimal points before you carry out the operation.

Example

$$\begin{array}{r} 27.4 \\ +\ 6.19 \\ \hline 33.59 \end{array} \qquad \begin{array}{r} 278.635 \\ -\ 191.4 \\ \hline 87.235 \end{array}$$

Multiplying With Decimals When you multiply two numbers with decimals, the number of decimal places in the product is equal to the total number of decimal places in each number being multiplied.

Example

46.2 (one decimal place)
× 2.37 (two decimal places)
109.494 (three decimal places)

Dividing With Decimals To divide a decimal by a whole number, put the decimal point in the quotient above the decimal point in the dividend.

Example

$15.5 \div 5$

$$\begin{array}{r} 3.1 \\ 5\overline{)15.5} \end{array}$$

To divide a decimal by a decimal, you need to rewrite the divisor as a whole number. Do this by multiplying both the divisor and dividend by the same multiple of 10.

Example

$1.68 \div 4.2 = 16.8 \div 42$

$$\begin{array}{r} 0.4 \\ 42\overline{)16.8} \end{array}$$

Practice

Multiply 6.21 by 8.5.

Math Skills

Fractions

Focus Draw a circle on the board, and divide it into eight equal sections. Shade in one of the sections, and explain that one out of eight, or one eighth, of the sections is shaded. Also use the circle to show that four eighths is the same as one half.

Teach Write the fraction $\frac{3}{4}$ on the board. Ask: **What is the numerator?** *(Three)* **What is the denominator?** *(Four)* Emphasize that when adding and subtracting fractions, the denominators of the two fractions must be the same. If necessary, review how to find the least common denominator. Remind students that when multiplying and dividing, the denominators do not have to be the same.

Practice

$$\frac{3}{7} \div \frac{4}{5} = \frac{3}{7} \times \frac{5}{4} = \frac{15}{28}$$

Decimals

Focus Write the number *129.835* on the board. Ask: **What number is in the ones position?** *(9)* **The tenths position?** *(8)* **The hundredths position?** *(3)* Make sure students know that 0.8 is equal to $\frac{8}{10}$ and 0.03 is equal to $\frac{3}{100}$.

Teach Use the examples in the book to review addition, subtraction, multiplication, and division with decimals. Make up a worksheet of similar problems to give students additional practice. Also show students how a fraction is converted to a decimal by dividing the numerator by the denominator. For example, $\frac{1}{2}$ is equal to 0.5.

Practice

$6.21 \times 8.5 = 52.785$

Ratio and Proportion

Focus Differentiate a ratio from a fraction. Remind students that a fraction tells how many parts of the whole. In contrast, a ratio compares two different numbers. For example, $\frac{12}{22}$, or $\frac{6}{11}$, of a class are girls. But the ratio of boys to girls in the class is 10 to 12, or $\frac{5}{6}$.

Teach Use the example in the book to explain how to use a proportion to find an unknown quantity. Provide students with additional practice problems, if needed.

Practice

$6 \times 49 = 7x$
$294 = 7x$
$294 \div 7 = x$
$x = 42$

Percentage

Focus On the board, write $50\% = \frac{50}{100}$. Explain that a percentage is a ratio that compares a number to 100.

Teach Point out that when calculating percentages, you are usually using numbers other than 100. In this case, you set up a proportion. Go over the example in the book. Emphasize that the number representing the total goes on the bottom of the ratio, as does the 100%.

Practice

Students should set up the proportion

$$\frac{42 \text{ marbles}}{300 \text{ marbles}} = \frac{x\%}{100\%}$$

$42 \times 100 = 300x$

$4200 = 300x$

$4200 \div 300 = 14\%$

Ratio and Proportion

A **ratio** compares two numbers by division. For example, suppose a scientist counts 800 wolves and 1,200 moose on an island. The ratio of wolves to moose can be written as a fraction, $\frac{800}{1,200}$, which can be reduced to $\frac{2}{3}$. The same ratio can also be expressed as 2 to 3 or 2 : 3.

A **proportion** is a mathematical sentence saying that two ratios are equivalent. For example, a proportion could state that $\frac{800 \text{ wolves}}{1,200 \text{ moose}} = \frac{2 \text{ wolves}}{3 \text{ moose}}$. You can sometimes set up a proportion to determine or estimate an unknown quantity. For example, suppose a scientist counts 25 beetles in an area of 10 square meters. The scientist wants to estimate the number of beetles in 100 square meters.

Example

1. Express the relationship between beetles and area as a ratio: $\frac{25}{10}$, simplified to $\frac{5}{2}$.
2. Set up a proportion, with x representing the number of beetles. The proportion can be stated as $\frac{5}{2} = \frac{x}{100}$.
3. Begin by cross-multiplying. In other words, multiply each fraction's numerator by the other fraction's denominator.

   $5 \times 100 = 2 \times x$, or $500 = 2x$
4. To find the value of x, divide both sides by 2. The result is 250, or 250 beetles in 100 square meters.

Practice

Find the value of x in the following proportion: $\frac{6}{7} = \frac{x}{49}$.

Percentage

A **percentage** is a ratio that compares a number to 100. For example, there are 37 granite rocks in a collection that consists of 100 rocks. The ratio $\frac{37}{100}$ can be written as 37%. Granite rocks make up 37% of the rock collection.

You can calculate percentages of numbers other than 100 by setting up a proportion.

Example

Rain falls on 9 days out of 30 in June. What percentage of the days in June were rainy?

$$\frac{9 \text{ days}}{30 \text{ days}} = \frac{d\%}{100\%}$$

To find the value of d, begin by cross-multiplying, as for any proportion:

$9 \times 100 = 30 \times d \qquad d = \frac{900}{30} \qquad d = 30$

Practice

There are 300 marbles in a jar, and 42 of those marbles are blue. What percentage of the marbles are blue?

Significant Figures

The **precision** of a measurement depends on the instrument you use to take the measurement. For example, if the smallest unit on the ruler is millimeters, then the most precise measurement you can make will be in millimeters.

The sum or difference of measurements can only be as precise as the least precise measurement being added or subtracted. Round your answer so that it has the same number of digits after the decimal as the least precise measurement. Round up if the last digit is 5 or more, and round down if the last digit is 4 or less.

Example

Subtract a temperature of 5.2°C from the temperature 75.46°C.

$$75.46 - 5.2 = 70.26$$

5.2 has the fewest digits after the decimal, so it is the least precise measurement. Since the last digit of the answer is 6, round up to 3. The most precise difference between the measurements is 70.3°C.

Practice

Add 26.4 m to 8.37 m. Round your answer according to the precision of the measurements.

Significant figures are the number of nonzero digits in a measurement. Zeroes between nonzero digits are also significant. For example, the measurements 12,500 L, 0.125 cm, and 2.05 kg all have three significant figures. When you multiply and divide measurements, the one with the fewest significant figures determines the number of significant figures in your answer.

Example

Multiply 110 g by 5.75 g.

$$110 \times 5.75 = 632.5$$

Because 110 has only two significant figures, round the answer to 630 g.

Scientific Notation

A **factor** is a number that divides into another number with no remainder. In the example, the number 3 is used as a factor four times.

An **exponent** tells how many times a number is used as a factor. For example, $3 \times 3 \times 3 \times 3$ can be written as 3^4. The exponent ^{4} indicates that the number 3 is used as a factor four times. Another way of expressing this is to say that 81 is equal to 3 to the fourth power.

Example

$$3^4 = 3 \times 3 \times 3 \times 3 = 81$$

Scientific notation uses exponents and powers of ten to write very large or very small numbers in shorter form. When you write a number in scientific notation, you write the number as two factors. The first factor is any number between 1 and 10. The second factor is a power of 10, such as 10^3 or 10^6.

Example

The average distance between the planet Mercury and the sun is 58,000,000 km. To write the first factor in scientific notation, insert a decimal point in the original number so that you have a number between 1 and 10. In the case of 58,000,000, the number is 5.8.

To determine the power of 10, count the number of places that the decimal point moved. In this case, it moved 7 places.

$$58{,}000{,}000 \text{ km} = 5.8 \times 10^7 \text{ km}$$

Practice

Express 6,590,000 in scientific notation.

Significant Figures

Focus Measure the length of a paper clip using two different rulers. Use one ruler that is less precise than the other. Compare the two measurements. Ask: **Which measurement is more precise?** *(The ruler with the smallest units will give the more precise measurement.)*

Teach Give students the opportunity to take measurements of an object using tools with different precision. Encourage students to add and subtract their measurements, making sure that they round the answers to reflect the precision of the instruments. Go over the example for significant digits. Check for understanding by asking: **How many significant digits are in the number 324,000?** *(Three)* **In the number 5, 901?** *(Four)* **In the number 0.706?** *(Three)* If students need additional practice, create a worksheet with problems in multiplying and dividing numbers with various significant digits.

Practice

26.4 m + 8.37 m = 34.77 m
This answer should be rounded to 34.8 m because the least precise measurement has only one digit after the decimal. This number is rounded up to 8 because the last digit is more than 5.

Scientific Notation

Focus Write a very large number on the board, such as 100 million, using all the zeros. Then, write the number using scientific notation. Ask: **Why do you think scientists prefer to write very large numbers using scientific notation?** *(Possible answers include that it is easier to do calculations, convert units, and make comparisons with other numbers.)*

Teach Go over the examples, and ask: **In the second example, which numbers are the factors?** *(5.8 and 10^7)* **Which number is the exponent?** *(^{7})* Explain that very small numbers have a negative exponent because the decimal point is moved to the right to produce the first factor. For example, 0.00000628 is equal to 6.28×10^{-6}.

Practice

$6{,}590{,}000 = 6.59 \times 10^6$

Reading Comprehension Skills

Students can refer to this part of the Skills Handbook whenever they need to review a reading skill. You can use the activities provided here to teach or reinforce these skills.

All in One Teaching Resources

- Target Reading Skills Handbook

Using Prior Knowledge

Focus Explain to students that using prior knowledge helps connect what they already know to what they are about to read.

Teach Point out that prior knowledge might not be accurate because memories have faded or perspectives have changed. Encourage students to ask questions to resolve discrepancies between their prior knowledge and what they have learned.

Asking Questions

Focus Demonstrate to students how to change a text heading into a question to help them anticipate the concepts, facts, and events they will read about.

Teach Encourage students to use this reading skill for the next section they read. Instruct them to turn the text headings into questions. Also challenge students to write at least four *what, how, why, who, when,* or *where* questions. Then, have students evaluate the skill. Ask: **Did asking questions about the text help you focus on the reading and remember what you read?** *(Answers will vary, but encourage honesty.)* If this reading skill didn't help, challenge them to assess why not.

Previewing Visuals

Focus Explain to students that looking at the visuals before reading will help them activate prior knowledge and predict what they are about to read.

Teach Assign a section for students to preview the visuals. First, instruct them to write a sentence describing what the section will be about. Then, encourage them to write one or two questions for each visual to give purpose to their reading. Also have them list any prior knowledge about the subject.

Reading Comprehension Skills

Each section in your textbook introduces a Target Reading Skill. You will improve your reading comprehension by using the Target Reading Skills described below.

Using Prior Knowledge

Your prior knowledge is what you already know before you begin to read about a topic. Building on what you already know gives you a head start on learning new information. Before you begin a new assignment, think about what you know. You might look at the headings and the visuals to spark your memory. You can list what you know. Then, as you read, consider questions like these.

- How does what you learn relate to what you know?
- How did something you already know help you learn something new?
- Did your original ideas agree with what you have just learned?

Asking Questions

Asking yourself questions is an excellent way to focus on and remember new information in your textbook. For example, you can turn the text headings into questions. Then your questions can guide you to identify the important information as you read. Look at these examples:

Heading: Using Seismographic Data

Question: How are seismographic data used?

Heading: Kinds of Faults

Question: What are the kinds of faults?

You do not have to limit your questions to text headings. Ask questions about anything that you need to clarify or that will help you understand the content. *What* and *how* are probably the most common question words, but you may also ask *why, who, when,* or *where* questions.

Previewing Visuals

Visuals are photographs, graphs, tables, diagrams, and illustrations. Visuals contain important information. Before you read, look at visuals and their labels and captions. This preview will help you prepare for what you will be reading.

Often you will be asked what you want to learn about a visual. For example, after you look at the normal fault diagram below, you might ask: What is the movement along a normal fault? Questions about visuals give you a purpose for reading—to answer your questions.

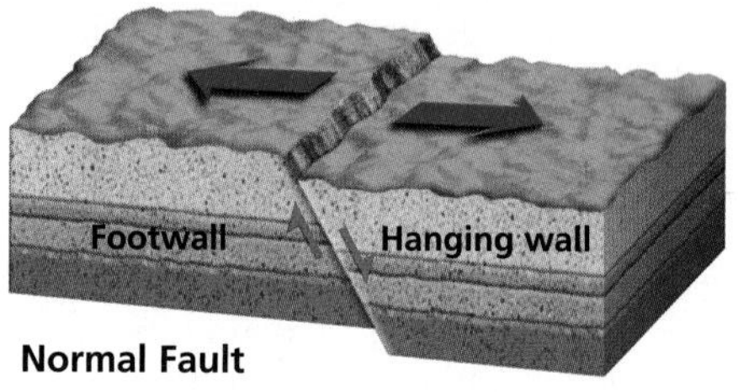

Normal Fault

Outlining

An outline shows the relationship between main ideas and supporting ideas. An outline has a formal structure. You write the main ideas, called topics, next to Roman numerals. The supporting ideas, called subtopics, are written under the main ideas and labeled A, B, C, and so on. An outline looks like this:

Technology and Society

I. Technology through history

II. The impact of technology on society

A.

B.

164 ♦ N

Outlining

Focus Explain that using an outline format helps organize information by main topic, subtopic, and details.

Teach Choose a section in the book, and demonstrate how to make an outline for it. Make sure students understand the structure of the outline by asking: **Is this a topic or a subtopic? Where does this information go in the outline? Would I write this heading next to a Roman numeral or a capital letter?** *(Answers depend on the section being outlined.)* Also show them how to indent and add details to the outline using numerals and lowercase letters.

Identifying Main Ideas

When you are reading science material, it is important to try to understand the ideas and concepts that are in a passage. Each paragraph has a lot of information and detail. Good readers try to identify the most important—or biggest—idea in every paragraph or section. That's the main idea. The other information in the paragraph supports or further explains the main idea.

Sometimes main ideas are stated directly. In this book, some main ideas are identified for you as key concepts. These are printed in boldface type. However, you must identify other main ideas yourself. In order to do this, you must identify all the ideas within a paragraph or section. Then ask yourself which idea is big enough to include all the other ideas.

Comparing and Contrasting

When you compare and contrast, you examine the similarities and differences between things. You can compare and contrast in a Venn diagram or in a table.

Venn Diagram A Venn diagram consists of two overlapping circles. In the space where the circles overlap, you write the characteristics that the two items have in common. In one of the circles outside the area of overlap, you write the differing features or characteristics of one of the items. In the other circle outside the area of overlap, you write the differing characteristics of the other item.

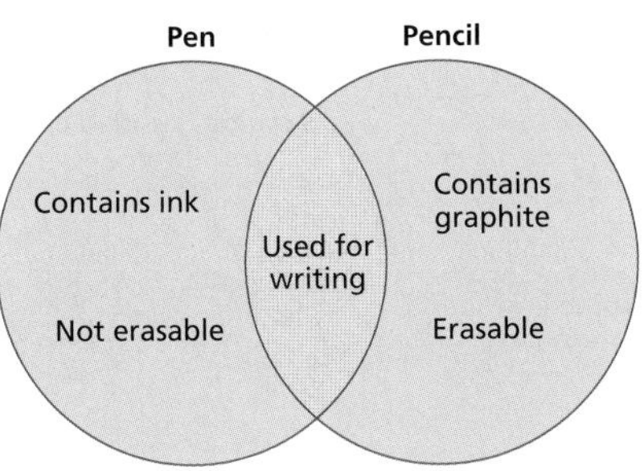

Table In a compare/contrast table, you list the characteristics or features to be compared across the top of the table. Then list the items to be compared in the left column. Complete the table by filling in information about each characteristic or feature.

Blood Vessel	Function	Structure of Wall
Artery	Carries blood away from heart	
Capillary		
Vein		

Identifying Supporting Evidence

A hypothesis is a possible explanation for observations made by scientists or an answer to a scientific question. Scientists must carry out investigations and gather evidence that either supports or disproves the hypothesis.

Identifying the supporting evidence for a hypothesis or theory can help you understand the hypothesis or theory. Evidence consists of facts—information whose accuracy can be confirmed by testing or observation.

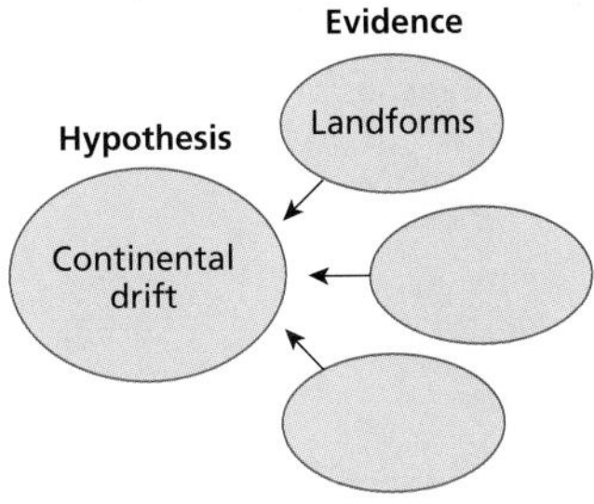

Reading Skills

Identifying Main Ideas

Focus Explain that identifying main ideas and details helps sort the facts from the information into groups. Each group can have a main topic, subtopics, and details.

Teach Tell students that paragraphs are often written so that the main idea is in the first or second sentence, or in the last sentence. Assign students a page in the book. Instruct them to write the main idea for each paragraph on that page. If students have difficulty finding the main idea, suggest that they list all of the ideas given in the paragraph, and then choose the idea that is big enough to include all the others.

Comparing and Contrasting

Focus Explain that comparing and contrasting information shows how concepts, facts, and events are similar or different. The results of the comparison can have importance.

Teach Point out that Venn diagrams work best when comparing two things. To compare more than two things, students should use a compare/contrast table. Have students make a Venn diagram or compare/contrast table using two or more different sports or other activities, such as playing musical instruments. Emphasize that students should select characteristics that highlight the similarities and differences in the activities.

Identifying Supporting Evidence

Focus Explain to students that identifying the supporting evidence will help them to understand the relationship between the facts and the hypothesis.

Teach Remind students that a hypothesis is neither right nor wrong, but it is either supported or not supported by the evidence from testing or observation. If evidence is found that does not support a hypothesis, the hypothesis can be changed to accommodate the new evidence, or it can be dropped.

Sequencing

Focus Tell students that organizing information from beginning to end will help them understand a step-by-step process.

Teach Encourage students to create a flowchart to show the things they did this morning to get ready for school. Remind students that a flowchart should show the correct order in which events occur. *(A typical flowchart might include: got up ➤ took a shower ➤ got dressed ➤ ate breakfast ➤ brushed teeth ➤ gathered books and homework ➤ put on jacket.)*

Then explain that a cycle diagram shows a sequence of events that is continuous. Point out the cycle diagram that shows how the weather changes with the seasons of the year. Ask: **Why is a cycle diagram used instead of a flowchart to show the sequence of the seasons?** *(A cycle diagram shows that the sequence is continuous, not just a series of events.)* Challenge students to make a sequence diagram for a section of the text. Have them explain why they chose either a cycle diagram or a flowchart. Remind them to include at least four steps in the sequence.

Relating Cause and Effect

Focus Explain to students that cause is the reason for what happens. The effect is what happens in response to the cause. Relating cause and effect helps students relate the reason for what happens to what happens as a result.

Teach Emphasize that not all events that occur together have a cause-and-effect relationship. For example, tell students that you went to the grocery store and your car stalled. Ask: **Is there a cause-and-effect relationship in this situation? Explain.** *(No. Going to the grocery store could not cause a car to stall. There must be another cause to make the car stall.)*

Sequencing

A sequence is the order in which a series of events occurs. A flowchart or a cycle diagram can help you visualize a sequence.

Flowchart To make a flowchart, write a brief description of each step or event in a box. Place the boxes in order, with the first event at the top of the page. Then draw an arrow to connect each step or event to the next.

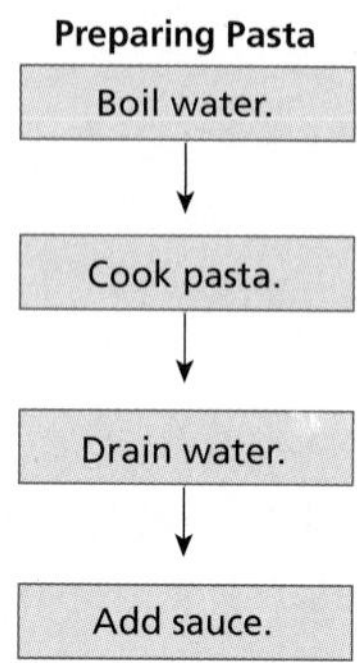

Cycle Diagram A cycle diagram shows a sequence that is continuous, or cyclical. A continuous sequence does not have an end because when the final event is over, the first event begins again. To create a cycle diagram, write the starting event in a box placed at the top of a page in the center. Then, moving in a clockwise direction, write each event in a box in its proper sequence. Draw arrows that connect each event to the one that occurs next.

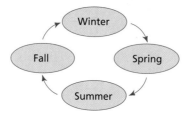

Seasons of the Year

Winter

Spring

Summer

Fall

Relating Cause and Effect

Science involves many cause-and-effect relationships. A cause makes something happen. An effect is what happens. When you recognize that one event causes another, you are relating cause and effect.

Words like *cause, because, effect, affect,* and *result* often signal a cause or an effect. Sometimes an effect can have more than one cause, or a cause can produce several effects.

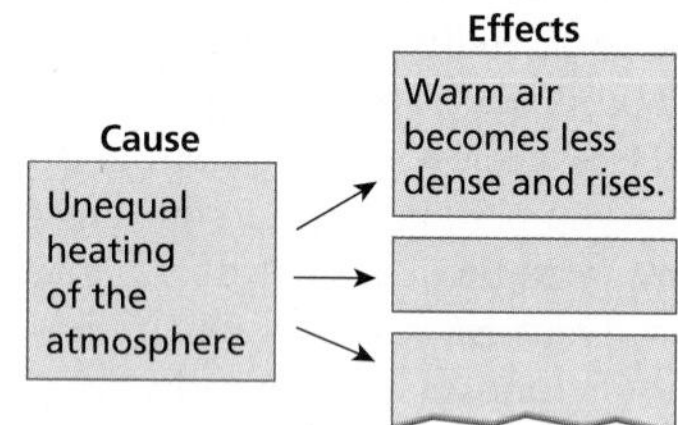

Concept Mapping

Concept maps are useful tools for organizing information on any topic. A concept map begins with a main idea or core concept and shows how the idea can be subdivided into related subconcepts or smaller ideas.

You construct a concept map by placing concepts (usually nouns) in ovals and connecting them with linking words (usually verbs). The biggest concept or idea is placed in an oval at the top of the map. Related concepts are arranged in ovals below the big idea. The linking words connect the ovals.

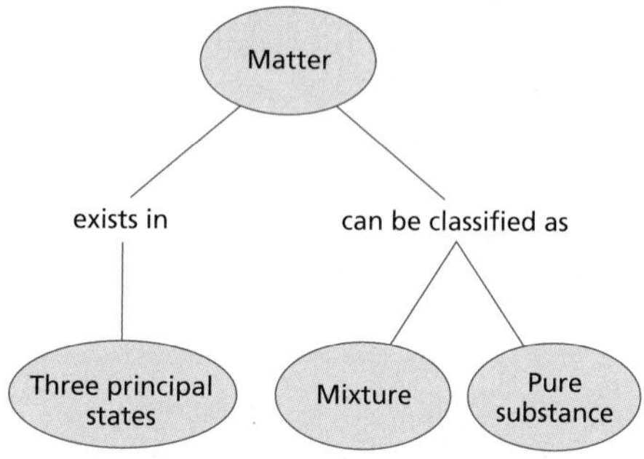

Concept Mapping

Focus Elicit from students how a map shows the relationship of one geographic area to another. Connect this idea to how a concept map shows the relationship between terms and concepts.

Teach Challenge students to make a concept map with at least three levels of concepts to organize information about types of transportation. All students should start with the phrase *Types of transportation* at the top of the concept map. After that point, their concepts may vary. *(For example, some students might place* private transportation *and* public transportation *at the next level, while other students might choose* human-powered *and* gas-powered.*)* Make sure students connect the concepts with linking words.

Building Vocabulary

Knowing the meaning of these prefixes, suffixes, and roots will help you understand the meaning of words you do not recognize.

Word Origins Many science words come to English from other languages, such as Greek and Latin. By learning the meaning of a few common Greek and Latin roots, you can determine the meaning of unfamiliar science words.

Prefixes A prefix is a word part that is added at the beginning of a root or base word to change its meaning.

Suffixes A suffix is a word part that is added at the end of a root word to change the meaning.

Greek and Latin Roots

Greek Roots	Meaning	Example
ast-	star	astronaut
geo-	Earth	geology
metron-	measure	kilometer
opt-	eye	optician
photo-	light	photograph
scop-	see	microscope
therm-	heat	thermostat
Latin Roots	**Meaning**	**Example**
aqua-	water	aquarium
aud-	hear	auditorium
duc-, duct-	lead	conduct
flect-	bend	reflect
fract-, frag-	break	fracture
ject-	throw	reject
luc-	light	lucid
spec-	see	inspect

Prefixes and Suffixes

Prefix	Meaning	Example
com-, con-	with	communicate, concert
de-	from; down	decay
di-	two	divide
ex-, exo-	out	exhaust
in-, im-	in, into; not	inject, impossible
re-	again; back	reflect, recall
trans-	across	transfer
Suffix	**Meaning**	**Example**
-al	relating to	natural
-er, -or	one who	teacher, doctor
-ist	one who practices	scientist
-ity	state of	equality
-ology	study of	biology
-tion, -sion	state or quality of	reaction, tension

Suffixes

Focus Explain to students that learning the meanings of common suffixes and recognizing them in words are two effective strategies for learning word meanings and building vocabulary.

Teach Remind students that a suffix is added to the end of a word to change its meaning. In addition, students can use suffixes to discover the part of speech of an unfamiliar word. On the chalkboard, draw a four-column chart. Label the columns Noun, Verb, Adjective, and Adverb. Choose a Key Term that has a familiar base word, such as *tension.* Ask: **What are the noun, verb, adjective, and adverb forms of this word?** *(Students should give all possible answers, which may include only two forms of the word.)* Ask: **What endings signal that the word is a noun, adjective, or adverb?** *(Students should list the suffixes.)* Challenge students to learn the meanings of suffixes and to use them to decode new words.

Building Vocabulary

Reading in a content area presents challenges different from those encountered when reading fiction. Science texts often have more new vocabulary and more unfamiliar concepts that place greater emphasis on inferential reasoning. Students who can apply vocabulary strategies will be more successful in reading and understanding a science textbook. Challenge students to use Greek and Latin word origins and the meanings of prefixes and suffixes to learn the Key Terms in each section.

Word Origins

Focus Explain that word origins describe the older, foreign words that many modern English words have come from. Many science words come from Greek and Latin.

Teach Tell students that most dictionaries give the word origin just before the definition. Choose a section that has a Key Term with a Greek or Latin word origin. Encourage students to learn the meaning of the root word. Ask: **How does knowing the word origin help you remember the meaning of the Key Term?** *(Answers will vary, but the meaning of the Latin or Greek root should provide a clue to the definition of the Key Term.)* Ask: **What other words do you know that come from the same word origin?** *(Students may mention other words related to the Key Term.)* Challenge students to use word origins to figure out the meanings of unfamiliar words as they read. Students should confirm their definitions as necessary by checking a dictionary.

Prefixes

Focus Tell students that learning the meaning of common prefixes can help them determine the meaning of words they don't recognize. They will also increase their vocabulary.

Teach Remind students that a prefix is a word part that is added at the beginning of a root word to change its meaning. List some of the familiar prefixes and meanings, such as *de-* and *re-*, on the chalkboard. Ask: **What words do you know that use these same prefixes?** *(Students should list at least two words for each prefix.)* Ask: **How does the prefix affect the meaning of the root word?** *(Students should explain how it changes the meaning.)* Challenge students to learn the meaning of common prefixes and to use the skill to increase their vocabulary.

- Complete student edition
- Video and audio
- Simulations and activities
- Section and chapter activities

Laboratory Safety

Laboratory safety is an essential element of a successful science class. Students need to understand exactly what is safe and unsafe behavior and what the rationale is behind each safety rule.

All in One Teaching Resources

- Laboratory Safety Teacher Notes
- Laboratory Safety Rules
- Laboratory Safety Symbols
- Laboratory Safety Contract

General Precautions

- Post safety rules in the classroom, and review them regularly with students before beginning every science activity.
- Familiarize yourself with the safety procedures for each activity before introducing it to your students.
- For open-ended activities like Chapter Projects, have students submit their procedures or design plans in writing and check them for safety considerations.
- Always act as an exemplary role model by displaying safe behavior.
- Know how to use safety equipment, such as fire extinguishers and fire blankets, and always have it accessible.
- Have students practice leaving the classroom quickly and orderly to prepare them for emergencies.
- Explain to students how to use the intercom or other available means of communication to get help during an emergency.
- Never leave students unattended while they are engaged in science activities.
- Provide enough space for students to safely carry out science activities.
- Instruct students to report all accidents and injuries to you immediately.

Safety Symbols

These symbols warn of possible dangers in the laboratory and remind you to work carefully.

Safety Goggles Wear safety goggles to protect your eyes in any activity involving chemicals, flames or heating, or glassware.

Lab Apron Wear a laboratory apron to protect your skin and clothing from damage.

Breakage Handle breakable materials, such as glassware, with care. Do not touch broken glassware.

Heat-Resistant Gloves Use an oven mitt or other hand protection when handling hot materials such as hot plates or hot glassware.

Plastic Gloves Wear disposable plastic gloves when working with harmful chemicals and organisms. Keep your hands away from your face, and dispose of the gloves according to your teacher's instructions.

Heating Use a clamp or tongs to pick up hot glassware. Do not touch hot objects with your bare hands.

Flames Before you work with flames, tie back loose hair and clothing. Follow instructions from your teacher about lighting and extinguishing flames.

No Flames When using flammable materials, make sure there are no flames, sparks, or other exposed heat sources present.

Corrosive Chemical Avoid getting acid or other corrosive chemicals on your skin or clothing or in your eyes. Do not inhale the vapors. Wash your hands after the activity.

Poison Do not let any poisonous chemical come into contact with your skin, and do not inhale its vapors. Wash your hands when you are finished with the activity.

Fumes Work in a ventilated area when harmful vapors may be involved. Avoid inhaling vapors directly. Only test an odor when directed to do so by your teacher, and use a wafting motion to direct the vapor toward your nose.

Sharp Object Scissors, scalpels, knives, needles, pins, and tacks can cut your skin. Always direct a sharp edge or point away from yourself and others.

Animal Safety Treat live or preserved animals or animal parts with care to avoid harming the animals or yourself. Wash your hands when you are finished with the activity.

Plant Safety Handle plants only as directed by your teacher. If you are allergic to certain plants, tell your teacher; do not do an activity involving those plants. Avoid touching harmful plants such as poison ivy. Wash your hands when you are finished with the activity.

Electric Shock To avoid electric shock, never use electrical equipment around water, or when the equipment is wet or your hands are wet. Be sure cords are untangled and cannot trip anyone. Unplug equipment not in use.

Physical Safety When an experiment involves physical activity, avoid injuring yourself or others. Alert your teacher if there is any reason you should not participate.

Disposal Dispose of chemicals and other laboratory materials safely. Follow the instructions from your teacher.

Hand Washing Wash your hands thoroughly when finished with the activity. Use antibacterial soap and warm water. Rinse well.

General Safety Awareness When this symbol appears, follow the instructions provided. When you are asked to develop your own procedure in a lab, have your teacher approve your plan before you go further.

End-of-Experiment Rules

- Always have students use warm water and soap for washing their hands.

Heating and Fire Safety

- No flammable substances should be in use around hot plates, light bulbs, or open flames.
- Test tubes should be heated only in water baths.
- Students should be permitted to strike matches to light candles or burners *only* with strict supervision. When possible, you should light the flames, especially when working with younger students.
- Be sure to have proper ventilation when fumes are produced during a procedure.
- All electrical equipment used in the lab should have GFI (Ground Fault Interrupter) switches.

Science Safety Rules

General Precautions
Follow all instructions. Never perform activities without the approval and supervision of your teacher. Do not engage in horseplay. Never eat or drink in the laboratory. Keep work areas clean and uncluttered.

Dress Code
Wear safety goggles whenever you work with chemicals, glassware, heat sources such as burners, or any substance that might get into your eyes. If you wear contact lenses, notify your teacher.

Wear a lab apron or coat whenever you work with corrosive chemicals or substances that can stain. Wear disposable plastic gloves when working with organisms and harmful chemicals. Tie back long hair. Remove or tie back any article of clothing or jewelry that can hang down and touch chemicals, flames, or equipment. Roll up long sleeves. Never wear open shoes or sandals.

First Aid
Report all accidents, injuries, or fires to your teacher, no matter how minor. Be aware of the location of the first-aid kit, emergency equipment such as the fire extinguisher and fire blanket, and the nearest telephone. Know whom to contact in an emergency.

Heating and Fire Safety
Keep all combustible materials away from flames. When heating a substance in a test tube, make sure that the mouth of the tube is not pointed at you or anyone else. Never heat a liquid in a closed container. Use an oven mitt to pick up a container that has been heated.

Using Chemicals Safely
Never put your face near the mouth of a container that holds chemicals. Never touch, taste, or smell a chemical unless your teacher tells you to.

Use only those chemicals needed in the activity. Keep all containers closed when chemicals are not being used. Pour all chemicals over the sink or a container, not over your work surface. Dispose of excess chemicals as instructed by your teacher.

Be extra careful when working with acids or bases. When mixing an acid and water, always pour the water into the container first and then add the acid to the water. Never pour water into an acid. Wash chemical spills and splashes immediately with plenty of water.

Using Glassware Safely
If glassware is broken or chipped, notify your teacher immediately. Never handle broken or chipped glass with your bare hands.

Never force glass tubing or thermometers into a rubber stopper or rubber tubing. Have your teacher insert the glass tubing or thermometer if required for an activity.

Using Sharp Instruments
Handle sharp instruments with extreme care. Never cut material toward you; cut away from you.

Animal and Plant Safety
Never perform experiments that cause pain, discomfort, or harm to animals. Only handle animals if absolutely necessary. If you know that you are allergic to certain plants, molds, or animals, tell your teacher before doing an activity in which these are used. Wash your hands thoroughly after any activity involving animals, animal parts, plants, plant parts, or soil.

During field work, wear long pants, long sleeves, socks, and closed shoes. Avoid poisonous plants and fungi as well as plants with thorns.

End-of-Experiment Rules
Unplug all electrical equipment. Clean up your work area. Dispose of waste materials as instructed by your teacher. Wash your hands after every experiment.

Handling Organisms Safely
- In an activity where students are directed to taste something, be sure to store the material in clean, *nonscience* containers. Distribute the material to students in *new* plastic or paper dispensables, which should be discarded after the tasting. Tasting or eating should never be done in a lab classroom.
- When growing bacterial cultures, use only disposable petri dishes. After streaking, the dishes should be sealed and not opened again by students. After the lab, students should return the unopened dishes to you.
- Two methods are recommended for the safe disposal of bacterial cultures. *First method:* Autoclave the petri dishes and discard them without opening. *Second method:* If no autoclave is available, carefully open the dishes (never have a student do this), pour full-strength bleach into the dishes, and let them stand for a day. Then pour the bleach from the petri dishes down a drain, and flush the drain with lots of water. Tape the petri dishes back together, and place them in a sealed plastic bag. Wrap the plastic bag with a brown paper bag or newspaper, and tape securely. Throw the sealed package in the trash. Thoroughly disinfect the work area with bleach.
- To grow mold, use a new, sealable plastic bag that is two to three times larger than the material to be placed inside. Seal the bag and tape it shut. After the bag is sealed, students should not open it. To dispose of the bag and mold culture, make a small cut near an edge of the bag, and cook the bag in a microwave oven on a high setting for at least one minute. Discard the bag according to local ordinance, usually in the trash.
- Students should wear disposable nitrile, latex, or food-handling gloves when handling live animals or nonliving specimens.

Using Glassware Safely
- Use plastic containers, graduated cylinders, and beakers whenever possible. If using glass, students should wear safety goggles.
- Use only nonmercury thermometers with anti-roll protectors.

Using Chemicals Safely
- When students use both chemicals and microscopes in one activity, microscopes should be in a separate part of the room from the chemicals so that when students remove their goggles to use the microscopes, their eyes are not at risk.

English and Spanish Glossary

alternating current Current consisting of charges that move back and forth in a circuit. (p. 97)
corriente alterna Corriente que consiste en cargas eléctricas que se mueven hacia adelante y hacia atrás en un circuito.

ammeter A device used to measure current in a circuit. (p. 64)
amperímetro Aparato usado para medir la corriente en un circuito.

amplitude The height of a wave from the center to a crest or trough. (p. 119)
amplitud Altura de una onda desde su parte media a la cresta o al valle.

amplitude modulation (AM) A change in the amplitude of a carrier wave to match the amplitude of a signal. (p. 119)
amplitud modulada (AM) Cambio en la amplitud de una onda portadora para que corresponda con la amplitud de la señal.

analog signal An electric current that is varied smoothly to represent information. (p. 109)
señal analógica Corriente eléctrica que varía levemente para representar información.

atom The smallest particle of an element that has the properties of that element. (p. 15)
átomo La partícula más pequeña de un elemento, que tiene las propiedades de ese elemento.

aurora A glowing region produced by the interaction of charged particles from the sun and atoms in the atmosphere. (p. 27)
aurora polar Área resplandeciente en la atmósfera de la Tierra producida por la interacción de partículas cargadas del Sol y los átomos de la atmósfera.

B

battery A combination of two or more electrochemical cells in series. (p. 56)
pila Combinación de dos o más celdas electroquímicas en serie.

binary system A number system using combinations of only two digits, 0 and 1. (p. 123)
sistema binario Sistema de números que usa combinaciones de sólo dos dígitos, 0 y 1.

central processing unit (CPU) Directs the operation of a computer, performs logical operations and calculations. (p. 125)
unidad central de procesamiento (CPU) Dirige la operación de una computadora, realiza operaciones y cálculos lógicos.

chat room A network feature that allows two or more users to exchange messages. (p. 135)
salón de charla Característica de una red que permite que dos o más usuarios intercambien mensajes.

chemical energy The energy stored in chemical compounds. (p. 55)
energía química Energía almacenada en los compuestos químicos.

chemical reaction A process in which substances change into new substances with different properties. (p. 55)
reacción química Proceso por el cual las sustancias químicas se convierten en nuevas sustancias químicas con propiedades diferentes.

circuit breaker A reusable safety switch that breaks the circuit when the current becomes too high. (p. 73)
interruptor de circuito Interruptor de seguridad que se puede volver a usar, que se usa para cortar el circuito cuando la corriente es demasiado alta.

170 • N

compass A device with a magnetized needle that can spin freely. (p. 22)
brújula Instrumento con una aguja imantada que puede girar libremente.

computer An electronic device that stores, processes, and retrieves information. (p. 123)
computadora Aparato electrónico que almacena, procesa y obtiene información.

computer network A group of computers connected by cables or telephone lines that allows people to share information. (p. 132)
red de computadoras Grupo de computadoras conectadas por cables o líneas telefónicas que permite que la gente comparta información.

computer programmer A person who uses computer languages to write programs, or sets of operation instructions, for computers. (p. 129)
programador de computadoras Persona que usa los lenguajes de computación para escribir programas o conjuntos de instrucciones de operaciones para computadoras.

computer virus A program that can enter a computer, destroy files, and disable the computer. (p. 134)
virus de computadoras Programa que puede entrar en una computadora, destruir documentos y estropearla.

conduction A method of charging an object by allowing electrons to flow by direct contact from one object to another object. (p. 38)
conducción Método para cargar un objeto que consiste en permitir que los electrones fluyan por contacto directo de un objeto a otro.

conductor A material through which charges can easily flow. (p. 47)
conductor Material a través del cual pueden fluir las cargas eléctricas fácilmente.

conservation of charge The law that states that charges are neither created nor destroyed but only transferred from one material to another. (p. 38)
conservación de la carga eléctrica Ley que enuncia que las cargas no se crean ni se destruyen, sino que sólo se transfieren de un material a otro.

D

digital signal Pulses of current used to represent information. (p. 109)
señal digital Pulsaciones de corriente que se usan para representar información.

diode An electronic component that consists of layers of two types of semiconductors. (p. 111)
diodo Componente electrónico que consiste en capas de dos tipos de semiconductores.

direct current Current consisting of charges that flow in only one direction in a circuit. (p. 96)
corriente directa Corriente que consiste en cargas eléctricas que fluyen en una sola dirección en un circuito.

dry cell An electrochemical cell in which the electrolyte is a paste. (p. 57)
celda seca Celda electroquímica en la que el electrolito es una pasta.

E

electrical energy The energy of moving electrical charges. (p. 86)
energía eléctrica Energía de cargas eléctricas que se mueven.

electric circuit A complete, unbroken path through which electric charges can flow. (p. 46)
circuito eléctrico Camino completo y continuo a través del cual pueden fluir las cargas eléctricas.

electric current The continuous flow of electric charges through a material. (p. 45)
corriente eléctrica Flujo continuo de cargas eléctricas a través de un material.

electric field The region around a charged object where the object's electric force interacts with other charged objects. (p. 36)
campo eléctrico Región alrededor de un objeto cargado en donde su fuerza eléctrica interactúa con otros objetos con carga eléctrica.

electric force The attraction or repulsion between electric charges. (p. 36)
fuerza eléctrica Atracción o repulsión entre cargas eléctricas.

electric generator A device that transforms mechanical energy into electrical energy. (p. 98)
generador eléctrico Instrumento que convierte la energía mecánica en energía eléctrica.

electric motor A device that transforms electrical energy to mechanical energy. (p. 88)
motor eléctrico Instrumento que convierte la energía eléctrica en energía mecánica.

electrochemical cell A device that transforms chemical energy into electrical energy. (p. 56)
celda electroquímica Instrumento que convierte la energía química en energía eléctrica.

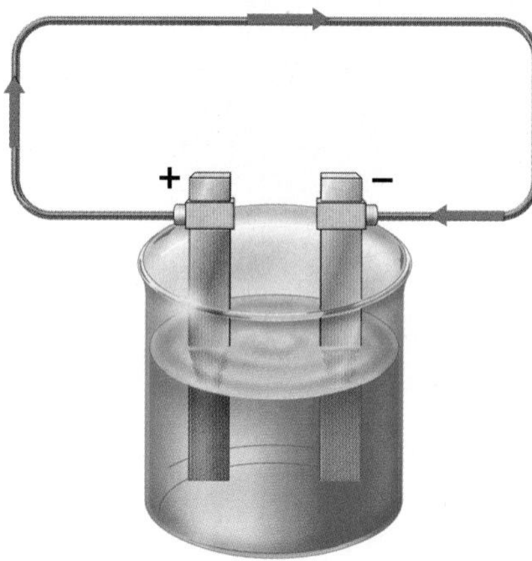

electrode A metal part of an electrochemical cell, which gains or loses electrons. (p. 56)
electrodo Parte metálica de una celda electroquímica que gana o pierde electrones.

electrolyte A liquid or paste that conducts electric current. (p. 56)
electrolito Líquido o pasta que conduce la corriente eléctrica.

electromagnet A magnet created by wrapping a coil of wire with a current around a ferromagnetic core. (p. 83)
electroimán Imán creado al enrollar una espiral de alambre con corriente alrededor de un núcleo ferromagnético.

electromagnetic induction The process of generating an electric current from the motion of a conductor through a magnetic field. (p. 94)
inducción electromagnética Proceso por el cual se genera una corriente eléctrica a partir del movimiento de un conductor a través de un campo magnético.

electromagnetic wave A wave made up of a combination of a changing electric field and changing magnetic field. (p. 118)
onda electromagnética Onda formada por una combinación de un campo eléctrico cambiante y un campo magnético cambiante.

electromagnetism The relationship between electricity and magnetism. (p. 81)
electromagnetismo Relación entre la electricidad y el magnetismo.

electron A negatively charged particle that is found outside the nucleus of an atom. (p. 15)
electrón Partícula con carga negativa que se halla fuera del núcleo de un átomo.

electronic signal A varying electric current that represents information. (p. 108)
señal electrónica Corriente eléctrica variable que representa información.

electronics The use of electric current to control, communicate, and process information. (p. 108)
electrónica Uso de la corriente eléctrica para controlar, comunicar y procesar información.

element One of about 100 basic materials that make up all matter. (p. 15)
elemento Uno de aproximadamente 100 materiales básicos que componen toda la materia.

encryption A process of coding information so that only the intended user can read it. (p. 134)
encriptación Proceso de codificación de la información para que sólo la pueda leer el usuario deseado.

energy The ability to move an object some distance. (p. 86)
energía Capacidad para mover un objeto a una determinada distancia.

ferromagnetic material A material that is strongly attracted to a magnet, and which can be made into a magnet. (p. 17)
material ferromagnético Material que es atraído fuertemente a un imán y el cual puede transformarse en un imán.

frequency The number of waves passing a given point each second. (p. 119)
frecuencia Número de ondas que pasan por un punto dado en un segundo.

frequency modulation (FM) A change in the frequency of a carrier wave to match the amplitude of a signal. (p. 119)
frecuencia modulada (FM) Cambio en la frecuencia de una onda portadora para que corresponda con la amplitud de la señal.

friction A method of charging an object by rubbing it against another object; the force that one object exerts on another when the two rub against each other. (p. 38)
fricción Método para cargar con electricidad un objeto que consiste en frotarlo contra otro objeto; fuerza que ejerce un objeto sobre otro cuando se frotan mutuamente.

fuse A safety device with a thin metal strip that will melt if too much current passes through a circuit. (p. 73)
fusible Elemento de seguridad que tiene una tira metálica delgada que se derrite si pasa demasiada corriente a través de un circuito.

galvanometer A device that uses an electromagnet to detect small amounts of current. (p. 87)
galvanómetro Instrumento que usa un electroimán para detectar pequeñas cantidades de corriente.

grounded Allowing charges to flow directly from the circuit into Earth in the event of a short circuit. (p. 72)
conectado a tierra Permitir que la carga fluya directamente del circuito a la Tierra en el caso de un cortocircuito.

hardware The permanent components of a computer, including the central processing unit and input, output, and memory storage devices. (p. 125)
hardware Componentes permanentes de una computadora, incluyendo la unidad central de procesamiento, dispositivos de entrada y salida, y dispositivos de registro de memoria.

induction A method of charging an object by means of the electric field of another object; the objects have no direct contact. (p. 38)
inducción Método para cargar un objeto mediante el campo eléctrico de otro objeto; objetos que no están en contacto directo.

input device A device that feeds data to a CPU; a keyboard is an input device. (p. 125)
dispositivo de entrada Dispositivo que envía información a una CPU; un teclado es un dispositivo de entrada.

insulator A material through which charges cannot easily flow. (p. 47)
aislante Material a través del cual las cargas eléctricas no pueden fluir con facilidad.

integrated circuit A circuit that has been manufactured on a chip (a tiny slice of semiconductor), which can contain thousands of diodes, transistors, and resistors. (p. 112)
circuito integrado Circuito que ha sido fabricado en un chip (una diminuta placa de un semiconductor), que puede contener miles de diodos, transistores y resistores.

intellectual property A story, poem, computer program, or similar product owned by the author. (p. 135)
propiedad intelectual Cuento, poema, programa de computadoras o producto similar que pertenece al autor.

Internet An international computer network that shares data, information, and news; the Internet links millions of businesses, schools, research organizations, and individual users. (p. 133)
Internet Red de computadoras internacional que comparte datos, información y noticias; la Internet conecta millones de negocios, escuelas, organizaciones de investigación y usuarios individuales.

magnet Any material that attracts iron and materials that contain iron. (p. 7)
imán Material que atrae hierro y materiales que contienen hierro.

magnetic declination The angle between geographic north and the north to which a compass needle points. (p. 24)
declinación magnética Ángulo entre el norte geográfico y el norte hacia donde apunta la alguja de una brújula.

magnetic domain A region in which the magnetic fields of all atoms are lined up in the same direction. (p. 16)
dominio magnético Área en la que los campos magnéticos de todos los átomos están alineados en la misma dirección.

magnetic field The region around a magnet where the magnetic force is exerted. (p. 9)
campo magnético Área alrededor de un imán en la cual se ejerce la fuerza magnética.

magnetic field lines Invisible lines that map out the magnetic field around a magnet. (p. 9)
líneas del campo magnético Líneas invisibles que representan el campo magnético alrededor de un imán.

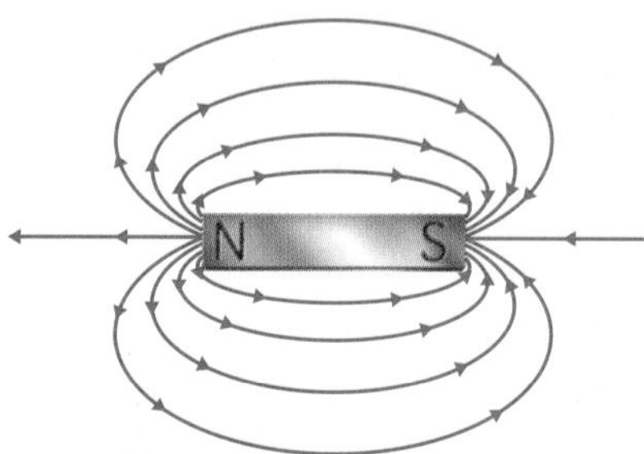

magnetic force A force produced when magnetic poles interact. (p. 8)
fuerza magnética Fuerza que se produce cuando interactúan los polos magnéticos.

magnetic pole The ends of a magnetic object, where the magnetic force is strongest. (p. 8)
polo magnético Extremo de un objeto magnético, donde la fuerza magnética es mayor.

magnetism The force of attraction or repulsion of magnetic materials. (p. 7)
magnetismo Atracción o repulsión de materiales magnéticos.

magnetosphere The region of Earth's magnetic field shaped by the solar wind. (p. 26)
magnetosfera Área del campo magnético de la Tierra formada por el viento solar.

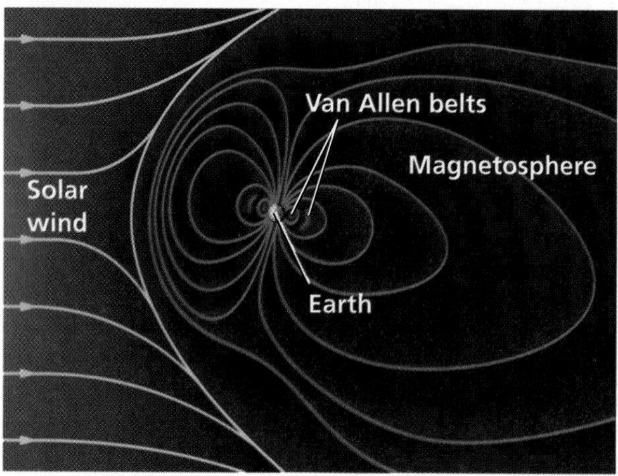

mechanical energy The energy an object has due to its movement or position. (p. 86)
energía mecánica Energía que tiene un objeto debido a su movimiento o posición.

neutron The small uncharged particle that is found in the nucleus of an atom. (p. 15)
neutrón Partícula pequeña sin carga que se haya en el núcleo de un átomo.

nucleus The core at the center of every atom. (p. 15)
núcleo Centro de un átomo.

Ohm's law The law that states that resistance is equal to voltage divided by current. (p. 61)
ley de Ohm Ley que enuncia que la resistencia es igual al voltaje dividido por la corriente.

output device A device that presents data from a computer; a monitor is an output device. (p. 125)
dispositivo de salida Dispositivo que presenta información de una computadora; un monitor es un dispositivo de salida.

parallel circuit An electric circuit with multiple paths. (p. 65)
circuito paralelo Circuito eléctrico con caminos múltiples.

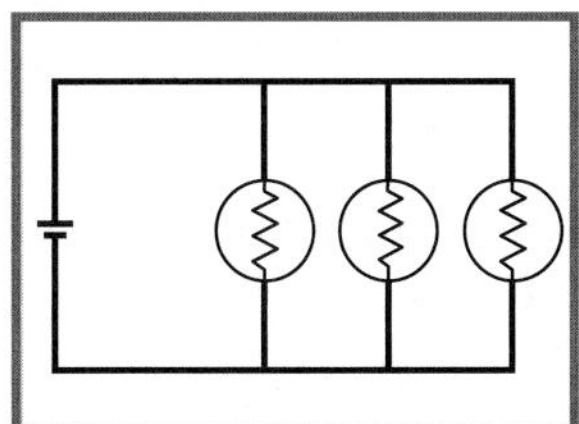

permanent magnet A magnet made of material that keeps its magnetism. (p. 18)
imán permanente Imán hecho de un material que mantiene su magnetismo.

power The rate at which one form of energy is transformed into another; the unit of power is the watt. (p. 68)
potencia Razón a la cual una forma de energía se convierte en otra; la unidad de potencia es el vatio.

proton A positively charged particle that is part of an atom's nucleus. (p. 15)
protón Partícula con carga positiva ubicada en el núcleo de un átomo.

resistence The measurement of how difficult it is for charges to flow through a material. (p. 50)
resistencia Medida de lo difícil que es para las cargas eléctricas fluir a través de un material.

semiconductor A material that conducts current under certain conditions. (p. 110)
semiconductor Material que conduce la corriente bajo ciertas condiciones.

series circuit An electric circuit with a single path. (p. 64)
circuito en serie Circuito eléctrico con un solo camino.

short circuit A connection that allows current to take an unintended path. (p. 71)
cortocircuito Conexión que permite que la corriente tome un camino no establecido.

software A detailed set of instructions that directs the computer hardware to perform operations on stored information. (p. 128)
software Conjunto de instrucciones detalladas que dirige el hardware de una computadora para que realice operaciones con la información almacenada.

solar wind Streams of electrically charged particles flowing at high speeds from the sun; solar wind pushes against Earth's magnetic field and surrounds it. (p. 26)
viento solar Corrientes de partículas con carga eléctrica que fluyen a gran velocidad desde el Sol; el viento solar empuja el campo magnético de la Tierra y lo rodea

solenoid A coil of wire with a current that acts as a bar magnet. (p. 82)
solenoide Espiral de alambre con una corriente que actúa como un imán de barra.

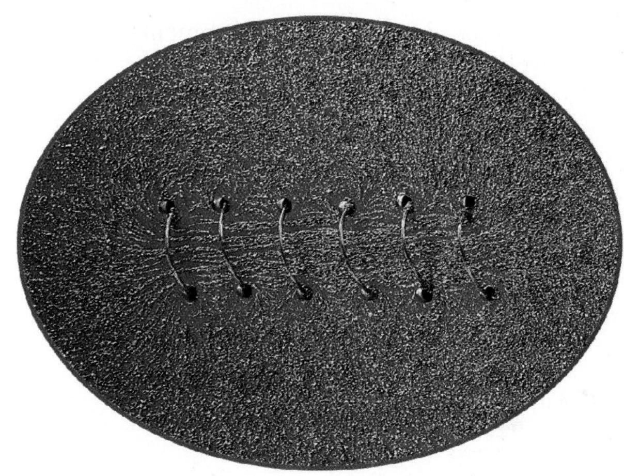

static discharge The loss of static electricity as electric charges transfer from one object to another. (p. 40)
descarga estática Pérdida de la electricidad estática cuando las cargas eléctricas se transfieren de un objeto a otro.

static electricity A buildup of charges on an object. (p. 37)
electricidad estática Acumulación de cargas eléctricas en un objeto.

step-down transformer A transformer that decreases voltage. (p. 101)
transformador reductor Transformador que disminuye el voltaje.

step-up transformer A transformer that increases voltage. (p. 100)
transformador elevador Transformador que aumenta el voltaje.

temporary magnet A magnet made from a material that easily loses its magnetism. (p. 18)
imán temporal Imán hecho de un material que pierde fácilmente su magnetismo.

terminal A convenient attachment point used to connect a cell or battery to a circuit. (p. 56)
terminal Punto de conexión conveniente que se usa para conectar una celda o batería a un circuito.

third prong The round prong of a plug that connects any metal pieces in an appliance to the safety grounding wire of a building. (p. 72)
tercer terminal Terminal redondeado de un enchufe que conecta cualquier parte de metal de un artefacto con el alambre a tierra de un edificio.

transformer A device that increases or decreases voltage. (p. 99)
transformador Instrumento que aumenta o disminuye el voltaje.

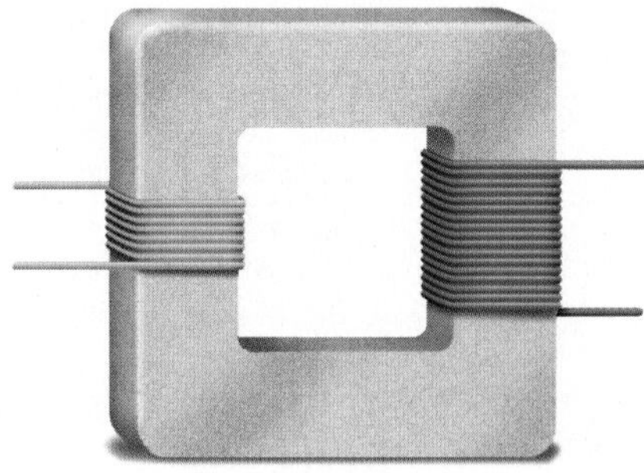

transistor An electronic component used to amplify an electronic signal or to switch current on and off. (p. 111)
transistor Componente electrónico que se usa para amplificar una señal electrónica o apagar y encender la corriente.

Van Allen belts Two doughnut-shaped regions 1,000–25,000 kilometers above Earth that contain electrons and protons traveling at high speed. (p. 26)
cinturones de Van Allen Par de regiones circulares ubicadas de 1,000 a 25,000 kilómetros de la Tierra; están formadas de electrones y protones que viajan a alta velocidad.

voltage The difference in electrical potential energy between two places in a circuit. (p. 49)
voltaje Diferencia en la energía potencial eléctrica entre dos lugares en un circuito.

voltage source A device that creates an electrical potential energy difference in an electric circuit; batteries and generators are voltage sources. (p. 49)
fuente de voltaje Instrumento que crea una diferencia en la energía potencial eléctrica en un circuito eléctrico; las pilas y los generadores son fuentes de voltaje.

voltmeter A device used to measure voltage, or electrical potential energy difference. (p. 66)
voltímetro Aparato usado para medir el voltaje o la diferencia de energía eléctrica potencial.

wet cell An electrochemical cell in which the electrolyte is a liquid. (p. 57)
celda húmeda Celda electroquímica en la que el electrolito es un líquido.

World Wide Web A part of the Internet that allows the displaying and viewing of text, pictures, video, and sound. (p. 133)
World Wide Web (WWW) Parte de la Internet que permite la presentación y visión de texto, fotos, video y sonido

Page numbers for key terms are printed in **boldface** type.
Page numbers for illustrations, maps, and charts are printed in *italics*.

Index

Teacher's Edition entries appear in blue type. The page on which a term is defined is indicated in **boldface** type.

Index

Page numbers for key terms are printed in **boldface** type.
Page numbers for illustrations, maps, and charts are printed in *italics*.

Index

Page numbers for key terms are printed in **boldface** type.
Page numbers for illustrations, maps, and charts are printed in *italics*.

Index

Acknowledgments

Staff Credits

Diane Alimena, Scott Andrews, Jennifer Angel, Michele Angelucci, Laura Baselice, Carolyn Belanger, Barbara A. Bertell, Suzanne Biron, Peggy Bliss, Stephanie Bradley, James Brady, Anne M. Bray, Sarah M. Carroll, Kerry Cashman, Jonathan Cheney, Joshua D. Clapper, Lisa J. Clark, Bob Craton, Patricia Cully, Patricia M. Dambry, Kathy Dempsey, Leanne Esterly, Emily Ellen, Thomas Ferreira, Jonathan Fisher, Patricia Fromkin, Paul Gagnon, Kathy Gavilanes, Holly Gordon, Robert Graham, Ellen Granter, Diane Grossman, Barbara Hollingdale, Linda Johnson, Anne Jones, John Judge, Kevin Keane, Kelly Kelliher, Toby Klang, Sue Langan, Russ Lappa, Carolyn Lock, Rebecca Loveys, Constance J. McCarty, Carolyn B. McGuire, Ranida Touranont McKneally, Anne McLaughlin, Eve Melnechuk, Natania Mlawer, Janet Morris, Karyl Murray, Francine Neumann, Baljit Nijjar, Marie Opera, Jill Ort, Kim Ortell, Joan Paley, Dorothy Preston, Maureen Raymond, Laura Ross, Rashid Ross, Siri Schwartzman, Melissa Shustyk, Laurel Smith, Emily Soltanoff, Jennifer A. Teece, Elizabeth Torjussen, Amanda M. Watters, Merce Wilczek, Amy Winchester, Char Lyn Yeakley. **Additional Credits:** Tara Alamilla, Louise Gachet, Allen Gold, Andrea Golden, Terence Hegarty, Etta Jacobs, Meg Montgomery, Stephanie Rogers, Kim Schmidt, Adam Teller, Joan Tobin.

Illustration

Kerry Cashman: 108; **David Corrente:** 16, 23, 84, 98, 100t, 104, 111, 118, 120, 122; **John Edwards:** 90–91, 100b, 121; **Ray Goudey:** 45, 48–49; **J/B Woolsey Associates:** 64–65, 76, 115, 119; **Richard McMahon:** 36, 50, 63, 86–87, 92, 95–97, 99b, 126–127, 136–137; **Morgan Cain & Associates:** 9–11, 19, 25, 30–31, 35, 40, 82–83; **Precision Graphics:** 55–57, 88, 99t, 119, 140; **Ted Smykel:** 15, 17, 24, 46, 59, 110. **All charts and graphs by Matt Mayerchak.**

Photography

Photo Research John Judge
Cover Image top, Tom Ives/Corbis; **bottom,** Thom Lang/Corbis

Page vi, Manfred Kage/Peter Arnold; **vii, viii,** Richard Haynes; **x, 1,** Tom Trower/Ames Research Center/NASA; **2 all,** Ames Research Center/NASA; **3b,** Tom Trower/Ames Research Center/NASA; **3t,** Ames Research Center/NASA.

Chapter 1
Pages 4–5, Wayne R. Bilenduke/Getty Images, Inc.; **5 inset,** Richard Haynes; **6b,** Marcello Bertinetti/Photo Researcher, Inc; **6t,** Richard Haynes; **7b,** Richard Haynes; **7t,** Russ Lappa; **8 both,** Richard Megna/Fundamental Photographs; **10,** Richard Megna/Fundamental Photographs; **11 both,** Richard Megna/Fundamental Photographs; **12b,** Richard Haynes; **12t,** Aaron Rezny/The Stock Market; **13,** Richard Haynes; **14 both,** Richard Haynes; **17 both,** Richard Haynes; **18, 20, 21,** Richard Haynes; **22b,** Sisse Brimberg/National Geographic Image; **22t,** Russ Lappa; **27,** Kennan Ward/Corbis; **28b,** Richard Haynes; **28t,** Sisse Brimberg/National Geographic Image.

Chapter 2
Pages 32–33,Owaki-Kulla/Corbis; **33 inset,** Richard Haynes; **34 both,** Richard Haynes; **37 all,** Richard Haynes; **38, 39,** Richard Haynes; **41,** Jeff Hunter/Getty Images, Inc.; **42, 43,** Richard Haynes; **44b,** Larry Lefever/Grant Heilman Photography, Inc.; **44t,** Russ Lappa; **46, 47, 48,** Richard Haynes; **49,** Peter Anderson/Dorling Kindersley; **49 inset,** Adrian Weinbrecht/Photo Library.com; **51,** Johan van Jaarsveld/Gallo Images/Corbis; **52,** Mark Burnett/Stock Boston; **53,** Richard Haynes; **54b,** Patitucci Photo/Raw Talent Photo; **54t,** Russ Lappa; **55,** J-L Charmet/Science Photo Library/Photo Researcher, Inc; **58,** Kevin Cruff/FPG International; **59,** Richard Haynes; **60,** Chris Rawlings/Getty Images, Inc.; **61,** Richard Haynes; **62,** Ron Kimball/Ron Kimball Stock; **63, 64, 65, 66,** Russ Lappa; **67b,** Justin Pumfrey/Getty Images, Inc.; **67t,** Russ Lappa; **68l,** Getty Images, Inc.; **68ml,** Getty Images, Inc.; **68mr,** Gamma Ray Studio Inc/Getty Images, Inc.; **68r,** Whirlpool; **70b,** Toni Micheals; **70t,** B. Daemmrich/Stock Market; **71b,** Joel Page/AP Wide World; **71t,** Russ Lappa; **73,** Richard Haynes.

Chapter 3
Pages 78–79, Justin Sullivan/Getty Images, Inc.; **79 inset,** Jon Chomitz; **80,** Russ Lappa; **81b,** Richard Megna/Fundamental Photographs; **81t,** Richard Haynes; **82,** Richard Megna/Fundamental Photographs; **84,** Dick Durrance II/The Stock Market; **85b,** Prentice Hall School Division; **85t,** Russ Lappa; **87,** Richard Haynes; **89,** Tim Ridley/Dorling Kindersley; **91l,** UHB Trust/Getty Images, Inc.; **91m,** CNRI/SPL/Photo Researchers, Inc.; **91r,** Alfred Pasieka/SPL/Photo Researchers, Inc.; **92l,** Russ Lappa; **92r,** Richard Haynes; **93b,** Zoran Milich/Masterfile; **93t,** Russ Lappa; **94,** Richard Haynes; **96 both,** Clive Streeter; **97l,** Corbis-Bettman; **97m,** Clive Streeter; **97r,** The Granger Collection; **102,** Richard Megna/Fundamental Photographs.

Chapter 4
Pages 106–107, Klaus Lahnstein/Getty Images, Inc.; **107 inset,** Richard Haynes; **108, 109,** Russ Lappa; **111b,** Richard Haynes; **111 all the rest,** Russ Lappa; **112 both,** Manfred Kage/Peter Arnold; **113, 114,** Richard Haynes; **116 inset,** Andrew Syred/Photo Researchers, Inc.; **116l,** Russ Lappa; **116r,** Chuck Savage/Corbis; **117l,** Russ Lappa; **117r,** Michael Newman/PhotoEdit; **120l,** Mark Richards/PhotoEdit; **120m,** Getty Images; **120r,** Sky Bonillo/PhotoEdit; **1221l,** David R. Frazier/Photo Library/Photo Researchers, Inc.; **122b,** Getty Images, Inc.; **122 inset,** Joe McDonald/McDonald Wildlife Photography, Inc.; **122t,** David Young-Wolff/Photo Edit; **123b,** L. Dematteis/The Image Works; **123t,** Richard Haynes; **124,** Andrew Syred/Science Photo Library/Photo Researchers; **125,** Russ Lappa; **126l,** The Granger Collection, NY; **126r,** Corbis-Bettman; **127l,** A/P Wide World Photos; **127m,** Camilla Smith/Rainbow; **127r,** Ryan McVay/Getty Images, Inc.; **128,** Peter Menzel Photography; **129,** Zach Holmes; **130, 131,** Richard Haynes **132,** Gurinder Osan/AP/Wide World Photos; **133l,** Ronnie Kaufman/Corbis; **133r,** Richard Vogel/AP/Wide World Photos; **134,** David Young-Wolff/Photo Edit; **135,** Sarah Swersey, artwork on CD by Rachel Swersey; **136–37 portraits of a boy,** Getty Images, Inc.; **137 image of space suit,** Roger Ressmeyer/Corbis; **138b,** David Young-Wolff/PhotoEdit; **138t,** Manfred Kage/Peter Arnold.

Pages 142b, Library of Congress; **142m,** U.S. Dept. of the Interior, National Park Service, Edison National Historic Site; **142t,** Dave King/Dorling Kindersley; **143,** U.S. Dept. of the Interior, National Park Service, Edison National Historic Site; **144–45,** AP/Wide World Photos; **145b,** Bettman/Corbis; **145t,** Smithsonian Institution, EMP-LAR-BB1, Courtesy of the General Electric Lighting Co.; **146b,**Brooks/Brown/Photo Researchers, Inc.; **146m,** U.S. Dept. of the Interior, National Park Service, Edison National Historic Site; **146t,** Everett Collection; **147b,** Tom McCarthy/PhotoEdit; **147t,** U.S. Geological Survey/Science Photo Library/Photo Researchers, Inc.; **148,** Tony Freeman/PhotoEdit; **149b,** Russ Lappa; **149m,** Richard Haynes; **149t,** Russ Lappa; **150,** Richard Haynes; **152,** Richard Haynes; **154,** Tanton Yachts; **155,** Richard Haynes; **157b,** Richard Haynes; **157t,** Dorling Kindersley; **159,** ImageStop/Phototake; **162,** Richard Haynes; **169,** Richard Haynes; **170,** Kennan Ward/Corbis; **171,** Richard Haynes; **175,** Richard Megna/Fundamental Photographs.